MAN IN LITERATURE
　　　Comparative World Studies in Translation

LITERATURE FROM GREEK AND ROMAN ANTIQUITY

RUSSIAN AND EASTERN EUROPEAN LITERATURE

TRANSLATIONS FROM THE FRENCH

ITALIAN LITERATURE IN TRANSLATION

BLACK AFRICAN VOICES

LITERATURE OF THE EASTERN WORLD

FROM SPAIN AND THE AMERICAS
　　　　　　Literature in Translation

TEUTONIC LITERATURE

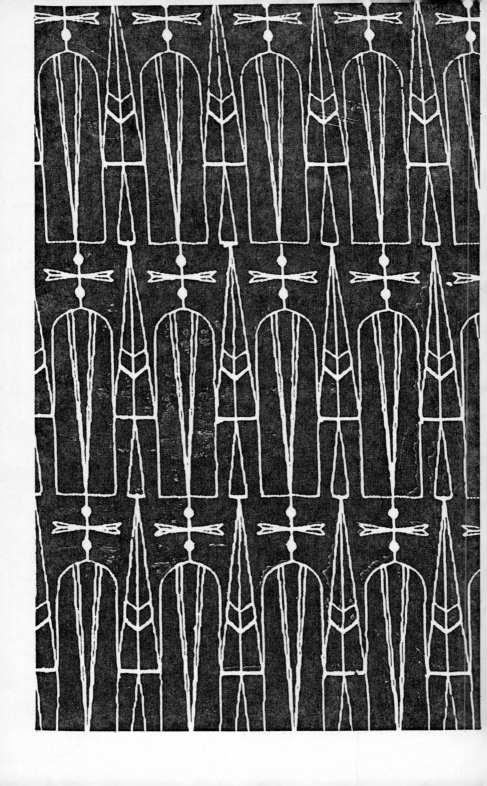

Teutonic Literature in English Translation

JAMES E. MILLER, JR.

ROBERT O'NEAL

HELEN M. McDONNELL

*Introductory Essay
"German and
Related Languages"
by Charlton Laird*

Scott, Foresman and Company

James E. Miller, Jr.

Professor of English, University of Chicago.
Awarded Fulbright to Italy, lectured at
Oriental Institute, Naples, and the University
of Rome, 1958–1959. Fulbright lecturer in
American Literature at University of Kyoto
and Doshisha University, Kyoto, Japan, 1968.
Elected to the Research Foundation of the
National Council of Teachers of English.
Author of *F. Scott Fitzgerald: His Art and His
Techniques* and *Quests Surd and Absurd: Essays
in American Literature.*

Robert O'Neal

Professor and Chairman of the English Department,
San Antonio College. Chairman of the Committee on
Comparative and World Literature, National Council
of Teachers of English. Author of *Teachers' Guide to
World Literature for the High School.* Contributor of
articles to *Modern Language Notes,* the *French Review,* and other professional magazines.

Helen M. McDonnell

Chairman, English Department, Ocean
Township High School, Oakhurst, New Jersey.
Member of the Committee on Comparative and
World Literature, National Council of Teachers
of English. Reviewer of books in English and English
education for *Scholastic Teacher* and contributor of
articles on education to magazines and books.

Editorial Direction: LEO B. KNEER

Development: MARGARET RAUSCH

with Ghia Brenner, Dorothy Koeber, Fitzgerald Higgins,
and Susan Berger

Design: ROBERT AMFT

The authors and editors of *Teutonic Literature In English Translation* wish to express their appreciation to the following teachers. Acting as reader-consultants, they chose from the many selections submitted to them those that they believed were most relevant to the interests and needs of today's youth. They tested their opinions against classroom use and contributed ideas that evolved during the give-and-take of class discussion.

SISTER EUGENE FOX, S.C.
Seton High School
Cincinnati, Ohio

MR. THOMAS GAGE
Concord High School
Concord, California

MRS. JEANNE LUCKETT
Provine High School
Jackson, Mississippi

MRS. ELIZABETH DRUM McDOWELL
Highland Heights High School
Nashville, Tennessee

MR. RONALD MIDKIFF
Rome City Schools
Rome, Georgia

MR. ELMER E. MOORE, JR.
Dobbs Ferry High School
Dobbs Ferry, New York

MR. ROBERT ROMANO
Concord-Carlisle High School
Concord, Massachusetts

Cover: A Cotton and Paper, double-faced tabby weave.
Germany, 1925; Courtesy of The Chicago Art Institute.
Frontispiece: A Cotton, Machine-made net with darned pattern.
Germany, Bauhaus, 1920; Courtesy of The Chicago Art Institute.

1

Translations from the GERMAN

2

Translation from the DUTCH

3

Translations from the SCANDINAVIAN

GERMAN AND RELATED LANGUAGES

Charlton Laird

Compare the following columns:

horn	Horn	cuerno	ahudkooklay
house	Haus	casa	teh-la
hundred	Hundert	cento	ituwumo

You will recognize the first column as English, and if you have studied German you will know that the words in the second column are the German equivalents of the English. If you have studied a Romance language you may recognize the third column as Spanish, but unless you have a very special background you will make nothing of the fourth column. In fact, to say that the items in this column are words would be somewhat misleading, although reading crosswise the symbols in all four columns are roughly equivalent. The fourth column is Kutenai, an American-Indian language, and like many languages it has no common written form and does not depend entirely upon what are called words in European languages. Comparing the columns, you would probably say that the first and second resemble each other more than either resembles any other column, and that both resemble the third column more than any other column suggests the fourth.

Now consider the following pictures:

Here again, the first two pictures suggest similarities, and the fourth is the most divergent, and asked to explain why, you probably could. You might say that the horse and the cow are more closely related to each other than either is to a cat or a clam. Pressed further, you might point out that the horse and the cow have hooves, and that they must have come from a

Professor of English and Comparative Literature at the University of Nevada in Reno, Charlton Laird is a scholar, linguist, and novelist. His many publications include The Miracle of Language, The World Through Literature, *and* Thunder on the River.

common hoof-footed ancestor. They would, however, be closer to a cat than to a clam because all three, the horse, the cow, and the cat, must have had a common ancestor with lungs, a backbone, and four legs, but no hard shell.

If you will now apply the analogy of the animal kingdom to language, you will guess at once why the first two columns of words are so nearly alike; they must have had a common ancestor, and not very far back in time, as time goes when we think in thousands and hundreds of thousands of years. The languages represented in the first two columns must be related to the language of the third column through a somewhat more remote ancestor, but if there is any relationship between the first three columns and the fourth, the connection must be remote indeed. That is, we might make similar diagrams for the languages and the living things, somewhat as follows:

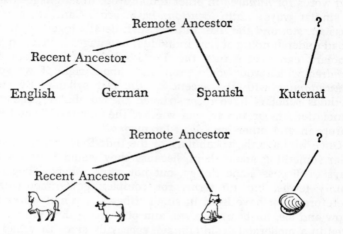

Of course an analogy is no proof. Fortunately, we can rely on analogy only to promote understanding, since we have evidence in great plenty, the results of detailed investigations of hundreds of languages all over the world. The evidence is overwhelming; languages tend to be related to other languages, to have ancestors and descendants, along with cousins as human beings do. The earliest ancestor of German and its relatives as yet identified is known as Proto [1]-Indo-European, a collection of dialects spoken in central or eastern Europe a few thousand years before the Christian era.

---

1. *Proto*, a Greek combining form meaning "first," "foremost," "earliest form of."

Only in a general way do we know who these Indo-Europeans were. They could not read or write, and archaeologists have not identified them. We know something of their language, however, since we can reconstruct it from its descendants, very much as you can know something of your ancestors from their descendants—unless you happen to be an Eskimo, you know that your ancestors were mostly not Eskimos.

Recalling the columns with which this essay started, you will notice that the English and German words began with *h* and the Spanish words with *c*. These are spelling differences, and in language study one must usually work with sounds, not with spellings. The *c* in Spanish represents a sound like that of our *k*, and for Old English the spelling *h* represented a sort of continuing *k*-sound, like the continuing sound of German *ch*. Thus the sounds historically are a little different, but not much, and words for *hundred* in other Indo-European languages begin in similar ways: Latin, *centum;* Irish, *cead;* Sanskrit, *catem;* Russian, *sto,* and the like. Putting such details together with a broad understanding of how individual languages have changed, scholars can reconstruct the Proto-Indo-European word for *hundred* which you would pronounce about right if we spell it *kumtomay,* with the accent on the last syllable. By such methods scholars have reconstructed the vocabulary, the pronunciation, the grammar, even some of the idioms of Proto-Indo-European and other long-dead languages.

Once we have the vocabulary of the Indo-Europeans, we can infer something about them, because they would have needed ways to discuss some things, but not some others. They had family terms, but no terms for complex government; they therefore must have lived in small tribes. They had words for snow and ice, for bears, wolves, and pine trees; they must have lived in a moderately cold climate, especially since they had no words for palm trees and for creatures like crocodiles and rhinoceroses. They had many words for edible wild creatures, both those that live on land and in the water; they must have been hunters and fishers. But they also had words for *herd, goose, goat, sheep, cow, dog,* and *horse,* so that they must have known about domesticating animals. Perhaps most significantly, they had words for honeybees and beech trees; it so happens that beech trees and honeybees were native to a small area, stretching from north of the Caspian Sea to about where Lithuania is now. Thus, if we could trust this evidence, we would know pretty certainly where the Indo-Europeans lived, but names for natural objects, especially for plants, are notoriously shifty, and even this word for *beech tree* (presumably the ancestor of our word *book,* German *Buch*) is in some areas used for oak trees. Still, this testimony from beech trees and honeybees is not at variance with the remainder of our evidence, so that western or southwestern Russia or central Europe north of the Balkan Peninsula is not a bad guess for the home of the Indo-Europeans.

Now we must remind ourselves of the phenomenon of dialect. In general, we call bodies of speech separate languages if their speakers cannot understand one another, and we call them dialects if speakers are aware of marked differences but can understand one another. These distinctions are not very sharp, and not precisely applied, so that Professor Uriel Weinreich has remarked, "A language is a dialect with an army and a navy." In fact, we should probably call Portuguese a dialect of Spanish except that Portugal was the center of a great empire; and we might now call Swedish, Danish, Norwegian, and Icelandic all dialects of a Norse or North Germanic language, except that each of these is the speech of a separate country. However that may be, all great languages consist of dialects, and Proto-Indo-European must have had them, too. Such dialects developed and specialized and some became languages as separate in space and character as Irish and Indic, on opposite sides of the world.

One of these dialects concerns us, because without it there would be neither English nor German, nor any other language represented in the book you are reading. We call it Proto-Germanic, and we know it must have grown in southern Scandinavia or northern central Europe, because languages that have come from there have common characteristics not shared by any other bodies of Indo-European speech. This dialect must have been growing into a language during the second pre-Christian millennium, that is, 1000–2000 B.C.; and knowing that, we can turn to archaeology for answers. We have evidence that hunters and fishers inhabited the Scandinavian peninsula from about 10,000 B.C. These people dominated the area until after 3000 B.C.; presumably they did not speak an Indo-European language. Then four successive cultures moved in: (1) people who lived by gathering seeds, shellfish, and the like; (2) people characterized by the fact that they built megalithic monuments [2]; (3) people characterized by using battle-axes, and (4) people known for their cemeteries marked by urn burials

---

2. *megalithic monuments,* monuments constructed of stones of great size.

in fields. One of the latter two probably brought an Indo-European dialect, which was imperfectly learned by the conquered people as a second language. This fact of conquest, and the imperfect learning of a foreign language, may account for the sharp and numerous differences between languages that have descended from Proto-Germanic when these are compared with other Indo-European tongues.

Now we can understand why the first two columns of symbols with which we started are so much alike; German and English are Germanic languages, descended during the past three or four thousand years from Proto-Germanic. Spanish is somewhat like English and German because it descends from Latin, which also descends from Indo-European, but by a different route and from a different dialect. None of these three languages much resembles Kutenai, which is not an Indo-European language. That is, all Indo-European languages have inheritances from Proto-Indo-European, and this is perhaps the most important fact about them. They rely mainly on words—not all languages do. They rely on sentences, which have subjects, verbs, and some sort of modifiers and complements—not all languages do, for some do not have verbs in our sense, and some incorporate the subject or the complement into the verb. They all have at least remnants of an inflectional or synthetic grammar, a grammar that works by changes of form like *boy–boys, who–whom.* They have similarities in sound; they are likely to have voiceless consonants like *p, t, k,* and the corresponding voiced consonants, *b, d, g;* they do not have glottal clicks—snapping sounds made in the glottis—common in Africa and the Americas.

Similarly, the fact that languages like English, German, Dutch, and Danish are Germanic languages has much to do with their character. Whether Proto-Germanic speech came down from Scandinavia into what was later Germany, brought by the Scandinavianized battle-axe people, or whether the urn-burial people introduced Indo-European speech to north-central Europe, including Scandinavia, or whether some other combination provided a new home for a new set of languages we do not know. We do know these languages changed relatively rapidly, and in their own ways. Germanic speakers simplified the grammar, using fewer case endings, fewer verb forms, fewer classes of nouns and verbs, less modification in adjectives. Most descendants of Indo-European have dropped some of the old forms, and developed new devices to replace the old prepositions, for example—but the Germanic languages have pushed these changes farther than have their neighbors, the Romanic, Greek, and Slavic languages. They changed many sounds, and in the manner of languages, many of these changes fall into orderly patterns. The Germanic Sound Shift, for instance, explained in what is called Grimm's Law, accounts for the fact that where a sound like *p* occurs in many Indo-European languages, a sound like *f* (whether or not spelled with a *v*) occurs in Germanic languages as in *fish*, for which the Latin is *pisces* and the German *Fisch*, in *father* where the Latin is *pater* and the German *Vater*.

And most interestingly, the stress or accent was different in Proto-Germanic. Indo-European had a variable accent, generally far on in a word, but in Germanic the accent was fixed on the root, which was commonly the first syllable. Thus words borrowed into a Germanic language from Latin or Greek, whether directly or indirectly, were likely to change their accent; the English word *labor* now rhymes with *sabre*, although it formerly rhymed with *poor*, being pronounced something like *leh-boor*, having come from Latin through French. More broadly, while the Romance languages developed poetry rhyming on the last syllable, the Germanic languages developed poetry with alliteration, which is rather like rhyming on the first syllable. For example, the Old English *Beowulf* has lines like the following:

Monigum	maegthum	meodsetla	ofteah
(Many	a time	the mead benches	he tore down)

All the Old Germanic poetry we know is of this sort.

We have noticed that all languages work through dialects, and Proto-Germanic was no exception. We have no direct early evidence of these dialects, since the Germanic peoples had to learn writing from the Greeks and Romans, or those who had learned from them. We can discover something from Classical writers like Tacitus, and from scattered finds. A drinking horn dug up near Jutland, dated about 400 A.D., has an inscription which reads in Runic futhark,[3] "I, Hlewagast of the Holting clan, made the horn." Enough weapons and other objects bearing inscriptions have survived in Scandinavia to make clear the fact that dialects to the north were distinct from those further south. Thus there was a North Germanic dialect—what is often called Old Norse—the ancestor of languages like Danish, Swedish, Norwegian, and Icelandic. The Old English dia-

---

3. *Runic futhark*, the runic or ancient Scandinavian alphabet.

lects are similar to Old Norse, but different. The oldest extended compositions in a Germanic dialect have survived in England, in works which must have been composed about 700 A.D. or earlier.

Farther south the situation is not so clear; Jacob Grimm, the propounder of Grimm's Law and one of the Brothers Grimm who collected the fairy tales that go by their name, thought he could identify East Germanic, made up of Gothic and other dialects that have not survived, and West Germanic, which included everything else except North Germanic. This was a good guess for a century and a half ago, but scholars can now refine it somewhat. They rely more on north and south than on east and west, and distinguish Low Germanic along the coast and High Germanic toward the Alps, with some blending between. From Low Germanic come Modern English, Dutch, Flemish, Frisian, and many north-German dialects, like Old Saxon. To the south, Old High German breaks into two belts of speech, one in Bavaria and other highlands to the south, the other across what is now central Germany. This High German was named for its physical altitude; but partly because culture flowed north from Italy, the dialect was "high" also in the sense that it often included fashionable speech. But other areas were important, too —the Hanseatic towns along the sea, modern cities like Hamburg, Bremen, and Berlin, and especially prosperous river valleys like the Rhineland—so that Professor John T. Waterman, in a recent authoritative survey, can write, "It now seems certain that the German language gradually took shape, from the fifth century on, as the result of the mergings and blendings of the dialects spoken by three tribal groups: The North Sea Germans (Saxons), the Weser-Rhine Germans (Franks), and the Elbe Germans (Alemmanians, Bavarians, the Langobardians)." Conventionally, German is divided into Old High German, from the beginnings to about 1050; Middle High German, 1050–1350; Early New High German, 1350–1600; New High German, 1600—the present.

Thus the Germanic languages and dialects from Icelandic to East Prussian, from Afrikaans to the speech of Spitsbergen fishermen, and developments from such speech as these that have been carried around the world, are rooted in the language habits that have sprung from Proto-Indo-European through Proto-Germanic. One should add, however, that language grows not only from within. It is also enriched from without. Germanic speakers have been great borrowers, and here once more we can notice a broad principle: wherever languages come in contact, they borrow from one another, with the direction of greatest borrowing from the more advanced cultures to the less advanced. So far as the Germanic languages are concerned, the direction is in no doubt; probably the great fact of western European history is that the culture of the Mediterranean areas, enriched with the culture of Greece and Rome, of Alexandria and the Hellenic cities, was flowing north toward the relatively unsophisticated Germanic tribes. This trend is now somewhat reversed, or at least redirected, but it dominated European history and influenced the growth of language for centuries.

For German, and for the Germanic languages generally, early borrowings came from Greek and Latin, sometimes Greek through Latin. For example, the word for "church," *die Kirche*, comes from a Low Greek word like *kurikon*, meaning "the house of the Lord"; but the German for "cross," *das Kreuz*, seems to come from Latin *crux*, having to do with torture on the cross, a word not found in Greek. During the long period of the hegemony of France, and to a somewhat lesser degree of cities like Amsterdam, many Latin words swept north into France and then worked east. For example, consider *der Ritter*, German for a knight. In French the word was something like *chevalier*, from Latin *caballus* (horse), meaning one who could afford a horse to ride. By what is called loan translation it became *ridder* in Dutch, that is, a rider, and with the Dutch voiced consonants replaced by German voiceless consonants, *Ritter* in German. Later there was a flow of English words into German, including terms like *die Banknote* and *das Beefsteak*, which any user of English can guess. Now there seems to be a minor flood of Americanisms, words like *Bluejeans, Date, Jazz, Jeep, Quiz,* and *Striptease*, with no change except the capitalizing of the first letter; meanwhile, *eine Milchbar* is something like a soda fountain, and *ein Mixer* is not a blender but a bartender, mixing *Mixedrinks* (cocktails). Meanwhile, other languages have borrowed from German, appropriating words like *Blitzkrieg* (lightning war) and *Märchen* (folktales).

Thus modern German, like all other languages we know, is the result of minglings of native dialects with streams of influence from abroad, both the native growths and the foreign borrowings reflecting the life and times of the users of the language.

Heinrich Heine[1] (1797–1856)

ABENDDÄMMERUNG

Am blassen Meeresstrande
Sass ich gedankenbekümmert und einsam.
Die Sonne neigte sich tiefer, und warf
Glührote Streifen auf das Wasser,
5 Und die weissen, weiten Wellen,
Von der Flut gedrängt,
Schäumten und rauschten näher und näher—
Ein seltsam Geräusch, ein Flüstern und Pfeifen,
Ein Lachen und Murmeln, Seufzen und Sausen,
10 Dazwischen ein wiegenliedheimliches Singen—
Mir war als hört ich verscholl'ne Sagen,
Uralte, liebliche Märchen,
Die ich einst, als Knabe,
Von Nachbarskindern vernahm,
15 Wenn wir am Sommerabend,
Auf den Treppensteinen der Hausthür,
Zum stillen Erzählen niederkauerten,
Mit kleinen, horchenden Herzen
Und neugierklugen Augen;
20 Während die grossen Mädchen,
Neben duftenden Blumentöpfen,
Gegenüber am Fenster sassen,
Rosengesichter,
Lächelnd und mondbeglänzt.

---

1. *Heinrich Heine* (hīn′riH hī′nə).

TWILIGHT

Translated from the German by

Aaron Kramer

I sat on the pale sea-sand
Grieved by my thoughts and lonely.
The sun sank ever lower, and threw
Red hot streaks upon the water,
5 And the white, the far-away billows,
Urged on by the flood,
Sparkled and murmured nearer and nearer—
A singular noise, a whispering and piping,
A laughing and murmuring, sighing and whistling,
10 Through all a mysterious cradle-song humming—
I thought I was hearing forgotten legends,
Ancient, lovely fables,
That I once, as a boy,
Learned from the neighbors' children,
15 When on a summer's evening,
On the steps before the street-door,
We squatted down to the quiet telling,
With little, hearkening hearts
And curious-clever eyes;—
20 While, opposite us at the window,
By fragrant flower-pots,
The grown-up girls were sitting,
Rosy-faced,
Smiling and lit by the moon.

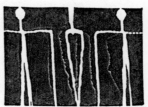

"Twilight" by Heinrich Heine, translated by Aaron Kramer from THE
POETRY AND PROSE OF HEINRICH HEINE, selected and edited with
an introduction by Frederic Ewen. Copyright 1948 by The Citadel Press.
Reprinted by permission of The Citadel Press, Inc.

EVENING TWILIGHT

Translated from the German by
John Todhunter

On the wan sea-strand
Lonely I lay, and in sorrowful brooding.
The sun sank lower and lower, and flung
His red rays, glowing, on the water,
5 And I watched the far white billows,
In the grip of the flood,
Foaming and roaring, nigher and nigher—
Strange medley of sounds! a whispering and wailing,
A laughing and murmuring, sobbing and sighing,
10 Low voices, the while, a strange lullaby singing.
Methought I heard long-forgotten legends,
World-old adorable folk-tales,
That long since in boyhood
From neighbors' children I learnt;
15 When, of a summer evening,
On the steps of stone by the house-door,
We squatted for quiet story-telling,
With small hearts eagerly listening
And young eyes keen for wonders;
20 While the fair grown-up maidens
Sat, 'mid balm-breathing pots of flowers,
At a window over the way there,
With rosy faces,
Smiling and lit by the moon.

1

Translations from the GERMAN

Hans Arp (1887–1966)

BAOBAB

Translated from the German by
Christopher Middleton

And she gave birth to a strong healthy boy
who was named Baobab.
The boy grew and grew,
and did not stop growing
5 and grew as high as the blue of the sky itself.
Baobab's compatriots liked to look into the eyes
of whomsoever they might be talking to.
But this was no longer possible in the case
of a person as tall as Baobab was.

---

10 So they lifted a lot of earth
   and dug a chasmic hole,
   into which Baobab willingly inserted himself,
   for he too found it unbearable
   not to be able to look into the eyes
15 of whomsoever he might be talking to.
   The earth they lifted
   they threw over the edge of their small star
   into the emptiness.
   After Baobab had spent
20 a hundred years in this hole,
   he began to disappear.
   Every day he grew smaller and smaller,
   till at length he disappeared altogether.
   Now the inhabitants of the small star
25 were left with nothing but a chasmic hole
   and a narrow strip of land around the hole,
   and they looked alternately
   into the chasmic hole on their small star
   and over the edge of their small star into the emptiness.

Heinrich Böll [1] (1917–   )

ENTER AND EXIT

Translated from the German by
Leila Vennewitz

WHEN THE WAR BROKE OUT

I WAS LEANING out of the window, my arms resting on the sill, I had rolled up my shirtsleeves and was looking beyond the main gate and guardroom across to the divisional headquarters telephone exchange, waiting for my friend Leo to give me the prearranged signal: come to the window, take off his cap, and put it on again. Whenever I got the chance I would lean out of the window, my arms on the sill; whenever I got the chance I would call a girl in Cologne and my mother—at army expense —and when Leo came to the window, took off his cap, and put it on again, I would run down to the barrack square and wait in the public callbox till the phone rang.

The other telephone operators sat there bareheaded, in their undershirts, and when they leaned forward to plug in or unplug, or to push up a flap, their identity disks would dangle out of their undershirts and fall back again when they straightened up. Leo was the only one wearing a cap, just so he could take it off to give me the signal. He had a heavy, pink face, very fair hair, and came from Oldenburg. The first expression you noticed on his face was guileless; the second was: incredibly guileless, and no one paid enough attention to Leo to notice more than those two expressions; he looked as uninteresting as the boys whose faces appear on advertisements for cheese.

It was hot, afternoon; the alert that had been going on for days had become stale, transforming all time as it passed into stillborn Sunday hours. The barrack square lay there blind and empty, and I was glad I could at least keep my head out of the camaraderie of my roommates. Over there the operators were plugging and unplugging, pushing up flaps, wiping off sweat, and Leo was sitting there among them, his cap on his thick fair hair.

All of a sudden I noticed the rhythm of plugging and unplugging had altered; arm movements were no longer routine, mechanical, they became hesitant, and Leo threw his arms up over his head three times: a signal we had not arranged but from which I could tell that something out of the ordinary had happened; then I saw an operator take his steel helmet from the switchboard and put it on; he looked ridiculous, sitting there sweating in his undershirt, his identity disk dangling, his steel helmet on his head—but I couldn't laugh at him; I realized that putting on a steel helmet meant something like "ready for action," and I was scared.

The ones who had been dozing on their beds behind me in the room got up, lit cigarettes, and formed the two customary groups: three probationary teachers, who were still hoping to be discharged as being "essential to the nation's educational system," resumed their discussion of Ernst Jünger [2]; the other two, an orderly and an office clerk, began discussing the female form; they didn't tell dirty stories, they didn't laugh, they discussed it just as two exceptionally boring geography teachers might have discussed the conceivably interesting topography of the Ruhr valley. Neither subject interested me. Psychologists, those interested in psychology, and those about to complete an adult education course in psychology, may be interested to learn that my desire to call the girl in Cologne became more urgent than in previous weeks; I went to my locker, took out my cap, put it on, and leaned out of the window, my arms on the sill, wearing my cap: the signal for Leo that I had to speak to him at once. To show he understood, he waved to me, and I put on my tunic, went out of the room, down the stairs, and stood at the entrance to headquarters, waiting for Leo.

It was hotter than ever, quieter than ever, the barrack

---

2. *Ernst Jünger* (1895–   ), novelist and essayist whose writings celebrated warfare.

squares were even emptier, and nothing has ever approximated my idea of hell as closely as hot, silent, empty barrack squares. Leo came very quickly; he was also wearing his steel helmet now, and was displaying one of his other five expressions which I knew: dangerous for everything he didn't like; this was the face he sat at the switchboard with when he was on evening or night duty, listened in on secret official calls, told me what they were about, suddenly jerked out plugs, cut off secret official calls so as to put through an urgent secret call to Cologne, for me to talk to the girl; then it would be my turn to work the switchboard, and Leo would first call his girl in Oldenburg, then his father; meanwhile Leo would cut thick slices from the ham his mother had sent him, cut these into cubes, and we would eat cubes of ham. When things were slack, Leo would teach me the art of recognizing the caller's rank from the way the flaps fell; at first I thought it was enough to be able to tell the rank simply by the force with which the flap fell: corporal, sergeant, etc., but Leo could tell exactly whether it was an officious corporal or a tired colonel demanding a line; from the way the flap fell he could even distinguish between angry captains and annoyed lieutenants—nuances which are very hard to tell apart, and as the evening went on his other expressions made their appearance: fixed hatred; primordial malice; with these faces he would suddenly become pedantic, articulate his "Are you still talking?" his "Yessirs," with great care, and with unnerving rapidity switch plugs so as to turn an official call about boots into one about boots and ammunition, and the other call about ammunition into one about ammunition and boots, or the private conversation of a sergeant-major with his wife might be suddenly interrupted by a lieutenant's voice saying: "I insist the man be punished, I absolutely insist." With lightning speed Leo would then switch the plugs over so that the boot partners were talking about boots again and the others about ammunition, and the sergeant-major's wife could resume discussion of her stomach trouble with her husband. When the ham was all gone, Leo's relief had arrived, and we were walking across the silent barrack square to our room, Leo's face would wear its final expression: foolish, innocent in a way that had nothing to do with childlike innocence.

Any other time I would have laughed at Leo, standing there wearing his steel helmet, that symbol of inflated importance. He looked past me, across the first, the second barrack square, to the stables; his expressions alternated from three to five, from five to four, and with his final expression he said: "It's war, war,

war—they finally made it." I said nothing, and he said: "I guess you want to talk to her?" "Yes," I said.

"I've already talked to mine," he said. "She's not pregnant, I don't know whether to be glad or not. What d'you think?" "You can be glad," I said, "I don't think it's a good idea to have kids in wartime."

"General mobilization," he said, "state of alert, this place is soon going to be swarming—and it'll be a long while before you and I can go off on our bikes again." (When we were off duty we used to ride our bikes out into the country, onto the moors, the farmers' wives used to fix us fried eggs and thick slices of bread and butter.) "The first joke of the war has already happened," said Leo: "In view of my special skills and services in connection with the telephone system, I have been made a corporal—now go over to the public callbox, and if it doesn't ring in three minutes I'll demote myself for incompetence."

In the callbox I leaned against the "Münster Area" phone book, lit a cigarette, and looked out through a gap in the frosted glass across the barrack square; the only person I could see was a sergeant-major's wife, in Block 4 I think; she was watering her geraniums from a yellow jug; I waited, looked at my wristwatch: one minute, two, and I was startled when it actually rang, and even more startled when I immediately heard the voice of the girl in Cologne: "Maybach's Furniture Company," and I said: "Marie, it's war, it's war"—and she said: "No." I said: "Yes it is," then there was silence for half a minute, and she said: "Shall I come?" and before I could say spontaneously, instinctively, "Yes, please do," the voice of what was probably a fairly senior officer shouted: "We need ammunition, and we need it urgently." The girl said: "Are you still there?" The officer yelled: "God damn it!" Meanwhile I had had time to wonder about what it was in the girl's voice that had sounded unfamiliar, ominous almost: her voice had sounded like marriage, and I suddenly knew I didn't feel like marrying her. I said: "We're probably pulling out tonight." The officer yelled: "God damn it, God damn it!" (evidently he couldn't think of anything better to say), the girl said: "I could catch the four o'clock train and be there just before seven," and I said, more quickly than was polite: "It's too late, Marie, too late"—then all I heard was the officer, who seemed to be on the verge of apoplexy. He screamed: "Well, do we get the ammunition or don't we?" And I said in a steely voice (I had learned that from Leo): "No, no, you don't get any ammunition, even if it chokes you." Then I hung up.

It was still daylight when we loaded boots from railway cars onto trucks, but by the time we were loading boots from trucks onto railway cars it was dark, and it was still dark when we loaded boots from railway cars onto trucks again, then it was daylight again, and we loaded bales of hay from trucks onto railway cars, and it was still daylight, and we were still loading bales of hay from trucks onto railway cars; but then it was dark again, and for exactly twice as long as we had loaded bales of hay from trucks onto railway cars, we loaded bales of hay from railway cars onto trucks. At one point a field kitchen arrived, in full combat rig; we were given large helpings of goulash and small helpings of potatoes, and we were given real coffee and cigarettes which we didn't have to pay for; that must have been at night, for I remember hearing a voice say: real coffee and cigarettes for free, the surest sign of war; I don't remember the face belonging to this voice. It was daylight again when we marched back to barracks, and as we turned into the street leading past the barracks we met the first battalion going off. It was headed by a marching band playing "Must I then, must I then," followed by the first company, then their armored vehicles, then the second, third and finally the fourth with the heavy machine guns. On not one face, not one single face, did I see the least sign of enthusiasm; of course there were some people standing on the sidewalks, some girls too, but not once did I see anybody stick a bunch of flowers onto a soldier's rifle; there was not even the merest trace of a sign of enthusiasm in the air.

Leo's bed was untouched; I opened his locker (a degree of familiarity with Leo which the probationary teachers, shaking their heads, called "going too far"); everything was in its place: the photo of the girl in Oldenburg, she was standing, leaning against her bicycle, in front of a birch tree; photos of Leo's parents; their farmhouse. Next to the ham there was a message: "Transferred to area headquarters. In touch with you soon, take all the ham, I've taken what I need. Leo." I didn't take any of the ham, and closed the locker; I was not hungry, and the rations for two days had been stacked up on the table: bread, cans of liver sausage, butter, cheese, jam and cigarettes. One of the probationary teachers, the one I liked least, announced that he had been promoted to Pfc. and appointed room senior for the period of Leo's absence; he began to distribute the rations; it took a very long time; the only thing I was interested in was the cigarettes, and these he left to the last because he was a nonsmoker. When I finally got the cigarettes I tore open the pack, lay down on the bed in my clothes and smoked; I watched the others eating. They spread liver sausage an inch thick on the bread and discussed the "excellent quality of the butter," then they drew the black-out blinds and lay down on their beds; it was very hot, but I didn't feel like undressing; the sun shone into the room through a few cracks, and in one of these strips of light sat the newly promoted Pfc. sewing on his Pfc.'s chevron. It isn't so easy to sew on a Pfc.'s chevron: it has to be placed at a certain prescribed distance from the seam of the sleeve; moreover, the two open sides of the chevron must be absolutely straight; the probationary teacher had to take off the chevron several times, he sat there for at least two hours, unpicking it, sewing it back on, and he did not appear to be running out of patience; outside the band came marching by every forty minutes, and I heard the "Must I then, must I then," from Block 7, Block 2, from Block 9, then from over by the stables—it would come closer, get very loud, then softer again; it took almost exactly three "Must I thens" for the Pfc. to sew on his chevron, and it still wasn't quite straight; by that time I had smoked the last of my cigarettes and fell asleep.

That afternoon we didn't have to load either boots from trucks onto railway cars or bales of hay from railway cars onto trucks; we had to help the quartermaster-sergeant; he considered himself a genius at organization; he had requisitioned as many assistants as there were items of clothing and equipment on his list, except that for the groundsheets he needed two; he also required a clerk. The two men with the groundsheets went ahead and laid them out, flicking the corners nice and straight, neatly on the cement floor of the stable; as soon as the groundsheets had been spread out, the first man started off by laying two neckties on each groundsheet; the second man, two handkerchiefs; I came next with the mess kits, and while all the articles in which, as the sergeant said, size was not a factor were being distributed, he was preparing, with the aid of the more intelligent members of the detachment, the objects in which size was a factor: tunics, boots, trousers, and so on; he had a whole pile of paybooks lying there, he selected the tunics, trousers and boots according to measurements and weight, and he insisted everything would fit, "unless the bastards have got too fat as civilians"; it all had to be done at great speed, in one continuous operation, and it was done at great speed, in one continuous operation, and when everything had been spread out the reservists came in, were conducted to their groundsheets, tied the ends together, hoisted their bundles onto their backs, and went to their rooms to put on their uniforms. Only occasionally did something have to be exchanged, and then it was always because someone had got too fat as a civilian. It was also only occasionally that something was missing: a shoe-cleaning brush or a spoon or fork, and it always turned out that someone else had two shoe-cleaning brushes or two spoons or forks, a fact which confirmed the sergeant's theory that we did not work mechanically enough, that we were "still using our brains too much." I didn't use my brain at all, with the result that no one was short a mess kit. While the first man of each company being equipped was hoisting his bundle onto his shoulder, the first of our own lot had to start spreading out the next groundsheet; everything went smoothly; meanwhile the newly promoted Pfc. sat at the table and wrote everything down in the paybooks; most of the time he had only to enter a one in the paybook, except with the neckties, socks, handkerchiefs, undershirts and underpants, where he had to write a two.

In spite of everything, though, there were occasionally some dead minutes, as the quartermaster-sergeant called them, and we were allowed to use these to fortify ourselves; we would sit on the bunks in the grooms' quarters and eat bread and liver sausage, sometimes bread and cheese or bread and jam, and when the sergeant had a few dead minutes himself he would come over and give us a lecture about the difference between rank and appointment; he found it tremendously interesting that he himself was a quartermaster-sergeant—"that's my appointment"—and yet had the rank of a corporal, "that's my rank," in this way, so he said, there was no reason, for example, why a Pfc. should not act as a quartermaster-sergeant, indeed even an ordinary private might; he found the theme endlessly fascinating and kept on concocting new examples, some of which betokened a well-nigh treasonable imagination: "It can actually happen, for instance," he said, "that a Pfc. is put in command of a company, of a battalion even."

For ten hours I laid mess kits on groundsheets, slept for six hours, and again for ten hours laid mess kits on groundsheets; then I slept another six hours and had still heard nothing from Leo. When the third ten hours of laying out mess kits began, the Pfc. started entering a two wherever there should have been a one, and a one wherever there should have been a two. He was relieved of his post, and now had to lay out neckties, and the second probationary teacher was appointed clerk. I stayed with the mess kits during the third ten hours too, the sergeant said he thought I had done surprisingly well.

During the dead minutes, while we were sitting on the bunks eating bread and cheese, bread and jam, bread and liver sausage, strange rumors were beginning to be peddled around. A story was being told about a rather well-known retired general who received orders by phone to go to a small island in the North Sea where he was to assume a top-secret, extremely important command; the general had taken his uniform out of the closet, kissed his wife, children and grandchildren goodbye, given his favorite horse a farewell pat, and taken the train to some station on the North Sea and from there hired a motorboat to the island in question; he had been foolish enough to send back the motorboat before ascertaining the nature of his command; he was cut off by the rising tide and—so the story went—had forced the farmer on the island at pistol point to risk his life and row him back to the mainland. By afternoon there was already a variation to the tale: some sort of a struggle had taken place in the boat between the general and the farmer, they had both been swept overboard and drowned. What I couldn't stand was that this story—and a number of others—was considered criminal all right, but funny as well, while to me they seemed neither one nor the other; I couldn't accept the grim accusation of sabotage, which was being used like some kind of moral tuning-fork, nor could I join in the laughter or grin with the others. The war seemed to deprive what was funny of its funny side.

At any other time the "Must I thens" which ran through my dreams, my sleep, and my few waking moments, the countless men who got off the streetcars and came hurrying into the barracks with their cardboard boxes and went out again an hour later with "Must I then"; even the speeches which we sometimes listened to with half an ear, speeches in which the words "united effort" were always occurring—all this I would have found funny, but everything which would have been funny before was not funny any more, and I could no longer laugh or smile at all the things which would have seemed laughable; not even the sergeant, and not even the Pfc., whose chevron was still not quite straight and who sometimes laid out three neckties on the groundsheet instead of two.

It was still hot, still August, and the fact that three times sixteen hours are only forty-eight, two days and two nights, was something I didn't realize until I woke up about eleven on Sunday and for the first time since Leo had been transferred was able to lean out of the window, my arms on the sill; the probationary teachers, wearing their walking-out dress, were ready for church and looked at me in a challenging kind of way, but all I said was: "Go ahead, I'll follow you," and it was obvious that they were glad to be able to go without me for once. Whenever we had gone to church they had looked at me as if they would like to excommunicate me, because something or other about me or my uniform was not quite up to scratch in their eyes: the way my boots were cleaned, the way I had tied my tie, my belt or my hair-cut; they were indignant not as fellow-soldiers (which, objectively speaking, I agree would have been justified), but as Catholics; they would rather I had not made it so unmistakably clear that we were actually going to one and the same church; it embarrassed them, but there wasn't a thing they could do about it, because my paybook is marked: R.C.

This Sunday there was no mistaking how glad they were to be able to go without me, I had only to watch them marching off to town, past the barracks, clean, upright, and brisk. Sometimes, when I felt bouts of pity for them, I was glad for their sakes that Leo was a Protestant: I think they simply couldn't have borne it if Leo had been a Catholic too.

The office clerk and the orderly were still asleep; we didn't have to be at the stable again till three that afternoon. I stood leaning out of the window for a while, till it was time to go, so as to get to church just in time to miss the sermon. Then, while I was dressing, I opened Leo's locker again: to my surprise it was empty, except for a piece of paper and a big chunk of ham; Leo had locked the cupboard again to be sure I would find the message and the ham. On the paper was written: "This is it —I'm being sent to Poland—did you get my message?" I put the paper in my pocket, turned the key in the locker, and finished dressing; I was in a daze as I walked into town and entered the church, and even the glances of the three probationary teachers, who turned round to look at me and then back to the altar again, shaking their heads, failed to rouse me completely. Probably they wanted to make sure quickly whether I hadn't come in *after* the Elevation of the Host so they could apply for my excommunication; but I really had arrived *before* the Elevation, there was nothing they could do, besides I wanted to remain a Catholic. I thought of Leo and was scared, I thought too of the girl in Cologne and had a twinge of conscience, but I was sure her voice had sounded like marriage. To annoy my roommates, I undid my collar while I was still in church.

After Mass I stood outside leaning against the church wall in a shady corner between the vestry and the door, took off my cap, lit a cigarette, and watched the faithful as they left the church and walked past me. I wondered how I could get hold of a girl with whom I could go for a walk, have a cup of coffee, and maybe go to a movie; I still had three hours before I had to lay out mess kits on groundsheets again. It would be nice if the girl were not too silly and reasonably pretty. I also thought about dinner at the barracks, which I was missing now, and that perhaps I ought to have told the office clerk he could have my chop and dessert.

I smoked two cigarettes while I stood there, watching the faithful standing about in twos and threes, then separating again, and just as I was lighting the third cigarette from the second a shadow fell across me from one side, and when I looked to the right I saw that the person casting the shadow was even blacker than the shadow itself: it was the chaplain who had read Mass. He looked very kind, not old, thirty perhaps, fair and just a shade too well-fed. First he looked at my open collar, then at my boots, then at my bare head, and finally at my cap, which I had put next to me on a ledge where it had slipped off onto the paving; last of all he looked at my cigarette, then into my face, and I had the feeling that he didn't like anything he saw there. "What's the matter?" he finally asked. "Are you in trouble?" And hardly had I nodded in reply to this question when he said: "Do you wish to confess?" Damn it, I thought, all they ever think of is confession, and only a certain part of that even. "No," I said, "I don't wish to confess." "Well, then," he said, "what's on your mind?" He might just as well have been asking about my stomach as my mind. He was obviously very impatient, looked at my cap, and I felt he was annoyed that I hadn't picked it up yet. I would have liked to turn his impatience into patience, but after all it wasn't I who had spoken to him, but he who had spoken to me, so I asked—to my annoyance, somewhat falteringly—whether he knew of some nice girl who would go for a walk with me, have a cup of coffee and maybe go to a movie in the evening; she didn't have to be a beauty queen, but she must be reasonably pretty, and if possible not from a good family, as these girls are usually so silly. I could give him the address of a chaplain in Cologne where he could make inquiries, call up if necessary, to satisfy himself I was from a good Catholic home. I talked a lot, toward the end a bit more coherently, and noticed how his face altered: at first it was almost kind, it had almost looked benign, that was in the early stage when he took me for a highly interesting, possibly even fascinating case of feeblemindedness and found me psychologically quite amusing. The transitions from kind to almost benign, from almost benign to amused were hard to distinguish, but then all of a sudden—the moment I mentioned the physical attributes the girl was to have—he went purple with rage. I was scared, for my mother had once told me it is a sign of danger when overweight people suddenly go purple in the face. Then he began to shout at me, and shouting has always put me on edge.

He shouted that I looked a mess, with my "field tunic" undone, my boots unpolished, my cap lying next to me "in the dirt, yes in the dirt," and how undisciplined I was, smoking one cigarette after another, and whether perhaps I couldn't tell the difference between a Catholic priest and a pimp. With my nerves strung up as they were I had stopped being scared of him, I was just plain angry. I asked him what my tie, my boots, my cap, had to do with him, whether he thought maybe he had to do my corporal's job, and: "Anyway," I said, "you fellows tell us all the time to come to you with our troubles, and when someone really tells you his troubles you get mad." "You fellows, eh?" he said, gasping with rage, "since when are we on such familiar terms?" "We're not on any terms at all," I said. I picked up my cap, put it on without looking at it, and left, walking straight across the church square. He called after me to at least do up my tie, and I shouldn't be so stubborn; I very nearly turned round and shouted that *he* was the stubborn one, but then I remembered my mother telling me it was all right to be frank with a priest but you should try and avoid being impertinent—and so, without looking back, I went on into town. I left my tie dangling and thought about Catholics; there was a war on, but the first thing they looked at was your tie, then your boots. They said you should tell them your troubles, and when you did they got mad.

I walked slowly through town, on the lookout for a café where I wouldn't have to salute anyone; this stupid saluting spoiled all cafés for me; I looked at all the girls I passed, I turned round to look at them, at their legs even, but there wasn't one whose voice would not have sounded like marriage. I was desperate, I thought of Leo, of the girl in Cologne, I was on the point of sending her a telegram; I was almost prepared to risk getting married just to be alone with a girl.

I stopped in front of the window of a photographer's studio, so I could think about Leo in peace. I was scared for him. I saw my reflection in the shop window—my tie undone and my black boots unpolished, I raised my hands to button up my collar, but then it seemed too much trouble, and I dropped my hands again. The photographs in the studio window were very depressing. They were almost all of soldiers in walking-out dress; some had even had their pictures taken wearing their steel helmets, and I was wondering whether the ones in steel helmets were more depressing than the ones in peak caps when a sergeant came out of the shop carrying a framed photograph: the photo was fairly large, at least twenty-four by thirty, the frame was painted silver, and the picture showed the sergeant in walking-out dress and steel helmet; he was quite young, not much older than I was, twenty-one at most; he was just about to walk past me, he hesitated, stopped, and I was wondering whether to raise my hand and salute him, when he said: "Forget it—but if I were you I'd do up your collar, and your tunic too, the next guy might be tougher than I am." Then he laughed and went off, and ever since then I have preferred (relatively, of course) the ones who have their pictures taken in steel helmets to the ones who have their pictures taken in peak caps.

Leo would have been just the person to stand with me in front of the photo studio and look at the pictures; there were also some bridal couples, first communicants, and students wearing colored ribbons and fancy fobs over their stomachs, and I stood there wondering why they didn't wear ribbons in their hair; some of them wouldn't have looked bad in them at all. I needed company and had none.

Probably the chaplain thought I was suffering from lust, or that I was an anticlerical Nazi; but I was neither suffering from lust nor was I anticlerical or a Nazi. I simply needed company, and not male company either, and that was so simple that it was terribly complicated; of course there were loose women in town as well as prostitutes (it was a Catholic town), but the loose women and the prostitutes were always offended if you weren't suffering from lust.

I stood for a long time in front of the photo studio; to this day I still always look at photo studios in strange cities; they are all much the same, and all equally depressing, although not everywhere do you find students with colored ribbons. It was nearly one o'clock when I finally left, on the lookout for a café where I didn't have to salute anyone, but in all the cafés they were sitting around in their uniforms, and I ended up by going to a movie anyway, to the first show at one-fifteen. All I remember was the newsreel: some very ignoble-looking Poles were maltreating some very noble-looking Germans; it was so empty in the movie that I could risk smoking during the show; it was hot that last Sunday in August 1939.[3]

When I got back to barracks it was way past three; for some reason the order to put down groundsheets at three o'clock and spread out mess kits and neckties on them had been countermanded; I came in just in time to change, have some bread and liver sausage, lean out of the window for a few minutes, listen to snatches of the discussion about Ernst Jünger and the other one about the female form; both discussions had become more serious, more boring; the orderly and the office clerk were now weaving Latin expressions into their remarks, and that made the whole thing even more repulsive than it was in the first place.

At four we were called out, and I had imagined we would be loading boots from trucks onto railway cars again or from railway cars onto trucks, but this time we loaded cases of soap powder, which were stacked up in the gym, onto trucks, and from the trucks we unloaded them at the parcel-post office, where they were stacked up again. The cases were not heavy, the addresses were typewritten; we formed a chain, and so one case after another passed through my hands; we did this the whole of Sunday afternoon right through till late at night, and there were scarcely any dead minutes when we could have had a bite to eat; as soon as a truck was fully loaded, we drove to the main post office, formed a chain again, and unloaded the cases. Sometimes we overtook a Must-I-then column, or met one coming the other way; by this time they had three bands, and it was all going much faster. It was late, after midnight, when we had driven off with the last of the cases, and my hands remembered the number of mess kits and decided there was very little difference between cases of soap powder and mess kits.

I was very tired and wanted to throw myself on the bed fully dressed, but once again there was a great stack of bread and cans of liver sausage, jam and butter, on the table, and the others insisted it be distributed; all I wanted was the cigarettes, and I had to wait till everything had been divided up exactly, for of course the Pfc. left the cigarettes to the last again; he took an abnormally long time about it, perhaps to teach me moderation and discipline and to convey his contempt for my craving; when I finally got the cigarettes, I lay down on the bed

---

3. *that last Sunday in August 1939.* The German invasion of Poland began on September 1, 1939.

in my clothes and smoked and watched them spreading their bread with liver sausage, listened to them praising the excellent quality of the butter, and arguing mildly as to whether the jam was made of strawberries, apples and apricots, or of strawberries and apples only. They went on eating for a long time, and I couldn't fall asleep; then I heard footsteps coming along the passage and knew they were for me: I was afraid, and yet relieved, and the strange thing was that they all, the office clerk, the orderly and the three probationary teachers who were sitting round the table, stopped their chewing and looked at me as the footsteps drew closer; now the Pfc. found it necessary to shout at me; he got up and yelled, calling me by my surname: "Damn it, take your boots off when you lie down."

There are certain things one refuses to believe, and I still don't believe it, although my ears remember quite well that all of a sudden he called me by my surname; I would have preferred it if we had used surnames all along, but coming so suddenly like that it sounded so funny that, for the first time since the war started, I had to laugh. Meanwhile the door had been flung open and the company clerk was standing by my bed; he was pretty excited, so much so that he didn't bawl me out, although he was a corporal, for lying on the bed with my boots and clothes on, smoking. He said: "You there, in twenty minutes in full marching order in Block 4, understand?" I said: "Yes" and got up. He added: "Report to the sergeant-major over there," and again I said yes and began to clear out my locker. I hadn't realized the company clerk was still in the room; I was just putting the picture of the girl in my trouser pocket when I heard him say: "I have some bad news, it's going to be tough on you but it should make you proud too; the first man from this regiment to be killed in action was your roommate, Corporal Leo Siemers."

I had turned round during the last half of this sentence, and they were all looking at me now, including the corporal; I had gone quite pale, and I didn't know whether to be furious or silent; then I said in a low voice: "But war hasn't been declared yet, he can't have been killed—and he wouldn't have been killed," and I shouted suddenly: "Leo wouldn't get killed, not him . . . you know he wouldn't." No one said anything, not even the corporal, and while I cleared out my locker and crammed all the stuff we were told to take with us into my pack, I heard him leave the room. I piled up all the things on the stool so I didn't have to turn around; I couldn't hear a sound from the others, I couldn't even hear them chewing. I packed all my stuff very quickly; the bread, liver sausage, cheese and butter I left in the locker and turned the key. When I had to turn around I saw they had managed to get into bed without a sound; I threw my locker key onto the office clerk's bed, saying: "Clear out everything that's still in there, it's all yours." I didn't care for him much, but I liked him best of the five; later on I was sorry I hadn't left without saying a word, but I was not yet twenty. I slammed the door, took my rifle from the rack outside, went down the stairs and saw from the clock over the office door downstairs that it was nearly three in the morning. It was quiet and still warm that last Monday of August 1939. I threw Leo's locker key somewhere onto the barrack square as I went across to Block 4. They were all there, the band was already moving into position at the head of the company, and some officer who had given the united effort speech was walking across the square, he took off his cap, wiped the sweat from his forehead and put his cap on again. He reminded me of a streetcar conductor who takes a short break at the terminus.

The sergeant-major came up to me and said: "Are you the man from staff headquarters?" and I said: "Yes." He nodded; he looked pale and very young, somewhat at a loss; I looked past him toward the dark, scarcely distinguishable mass; all I could make out was the gleaming trumpets of the band. "You wouldn't happen to be a telephone operator?" asked the sergeant-major. "We're short one here." "As a matter fact I am," I said quickly and with an enthusiasm which seemed to surprise him, for he looked at me doubtfully. "Yes, I'm one," I said, "I've had practical training as a telephone operator." "Good," he said, "you're just the man I need, slip in somewhere there at the end, we'll arrange everything en route." I went over toward the right where the dark gray was getting a little lighter; as I got closer I even recognized some faces. I took my place at the end of the company. Someone shouted: "Right turn—forward march!" and I had hardly lifted my foot when they started playing their "Must I then."

WHEN THE WAR WAS OVER

IT WAS just getting light when we reached the German border: to our left, a broad river, to our right a forest, even from its edges you could tell how deep it was; silence fell in the boxcar; the train passed slowly over patched-up rails, past shelled houses, splintered telegraph poles. The little guy sitting next to me took off his glasses and polished them carefully.

"Christ," he whispered to me, "d'you have the slightest idea where we are?"

"Yes," I said, "the river you've just seen is known here as the Rhine, the forest you see over there on the right is called the Reich Forest—and we'll soon be getting into Cleves."

"D'you come from around here?"

"No, I don't." He was a nuisance; all night long he had driven me crazy with his high-pitched schoolboy's voice, he had told me how he had secretly read Brecht, Tucholsky and Walter Benjamin, as well as Proust and Karl Kraus; that he wanted to study sociology, and theology too, and help create a new order for Germany, and when we stopped at Nimwegen at daybreak and someone said we were just coming to the German border, he nervously asked us all if there was anyone who would trade some thread for two cigarette butts, and when no one said anything I offered to rip off my collar tabs known—I believe—as insignia and turn them into dark-green thread; I took off my tunic and watched him carefully pick the things off with a bit of metal, unravel them, and then actually start using the thread to sew on his ensign's piping around his shoulder straps. I asked him whether I might attribute this sewing job to the influence of Brecht, Tucholsky, Benjamin or Karl Kraus, or was it perhaps the subconscious influence of Jünger which made him restore his rank with Tom Thumb's weapon; he had flushed and said he was through with Jünger, he had written him off; now, as we approached Cleves, he stopped sewing and sat down on the floor beside me, still holding Tom Thumb's weapon.

"Cleves doesn't convey anything to me," he said, "not a thing. How about you?"

"Oh yes," I said, "Lohengrin, 'Swan' margarine, and Anne of Cleves, one of Henry the Eighth's wives."

"That's right," he said, "Lohengrin—although at home we always had 'Sanella.' Don't you want the butts?"

"No," I said, "take them home for your father. I hope he'll punch you in the nose when you arrive with that piping on your shoulder."

"You don't understand," he said, "Prussia, Kleist, Frankfurt-on-the-Oder, Potsdam, Prince of Homburg, Berlin."

"Well," I said, "I believe it was quite a while ago that Prussia took Cleves—and somewhere over there on the other side of the Rhine there is a little town called Wesel."

"Oh of course," he said, "that's right, Schill."

"The Prussians never really established themselves beyond the Rhine," I said, "they only had two bridgeheads: Bonn and Koblenz."

"Prussia," he said.

"Blomberg," I said. "Need any more thread?" He flushed and was silent.

The train slowed down, everyone crowded round the open sliding door and looked at Cleves; English guards on the platform, casual and tough, bored yet alert: we were still prisoners; in the street a sign: To Cologne. Lohengrin's castle up there among the autumn trees. October on the Lower Rhine, Dutch sky; my cousins in Xanten, aunts in Kevelaer; the broad dialect and the smugglers' whispering in the taverns; St. Martin's Day processions, gingerbread men, Breughelesque carnival,[4] and everywhere the smell, even where there was none, of honey cakes.

"I wish you'd try and understand," said the little guy beside me.

"Leave me alone," I said; although he wasn't a man yet, no doubt he soon would be, and that was why I hated him; he was offended and sat back on his heels to add the final stitches to his braid; I didn't even feel sorry for him: clumsily, his thumb smeared with blood, he pushed the needle through the blue cloth of his air-force tunic; his glasses were so misted over I couldn't make out whether he was crying or whether it just looked like it; I was close to tears myself: in two hours, three at most, we would be in Cologne, and from there it was not far to the one I had married, the one whose voice had never sounded like marriage.

The woman emerged suddenly from behind the freight shed, and before the guards knew what was happening she was standing by our boxcar and unwrapping a blue cloth from what I first took to be a baby: a loaf of bread; she handed it to me, and I took it; it was heavy, I swayed for a moment and almost fell forward out of the train as it started moving; the bread was dark, still warm, and I wanted to call out "Thank you, thank you," but the words seemed ridiculous, and the train was moving faster now, so I stayed there on my knees with the heavy loaf in my arms; to this day all I know about the woman is that she was wearing a dark headscarf and was no longer young.

---

4. *Breughelesque carnival.* The Flemish painter, Pieter Breughel (1525?–1569), painted scenes of peasant life.

When I got up, clasping the loaf, it was quieter than ever in the boxcar; they were all looking at the bread, and under their stares it got heavier and heavier; I knew those eyes, I knew the mouths belonged to those eyes, and for months I had been wondering where the borderline runs between hatred and contempt, and I hadn't found the borderline; for a while I had divided them up into sewers-on and non-sewers-on, when we had been transferred from an American camp (where the wearing of rank insignia was prohibited) to an English one (where the wearing of rank insignia was permitted), and I had felt a certain fellow-feeling with the non-sewers-on till I found out they didn't even have any ranks whose insignia they could have sewn on; one of them, Egelhecht, had even tried to drum up a kind of court of honor that was to deny me the quality of being German (and I had wished that this court, which never convened, had actually had the power to deny me this quality). What they didn't know was that I hated them, Nazis and non-Nazis, not because of their sewing and their political views but because they were men, men of the same species as those I had had to spend the last six years with; the words *man* and *stupid* had become almost identical for me.

In the background Egelhecht's voice said: "The first German bread—and he of all people is the one to get it."

He sounded as if he was almost sobbing, I wasn't far off it myself either, but they would never understand that it wasn't just because of the bread, or because by now we had crossed the German border, it was mainly because, for the first time in eight months, I had for one moment felt a woman's hand on my arm.

"No doubt," said Egelhecht in a low voice, "you will even deny the bread the quality of being German."

"Yes indeed," I said, "I shall employ a typical intellectual's trick and ask myself whether the flour this bread is made of doesn't perhaps come from Holland, England or America. Here you are," I said, "divide it up if you like."

Most of them I hated, many I didn't care about one way or the other, and Tom Thumb, who was now the last to join the ranks of the sewers-on, was beginning to be a nuisance, yet I felt it was the right thing to do, to share this loaf with them, I was sure it hadn't been meant only for me.

Egelhecht made his way slowly toward me: he was tall and thin, like me, and he was twenty-six, like me; for three months he had tried to make me see that a nationalist wasn't a Nazi, that the words *honor, loyalty, fatherland, decency,* could never lose their value—and I had always countered his impressive array of words with just five: Wilhelm II, Papen, Hindenburg, Blomberg, Keitel, and it had infuriated him that I never mentioned Hitler, not even that first of May when the sentry ran through the camp blaring through a megaphone: "Hitler's dead, Hitler's dead!"

"Go ahead," I said, "divide up the bread."

"Number off," said Egelhecht. I handed him the loaf, he took off his coat, laid it on the floor of the boxcar with the lining uppermost, smoothed the lining, placed the bread on it, while the others numbered off around us. "Thirty-two," said Tom Thumb, then there was a silence. "Thirty-two," said Egelhecht, looking at me, for it was up to me to say thirty-three; but I didn't say it, I turned away and looked out: the highway with the old trees: Napoleon's poplars, Napoleon's elms, like the ones I had rested under with my brother when we rode from Weeze to the Dutch border on our bikes to buy chocolate and cigarettes cheap.

I could sense that those behind me were terribly offended; I saw the yellow road signs: To Kalkar, to Xanten, to Geldern, heard behind me the sounds of Egelhecht's tin knife, felt the offendedness swelling like a thick cloud; they were always being offended for some reason or other, they were offended if an English guard offered them a cigarette, and they were offended if he did not; they were offended when I cursed Hitler, and Egelhecht was mortally offended when I did not curse Hitler; Tom Thumb had secretly read Benjamin and Brecht, Proust, Tucholsky and Karl Kraus, and when we crossed the German border he was sewing on his ensign's piping. I took the cigarette out of my pocket I had got in exchange for my staff Pfc. chevron, turned around, and sat down beside Tom Thumb. I watched Egelhecht dividing up the loaf: first he cut it in half, then the halves in quarters, then each quarter again in eight parts. This way there would be a nice fat chunk for each man, a dark cube of bread which I figured would weigh about sixty grams.

Egelhecht was just quartering the last eighth, and each man, every one of them, knew that the ones who got the center pieces would get at least ten to five grams extra, because the loaf bulged in the middle and Egelhecht had cut the slices all the same thickness. But then he cut off the bulge of the two center slices and said: "Thirty-three—the youngest starts." Tom Thumb glanced at me, blushed, bent down, took a piece of bread and put it directly into his mouth; everything went smoothly till Bouvier, who had almost driven me crazy with his planes he was always talking about, had taken his piece of bread; now it should have been my turn, followed by Egelhecht, but I didn't move. I would have liked to light my cigarette, but I had no matches and nobody offered me one. Those who already had their bread were scared and stopped chewing; the ones who hadn't got their bread yet had no idea what was happening, but they understood: I didn't want to share the loaf with them; they were offended, while the others (who already had their bread) were merely embarrassed; I tried to look outside: at Napoleon's poplars, Napoleon's elms, at the tree-lined road with its gaps, with Dutch sky caught in the gaps, but my attempt to look unconcerned was not successful; I was scared of the fight which was bound to start now; I wasn't much good in a fight, and even if I had been it wouldn't have helped, they would have beaten me up the way they did in the camp near Brussels when I had said I would rather be a dead Jew than a live German. I took the cigarette out of my mouth, partly because it felt ridiculous, partly because I wanted to get it through the fight intact, and I looked at Tom Thumb who, his face scarlet, was squatting on his heels beside me. Then Gugeler, whose turn it would have been after Egelhecht, took his piece of bread, put it directly into his mouth, and the others took theirs; there were three pieces left when the man came toward me whom I scarcely knew; he had not joined our tent till we were in the camp near Brussels; he was already old, nearly fifty, short, with a dark, scarred face, and whenever we began to quarrel he wouldn't say a word, he used to leave the tent and run along beside the barbed-wire fence like someone to whom this kind of trotting up and down is familiar. I didn't even know his first name; he wore some sort of faded tropical uniform, and civilian shoes. He came from the far end of the boxcar straight toward me, stopped in front of me and said in a surprisingly gentle voice: "Take the bread"—and when I didn't he shook his head and said: "You fellows have one hell of a talent for turning everything into a symbolic event. It's just bread, that's all, and the woman gave it to you, the woman—here you are." He picked up a piece of bread, pressed it into my right hand, which was hanging down helplessly, and squeezed my hand around it. His eyes were quite dark, not black, and his face wore the look of many prisons. I nodded, got my hand muscles moving so as to hold onto the bread; a deep sigh went through the car, Egelhecht took his bread, then the old man in the tropical uniform. "Damn it all," said the old fellow, "I've been away from Germany for twelve years, you're a crazy bunch, but I'm just beginning to understand you." Before

I could put the bread into my mouth the train stopped, and we got out.

Open country, turnip fields, no trees; a few Belgian guards with the lion of Flanders on their caps and collars ran along beside the train calling: "All out, everybody out!"

Tom Thumb remained beside me; he polished his glasses, looked at the station sign, and said: "Weeze—does this also convey something to you?"

"Yes," I said, "it lies north of Kevelaer and west of Xanten."

"Oh yes," he said, "Kevelaer, Heinrich Heine."

"And Xanten: Siegfried, in case you've forgotten."

Aunt Helen, I thought. Weeze. Why hadn't we gone straight through to Cologne? There wasn't much left of Weeze other than a spattering of red bricks showing through the treetops. Aunt Helen had owned a fair-sized shop in Weeze, a regular village store, and every morning she used to slip some money into our pockets so we could go boating on the River Niers or ride over to Kevelaer on our bikes; the sermons on Sunday in church, roundly berating the smugglers and adulterers.

"Let's go," said the Belgian guard, "get a move on, or don't you want to get home?"

I went into the camp. First we had to file past an English officer who gave us a twenty-mark bill, for which we had to sign a receipt. Next we had to go to the doctor; he was a German, young, and grinned at us; he waited till twelve or fifteen of us were in the room, then said: "Anyone who is so sick that he can't go home today need only raise his hand." A few of us laughed at this terribly witty remark; then we filed past his table one by one, had our release papers stamped, and went out by the other door. I waited for a few moments by the open door and heard him say: "Anyone who is so sick that—," then moved on, heard the laughter when I was already at the far end of the corridor, and went to the next check point: this was an English corporal, standing out in the open next to an uncovered latrine. The corporal said: "Show me your paybooks and any papers you still have." He said this in German, and when they pulled out their paybooks he pointed to the latrine and told them to throw the books into it, adding, "Down the hatch!" and then most of them laughed at this witticism. It had struck me anyway that Germans suddenly seemed to have a sense of humor, so long as it was foreign humor: in camp even Egelhecht had laughed at the American captain who had pointed to the barbed-wire entanglement and said: "Don't take it so hard, boys, now you're free at last."

The English corporal asked me too about my papers, but all I had was my release; I had sold my paybook to an American for two cigarettes; so I said: "No papers"—and that made him as angry as the American corporal had been when I had answered his question: "Hitler Youth, S.A., or Party?" with: "No." He had yelled at me and put me on K.P., he had sworn at me and accused my grandmother of various sexual offenses the nature of which, due to my insufficient knowledge of the American language, I was unable to ascertain; it made them furious when something didn't fit into their stereotyped categories. The English corporal went purple with rage, stood up and began to frisk me, and he didn't have to search long before he had found my diary: it was thick, cut from paperbags, stapled together, and in it I had written down everything that had happened to me from the middle of April till the end of September: from being taken prisoner by the American sergeant Stevenson to the final entry I had made in the train as we went through dismal Antwerp and I read on walls: *Vive le Roi!* [5] There were more than a hundred paperbag pages, closely written, and the furious corporal took it from me, threw it into the latrine, and said: "Didn't I ask you for your papers?" Then I was allowed to go.

We stood crowded around the camp gate waiting for the Belgian trucks which were supposed to take us to Bonn. Bonn? Why Bonn, of all places? Someone said Cologne was closed off because it was contaminated by corpses, and someone else said we would have to clear away rubble for thirty or forty years, rubble, ruins, "and they aren't even going to give us trucks, we'll have to carry away the rubble in baskets." Luckily there was no one near me whom I had shared a tent or sat in the boxcar with. The drivel coming from mouths I did not know was a shade less disgusting than if it had come from mouths I knew. Someone ahead of me said: "But then he didn't mind taking the loaf of bread from the Jew," and another voice said: "Yes, they're the kind of people who are going to set the tone." Someone nudged me from behind and asked: "A hundred grams of bread for a cigarette, how about it, eh?" and from behind he thrust his hand in front of my face, and I saw it was one of the pieces of bread Egelhecht had divided up in the train. I shook my head. Someone else said: "The Belgians are selling cigarettes at ten marks apiece." To me that seemed very cheap: in camp the Germans had sold cigarettes for a hundred and twenty marks

---

5. *Vive le Roi!* Long Live the King! [*French*]

apiece. "Cigarettes, anyone?" "Yes," I said, and put my twenty-mark bill into an anonymous hand.

Everyone was trading with everyone else. It was the only thing that seriously interested them. For two thousand marks and a threadbare uniform someone got a civilian suit, the deal was concluded and clothes were changed somewhere in the waiting crowd, and suddenly I heard someone call out: "But of *course* the underpants go with the suit—and the tie, too." Someone sold his wristwatch for three thousand marks. The chief article of trade was soap. Those who had been in American camps had a lot of soap, twenty cakes some of them, for they had been given soap every week but never any water to wash in, and the ones who had been in the English camps had no soap at all. The green and pink cakes of soap went back and forth.

Some of the men had discovered their artistic aspirations and shaped the soap into little dogs, cats, and gnomes and now it turned out that the artistic aspirations had lowered the exchange value: unsculptured soap rated higher than sculptured, a loss of weight being suspected in the latter.

The anonymous hand into which I had placed the twenty-mark bill actually reappeared and pressed two cigarettes into my left hand, and I was almost touched by so much honesty (but I was only almost touched till I found out that the Belgians were selling cigarettes for five marks; a hundred-per-cent profit was evidently regarded as a fair mark-up, especially among "comrades"). We stood there for about two hours, jammed together, and all I remember is hands: trading hands, passing soap from right to left, from left to right, money from left to right and again from right to left; it was as if I had fallen into a snakepit; hands from all sides moved every which way, passing goods and money over my shoulders and over my head in every direction.

Tom Thumb had managed to get close to me again. He sat beside me on the floor of the Belgian truck driving to Kevelaer, through Kevelaer, to Krefeld, around Krefeld to Neuss; there was silence over the fields, in the towns, we saw hardly a soul and only a few animals, and the dark autumn sky hung low; on my left sat Tom Thumb, on my right the Belgian guard, and we looked out over the tailboard at the road I knew so well: my brother and I had often ridden our bicycles along it. Tom Thumb kept trying to justify himself, but I cut him off every time, and he kept trying to be clever; there was no stopping him. "But Neuss," he said, "that can't remind you of anything. What on earth could Neuss remind anybody of?"

"Novesio Chocolate," I said, "sauerkraut and Quirinus, but I don't suppose you ever heard of the Thebaic Legion."

"No, I haven't," he said, and blushed again.

I asked the Belgian guard if it was true that Cologne was closed off, contaminated by corpses, and he said: "No—but it's a mess all right, is that where you're from?"

"Yes," I said.

"Be prepared for the worst . . . do you have any soap left?"

"Yes, I have," I said.

"Here," he said, pulling a pack of tobacco out of his pocket; he opened it and held out the pale-yellow, fresh fine-cut tobacco for me to smell. "It's yours for two cakes of soap—fair enough?"

I nodded, felt around in my coat pocket for the soap, gave him two cakes and put the tobacco in my pocket. He gave me his submachine gun to hold while he hid the soap in his pockets; he sighed as I handed it back to him. "These lousy things," he said, "we'll have to go on carrying them around for a while yet. You fellows aren't half as badly off as you think. What are you crying about?"

I pointed toward the right: the Rhine. We were approaching Dormagen. I saw that Tom Thumb was about to open his mouth and said quickly: "For God's sake shut up, can't you? Shut up." He had probably wanted to ask me whether the Rhine reminded me of anything. Thank God he was deeply offended now and said no more till we got to Bonn.

In Cologne there were actually some houses still standing; somewhere I even saw a moving streetcar, some people too, women even: one of them waved to us; from the Neuss-Strasse we turned into the Ring avenues and drove along them, and I was waiting all the time for the tears, but they didn't come; even the insurance buildings on the avenue were in ruins, and all I could see of the Hohenstaufen Baths was a few pale-blue tiles. I was hoping all the time the truck would turn off somewhere to the right, for we had lived on the Carolingian Ring; but the truck did not turn, it drove down the Rings: Barbarossa Square, Saxon Ring, Salian Ring, and I tried not to look, and I wouldn't have looked if the truck convoy had not got into a traffic jam up front at Clovis Square and we hadn't stopped in front of the house we used to live in, so I did look. The term "totally destroyed" is misleading; only in rare cases is it possible to destroy a house totally: it has to be hit three or four times and, to make certain, it should then burn down; the house we used to live in was actually, according to official terminology, totally destroyed, but not in the technical sense. That is to say, I could still recognize it, the front door and the doorbells, and I submit that a house where it is still possible to recognize the front door and the doorbells has not, in the strict technical sense, been totally destroyed; but of the house we used to live in there was more to be recognized than the doorbells and the front door: two rooms in the basement were almost intact, on the mezzanine, absurdly enough, even three: a fragment of wall was supporting the third room which would probably not have passed a spirit-level test; our apartment on the second floor had only one room intact, but it was gaping open in front, toward the street; above this, a high, narrow gable reared up, bare, with empty window sockets; however, the interesting thing was that two men were moving around in our living-room as if their feet were on familiar ground; one of the men took a picture down from the wall, the Terborch print my father had been so fond of, walked to the front, carrying the picture, and showed it to a third man who was standing down below in front of the house, but this third man shook his head like someone who is not interested in an object being auctioned, and the man up above walked back with the Terborch and hung it up again on the wall; he even straightened the picture; I was touched by this mark of neatness—he even stepped back to make sure the picture was really hanging straight, then nodded in a satisfied way. Meanwhile the second man took the other picture off the wall: an engraving of Lochner's painting of the Cathedral, but this one also did not appear to please the third man standing down below; finally the first man, the one who had hung the Terborch back on the wall, came to the front, formed a megaphone with his hands and shouted: "Piano in sight!" and the man below laughed, nodded, likewise formed a megaphone with hands and shouted: "I'll get the straps." I could not see the piano, but I knew where it stood: on the right in the corner I couldn't see into and where the man with the Lochner picture was just disappearing.

"Whereabouts in Cologne did you live?" asked the Belgian guard.

"Oh, somewhere over there," I said, gesturing vaguely in the direction of the western suburbs.

"Thank God, now we're moving again," said the guard. He picked up his submachine gun, which he had placed on the floor of the truck, and straightened his cap. The lion of Flanders on the front of his cap was rather dirty. As we turned into Clovis Square I could see why there had been a traffic jam: some kind of raid seemed to be going on. English military police cars were all over the place, and civilians were standing in them with their hands up, surrounded by a sizable crowd, quiet yet tense: a surprisingly large number of people in such a silent, ruined city.

"That's the black market," said the Belgian guard. "Once in a while they come and clean it up."

Before we were even out of Cologne, while we were still on the Bonn-Strasse, I fell asleep and I dreamed of my mother's coffee mill: the coffee mill was being let down on a strap by the man who had offered the Terborch without success, but the man below rejected the coffee mill; the other man drew it up again, opened the hall door and tried to screw the coffee mill onto where it had hung before: immediately to the left of the kitchen door, but now there was no wall there for him to screw it onto, and still the man kept on trying (this mark of tidiness touched me even in my dream). He searched with the forefinger of his right hand for the pegs, couldn't find them and raised his fist threateningly to the gray autumn sky which offered no support for the coffee mill; finally he gave up, tied the strap around the mill again, went to the front, let down the coffee mill and offered it to the third man, who again rejected it, and the other man pulled it up again, untied the strap and hid the coffee mill under his jacket as if it were a valuable object; then he began to wind up the strap, rolled it into a coil and threw it down into the third man's face. All this time I was worried about what could have happened to the man who had offered the Lochner without success, but I couldn't see him anywhere; something was preventing me from looking into the corner where the piano was, my father's desk, and I was upset at the thought that he might be reading my father's diaries. Now the man with the coffee mill was standing by the living-room door trying to screw the coffee mill onto the door panel, he seemed absolutely determined to give the coffee mill a permanent resting place, and I was beginning to like him, even before I discovered he was one of our many friends whom my mother had comforted while they sat on the chair beneath the coffee mill, one of those who had been killed right at the beginning of the war in an air raid.

Before we got to Bonn the Belgian guard woke me up. "Come on," he said, "rub your eyes, freedom is at hand," and I straightened up and thought of all the people who had sat on the chair beneath my mother's coffee mill: truant schoolboys, whom she helped to overcome their fear of exams, Nazis whom she tried to enlighten, non-Nazis whom she tried to fortify: they had all sat on the chair beneath the coffee mill, had received comfort and censure, defense and respite, bitter words had destroyed their ideals and gentle words had offered them those things which would outlive the times: mercy to the weak, comfort to the persecuted.

The old cemetery, the market square, the university. Bonn. Through the Koblenz Gate and into the park. "So long," said the Belgian guard, and Tom Thumb with his tired child's face said: "Drop me a line some time." "All right," I said. "I'll send you my complete Tucholsky."

"Wonderful," he said, "and your Kleist too?"

"No," I said, "only the ones I have duplicates of."

On the other side of the barricade, through which we were finally released, a man was standing between two big laundry baskets; in one he had a lot of apples, in the other a few cakes of soap; he shouted: "Vitamins, my friends, one apple—one cake of soap!" And I could feel my mouth watering; I had quite forgotten what apples looked like; I gave him a cake of soap, was handed an apple, and bit into it at once; I stood there watching the others come out; there was no need for him to call out now: it was a wordless exchange; he would take an apple out of the basket, be handed a cake of soap, and throw the soap into the empty basket; there was a dull thud when the soap landed; not everyone took an apple, not everyone had any soap, but the transaction was as swift as in a self-service store, and by the time I had just finished my apple he already had his soap basket half full. The whole thing took place swiftly and smoothly and without a word, and even the ones who were very economical and very calculating couldn't resist the sight of the apples, and I began to feel sorry for them. Home was welcoming its homecomers so warmly with vitamins.

It took me a long time to find a phone in Bonn; finally a girl in the post office told me that the only people to get phones were doctors and priests, and even then only those who hadn't been Nazis. "They're scared stiff of the Nazi Werewolf underground," she said. "I s'pose you wouldn't have a cigarette for me?" I took my pack of tobacco out of my pocket and said: "Shall I roll one for you?" but she said no, she could do it herself, and I watched her take a cigarette paper out of her coat pocket and quickly and deftly roll herself a firm cigarette. "Who do you want to call?" she said, and I said: "My wife," and she laughed and said I didn't look married at all. I also rolled myself a cigarette and asked her whether there was any chance of selling some soap; I needed money, train fare, and didn't have a pfennig. "Soap," she said, "let's have a look." I felt around in my coat lining and pulled out some soap, and she snatched it out of my hand, sniffed it, and said: "Real Palmolive! That's worth—worth—I'll give you fifty marks for it." I looked at her in amazement, and she said: "Yes, I know, you can get as much as eighty for it, but I can't afford that." I didn't want to take the fifty marks, but she insisted, she thrust the note into my coat pocket and ran out of the post office; she was quite pretty, with that hungry prettiness which lends a girl's voice a certain sharpness.

What struck me most of all, in the post office and as I walked slowly on through Bonn, was the fact that nowhere was there a student wearing colored ribbons, and the smells: everyone smelled terrible, all the rooms smelled terrible, and I could see why the girl was so crazy about the soap; I went to the station, tried to find out how I could get to Oberkerschenbach (that was where the one I married lived), but nobody could tell me; all I knew was that it was a little place somewhere in the Eifel district not too far from Bonn; there weren't any maps anywhere either, where I could have looked it up; no doubt they had been banned on account of the Nazi Werewolves. I always like to know where a place is, and it bothered me that I knew nothing definite about this place Oberkerschenbach and couldn't find out anything definite. In my mind I went over all the Bonn addresses I knew but there wasn't a single doctor or a single priest among them; finally I remembered a professor of theology I had called on with a friend just before the war; he had had some sort of trouble with Rome and the Index,[6] and we had gone to see him simply to give him our moral support; I couldn't remember the name of the street, but I knew where it was, and I walked along the Poppelsdorf Avenue, turned left, then left again, found the house and was relieved to read the name on the door.

The professor came to the door himself; he had aged a great deal, he was thin and bent, his hair quite white. I said: "You won't remember me, Professor, I came to see you some years

---

6. *Rome and the Index.* The Index is the official list of books that Catholics were forbidden to read at the time of the story.

ago when you had that stink with Rome and the Index—can I speak to you for a moment?" He laughed when I said stink, and said: "Of course," when I had finished, and I followed him into his study; I noticed it no longer smelled of tobacco, otherwise it was still just the same with all the books, files, and house plants. I told the professor I had heard that the only people who got phones were priests and doctors, and I simply had to call my wife; he heard me out—a very rare thing—then said that, although he was a priest, he was not one of those who had a phone, for: "You see," he said, "I am not a pastor." "Perhaps you're a Werewolf," I said; I offered him some tobacco, and I felt sorry for him when I saw how he looked at my tobacco; I am always sorry for old people who have to go without something they like. His hands trembled as he filled his pipe, and they did not tremble just because he was old. When he had at last got it lit—I had no matches and couldn't help him—he told me that doctors and priests were not the only people with phones. "These night clubs they're opening up everywhere for the soldiers," they had them, too, and I might try in one of these night clubs; there was one just around the corner. He wept when I put a few pipefuls of tobacco on his desk as I left, and he asked me as his tears fell whether I knew what I was doing, and I said, yes, I knew, and I suggested he accept the few pipefuls of tobacco as a belated tribute to the courage he had shown toward Rome all those years ago. I would have liked to give him some soap as well, I still had five or six pieces in my coat lining, but I was afraid his heart would burst with joy; he was so old and frail.

"Night club" was a nice way of putting it; but I didn't mind that so much as the English sentry at the door of this night club. He was very young and eyed me severely as I stopped beside him. He pointed to the notice prohibiting Germans from entering this night club, but I told him my sister worked there, I had just returned to my beloved fatherland and my sister had the house key. He asked me what my sister's name was, and it seemed safest to give the most German of all German girls' names, and I said: "Gretchen"; oh yes, he said, that was the blonde one, and let me go in; instead of bothering to describe the interior, I refer the reader to the pertinent "Fräulein literature" and to movies and TV; I won't even bother to describe Gretchen (see above); the main thing was that Gretchen was surprisingly quick in the uptake and, in exchange for a cake of Palmolive, was willing to make a phone call to the priest's house in Kerschenbach (which I hoped existed) and have the one I had married called to the phone. Gretchen spoke fluent English on the phone and told me her boy friend would try to do it through the army exchange; it would be quicker. While we were waiting I offered her some tobacco, but she had something better; I tried to pay her the agreed fee of a cake of soap in advance, but she said no, she didn't want it after all, she would rather not take anything, and when I insisted on paying she began to cry and confided that one of her brothers was a prisoner of war, the other one dead, and I felt sorry for her, for it is not pleasant when girls like Gretchen cry; she even let on that she was a Catholic, and just as she was about to get her first communion picture out of a drawer the phone rang, and Gretchen lifted the receiver and said: "Reverend," but I had already heard that it was not a man's voice. "Just a moment," Gretchen said and handed me the receiver. I was so excited I couldn't hold the receiver, in fact I dropped it, fortunately onto Gretchen's lap; she picked it up, held it against my ear, and I said: "Hallo—is that you?"

"Yes," she said. "—Darling, where are you?"

"I'm in Bonn," I said. "The war's over—for me."

"My God," she said, "I can't believe it. No—it's not true."

"It is true," I said, "it is—did you get my postcard?"

"No," she said, "what postcard?"

"When we were taken prisoner—we were allowed to write one postcard."

"No," she said, "for the last eight months I haven't had the slightest idea where you were."

"Those bastards," I said, "those dirty bastards—listen, just tell me where Kerschenbach is."

"I—" She was crying so hard she couldn't speak, I heard her sobbing and gulping till at last she was able to whisper: "—at the station in Bonn, I'll meet you," then I could no longer hear her, someone said something in English that I didn't understand.

Gretchen put the receiver to her ear, listened a moment, shook her head and replaced it. I looked at her and knew I couldn't offer her the soap now. I couldn't even say "Thank you," the words seemed ridiculous. I lifted my arms helplessly and went out.

I walked back to the station, in my ear the woman's voice which had never sounded like marriage. ∎

Bertolt Brecht (1898–1956)

GENERAL, THAT TANK

Translated from the German by
Christopher Middleton

General, that tank of yours is some car.
It can wreck a forest, crush a hundred men.
But it has one failing:
It needs a driver.

5 General, you've got a good bomber there.
It can fly faster than the wind, carry more than an elephant
      can.
But it has one failing:
It needs a mechanic.

General, a man is a useful creature.
10 He can fly, and he can kill.
But he has one failing:
He can think.

RETURN

Translated from the German by
Christopher Middleton

Hometown, how will it look then?
Behind the swarms of bombers
I have come home.
But where's the town? Where the towering
5 Mountains of smoke stand.
There in the flames,
It's there.

Hometown, how will it receive me then?
Before me the bombers come. Death-bearing swarms
10 Announce my return. Raging fires
Precede the homecoming son.

IRON

Translated from the German by
Michael Hamburger

In a dream last night
I saw a great gale rage.
It gripped the scaffolding
Tore down the supports
5 Of solid iron.
But whatever was made of wood
Bent and remained.

CHANGING THE WHEEL

Translated from the German by
Michael Hamburger

I sit on the roadside bank.
The driver changes a wheel.
I do not like the place I have come from.
I do not like the place I am going to.
5 Why do I watch him changing the wheel
With impatience?

TO POSTERITY

Translated from the German by

Michael Hamburger

I

Truly, the age I live in is bleak.
The guileless word is foolish. A smooth brow
Denotes insensitiveness. The laughing man
Has only not yet received
5 The dreadful news.

What times are these when a conversation
About trees is almost a crime.
Because it includes a silence about so many misdeeds!
That one there calmly crossing the street,
10 Hasn't he ceased to be at home to
His friends in need?

True enough: I still earn my living.
But, believe me, it's only luck.
Nothing I do gives me the right to eat my fill.
15 It happens that I've been spared. (When my luck gives out
I shall be lost.)

They tell me: Eat and drink. Be glad that you can!
But how can I eat and drink, when
From the hungry man I snatch what I eat, and
20 My glass of water deprives the man dying of thirst?
And yet I eat and drink.

And I'd also like to be wise.
In the old books you read what is wise:
To keep out of the strife of the world and spend
25 Your brief span without fear.
And to refrain from violence
Render good for evil
Not fulfil one's desires, but forget
Is accounted wise.
30 All these are beyond me:
Truly, the age I live in is bleak.

II

I came into the cities at the time of disorder
When hunger was rife.
I mixed with men at the time of rebellion
35 And revolted as they did.
So passed the time
Granted to me on earth.

I ate my meals between battles.
I lay down to sleep between the murderers.
40 Love I pursued unheeding
And on nature looked without patience.
So passed the time
Granted to me on earth.

The streets led into morasses in my time.
45 Speech betrayed me to the butcher.
There was little I could do. Yet the rulers
Sat more secure but for me, that was my hope.
So passed the time
Granted to me on earth.

50 My resources were not great. The goal
Lay far ahead.
It was clearly visible, if for me
Scarcely attainable.
So passed the time
55 Granted to me on earth.

III

You that will emerge from the deluge
In which we drowned,
When you speak of our shortcomings
Remember too
60 The bleak age
Which you have escaped.

For, changing countries more often than shoes, we walked
Through the wars of the classes, despairing
When there was injustice only and no rebellion.

65 And yet we know well:
Even hatred of vileness
Distorts a man's features.
Even anger at injustice
Makes hoarse his voice. Ah, we
70 Who desired to prepare the soil for kindness
Could not ourselves be kind.

But you, when the times permit
Men to be the helpers of men
Remember us
75 With indulgence.

Hans Werner Cohn (1916–)

OF THE MAN WHO SITS IN THE CELLAR

Translated from the German by
Christopher Middleton

The man sits in the cellar
and he wilts:
a potato sprout in the corner.
His hands hang limp over his knees
5 his shoulders swallow his head.

Sometimes the woman
comes into the cellar
and combs his hair
and cleans his ears
10 and pulls him by the arm
as on a lead
into the best room:
there her lady friends sit round the table.
They say: how nice! they say: how clever!
15 For in the light he does not look at all bad,
the man,
and thoughts thrive
in the cellar air
and now he trundles them out for the lady friends,
20 the man.
The performance over, the woman pulls the man
back into the cellar.

It is her moment.
True: he looks forward to it
25 for a little light
pierces the velvet
of the curtains
in the best room.
Yet: it is her moment.

30 His moment comes
his moment comes
at night.
The woman lies in bed
but the man is awake.
35 His moment comes.
His head thrusts up
between the shoulders
and thumps on the ceiling
savage and red
40 in heart beat.
The hands clench
savage and red
and pound in heart beat
on the cellar door.

45 The woman lies in bed
bathed in fear
in fear.

Heimito von Doderer (1896–1966)

THE MAGICIAN'S ART

Translated from the German by Astrid Ivask

To PAN, the great god of summer, sacrificial offerings of camphor and naphthalene are brought by the city; the cool fragrance is pleasing to him in abandoned, half-darkened habitations, circling the shrouded furniture as a faintest whiff. Meanwhile the inhabitants of such rooms are walking in real woods, or standing in gardens on very narrow gravel paths between flower-beds adorned with glass globes of various colours. Dark woods encircle the foot of the distant mountain range like a discarded garment; rocks, already bare, shimmer milky and mild under the high summer skies, accented only here and there by a patch of snow.

The city has sunk below the horizon. In this heat she sinks into herself and becomes lonely, because so many have left her, and becomes lonelier still above the steaming asphalt, even though hundreds and thousands of people are still running and riding about. The city is in a meditative mood. She now has many hollow spaces for withdrawal, caverns and cavities, shaded and freshly camphorized. At long last furniture attains to a life of its own. But the city's meditations are not confined to sealed-off chambers alone. In front of a small inn, "To the City of Paris," tables with shiny beer mugs are standing on the sidewalk of a by-street. A cool and cellary smell wafts from the vaults, a smell of barrels perhaps, of wine casks and beer barrels. Only now does one notice that the moon has risen above the street. The evening stays very warm.

Reprinted by permission of Biederstein Verlag and Astrid Ivask from *The Literary Review* (Autumn, 1961, Volume 5, Number 1), published by Fairleigh Dickinson University, Rutherford, New Jersey, and later included in MODERN STORIES FROM MANY LANDS, published by Manyland Books, Inc., Copyright © 1963, *The Literary Review*.

Summer in the hot streets of Vienna is not the best of seasons for innkeepers, even though the heat makes beer flow more abundantly, especially when the temperature reaches six mugs in the shade, as a local saying has it. Daily a stream of people leaves the city after working hours, not to mention weekends, when the Vienna yard inns are favoured on account of their arbours, where moonlight transforms the jagged grape leaves into paper cut-outs or, on occasion, into the metallic rigidity of tin.

A stream of people abandons the city, which then begins to meditate in the forsaken inns and among the tables and potted laurel trees on a sidewalk.

The young innkeeper of "The City of Paris" and his wife were determined to get things going again after a succession of hot days that were continuing obstinately, as if intending to chase the very last customer into the verdure of the Prater or to the "Heuriger" in the suburb of Sievering. It would certainly take some doing to counteract this pitiful state of affairs! But since an innkeeper knows most of his customers rather intimately, he also commands a wealth of personal contacts, maybe more so than any other kind of businessman, thus having connections with all sorts of professions and walks of life, down to the very oddest. This is especially true if the innkeeper himself has an attractive and pleasing personality, as was certainly the case with Franz Blauensteiner, not to speak of his beautiful wife Elly, who in addition to a typically Viennese plumpness displayed a pair of shapely legs and thus, as a fair specimen of Viennese womanhood, bounced busily and merrily about the inn.

They knew everyone. And more than that: they recognized, sooner or later, everybody's real worth. They recognized, for instance, the exact relationship of an engaged couple whose feminine half had dyed her hair a fashionable Titian red, matching it with slacks and a loud shirt, while her partner, gentle and quiet, was always seen in one and the same respectable, though ill-fitting dress-suit. He was an employee of a private firm and devoted nearly all of his leisure hours to the peaceful art of bee-keeping, which is a fair indication that this young man was an introspective sort of character. She, on the other hand, would have much preferred riding a motorcycle, since she belonged, even in the absence of such a vehicle, basically to that group of people who keep up with the times, in other words, have a great capacity for making noise with whatever apparatus might best suit the case. "How in the world did she get hold of him, of all people?" "It's just the attraction of opposites," was Mrs. Elly's opinion, and furthermore: "She has bagged him safely, and it is evident who has the upper hand. She would not think of giving up that." "He probably has a lot of money and she knows it," said the innkeeper, whose opinions of the motives of human behavior were clearly down-to-earth. His wife, though no less outspoken, proceeded with more consideration, and ultimately penetrated deeper. Only as a team did they make a first-rate psychologist.

Thus they soon knew all there was to know about their male and female customers, their sore spots as well as what they took most pride in, be it a photograph of one's aunt, because she had been the widow of an Imperial and Royal Captain or be it, as in the case of the old retired cloak room attendant of the Vienna Court Opera, her intimacy with famous stage artists of her time ("such voices as in my time you just don't hear today"), this being documented by a vast number of photographs, complete with dedications. Through large, gold-rimmed spectacles the face of a bygone time seemed to be gazing at one, while reminiscences poured forth, the face of a time which, even while it lasted, was ultimately more preoccupied with the business of social appearances than with that of existence. . . . Then there was the fat little wife of a Civil Servant, her face all nose and looking exactly like a hoopoe. Her daughter appeared so satisfied with the world around her, her dachshund and, above all, herself, that the very world around her could hardly stand it; furthermore we must mention the civil engineer Anton Rieger, ever alone and ever a trifle sad, a truly handsome man, and head of a thriving business firm besides. The Blauensteiners knew him perhaps of all their customers most profoundly and could tell from slight indications, occurring toward midnight— certain gestures of his hands, maybe, and the recurrence of certain words—that his way home that night would be that of a straying star through the night and nightclubs of the city; this fate befell the inveterate bachelor from time to time.

We shall meet several other customers, but only after the magician's performance by which the Blauensteiners meant to awaken the place to life again in spite of the heat of July. They had, of course, connections even to this out-of-the-way profession, which is, nevertheless, a great favourite with the Viennese and has in that city a particularly venerable tradition. Around 1870 or '80 there lived in Vienna the famous Kratki-Baschik who, by changing the final vowel of his Bohemian name, Kratky, and by adding the incomprehensible "Baschik," had arrived at an Arabian- or Turkish-sounding name, in short, an

Oriental one. There does exist in Turkish a word somewhat similar to "Baschik," but of vastly different meaning. . . . Well, what difference did it make! Everybody knew Kratki-Baschik in those days. He resided in the Wurstelprater, the beloved amusement park, and was a magician by profession and owner of a collection of curiosities besides. All kinds of rarely seen things, preserved in alcohol, were on view there. Down to this day any somewhat weird fellow is characterized by the saying: "He belongs in Kratki-Baschik's collection." His pupils and followers in the second and third generation have multiplied and increased in numbers manifold; they organize conventions and contests; few of them are magicians by profession and earn their living as prominent exponents of this art; most are amateurs, although some have developed their art to a high degree of excellence.

Mr. Blauensteiner had procured himself the services of one such amateur and on the appointed night there was only standing room left at the inn, since the magician charged no fee, obliging everyone by a free performance. One might have called him a Sunday magician, as we are used to talking about Sunday painters. This one was a Senior Secretary of the Magistrate by profession. The magician's art involves, by the way, considerable expense, for even a magician cannot get around money and conjure up something out of nothing. The required paraphernalia can, besides being expensive, also be rather complex and even bulky. The crowd watched them being brought in: coffers, tubular pipes, even an odd-looking piece shaped like an old-fashioned contraption for giving electrical treatment, complete with circular window and shining brass parts. The evening was a big success, not only for the innkeeper, but also for the gentleman who so obligingly displayed his art, wearing a detachable white goatee during the performance. Mr. Blauensteiner called this regular customer, whose name was a little difficult to remember, from now on only "Kratki-Baschik," having found out where the gentleman's sympathies lay.

Soon after the beginning of the presentation such feats of magic were performed by this rather important official of the Civil Service, that the audience had forcefully to remind itself of its being all the result of manual dexterity and a skillful display of tricks. Yet even this rational explanation seemed, for several moments, to be suspended. This happened when a beautiful, coloured silk handkerchief of a young gentleman and a twenty-shilling bill of another were chopped and torn to bits in an apparatus—both men silently gave their possessions up for lost—only to be extracted, completely intact and under the very eyes of some spectators: the bill from the innkeeper's bushy hair and the handkerchief from the collar of his shirt. An enormous burst of laughter, applause, and many exclamations of surprise followed. The official of the Magistrate was profusely thanked for the very entertaining evening. The performance having lasted long enough, the consumption of drink keeping pace with the general enthusiasm, he could now pack up his curious and complicated equipment and call for a taxi. The crowd of patrons soon dispersed itself.

At the table of regular customers, only a few people remained with the host and hostess, some already known to us such as the ill-matched lovers and the civil engineer Rieger. Hoopoe, dachshund-daughter, and the member of the Vienna State Opera of the good old days were missing, and in view of the events that followed, we may call their absence a lucky coincidence. Not even the gold-rimmed spectacles of the *ancien régime* had accidentally been left at the inn, which circumstance often resulted in the lady's calling for them on the same evening. "Evening" would, in this case, hardly have done justice to the advanced hour of the night, for it was very late. Despite this hour, still present was a retired University Professor, Dr. Hugo Winkler, a gentleman commonly said to be seventy or more years of age, which seemed a correct assumption on account of his retirement; the gentleman himself, however, and especially his manner of speaking contradicted all evidence and made the above conjecture appear downright incredible: in his dialectics and willfullness he outdid a debating society, while in his capacity for enthusiasm he put a dozen secondary pupils to shame. Present was also a writer, a certain Dr. Döblinger. There is, admittedly, always a writer present. This one shared the whim of his profession: he did not much care to be addressed by his academic title; all writers evidently believe the splendour of their name sufficient to reduce to insignificance whatever titles they may possess.

"She is right, so very right!" cried the Professor emphatically, addressing the hostess, who in his particular case showed more forebearance than actual agreement with his views. "She is absolutely right!" (He was talking about the Titian-dyed redhead in slacks.) "Extraordinary achievement is what makes a man! A woman must simply demand it of him. It matters not whether he be a boxer, a poet, or a magician. But achieve the extraordinary he must! For the object of every endeavor is woman, nothing but woman, nothing else, nothing at all. What other ideals are there? What are you trying to tell me, gentlemen? Am I not right, Mr. Rieger? Woman is the goal of all human endeavor, woman alone!"

"Permit me, Professor," said Dr. Döblinger cautiously. "I cannot go along here without voicing an objection and venturing a counter argument—"

"No objections, no arguments!" interrupted the Professor with animation, his smooth head popping up like that of an aquatic acrobat above water. "I do not tolerate arguments and objections! In this case truth is as clear as daylight. One must but make up one's mind to see it—"

While this kind of dialectics soon reduced the Doctor to silence, it was evident that the bridegroom and bee-keeper (in his respectable, though ill-fitting suit), who had continued in the lowest of spirits, was now sinking into quite a depression. We should not overlook here the implicit and by no means inconsiderable compliment to the Senior Secretary Kratki-Baschik, whose performance had touched off this conversation about things extraordinary in general and extraordinary achievement in particular. The Professor was, of course, always intent upon reducing everything to basic principles. Not so Anton Rieger. He had kept his wits about him during the performance, using his engineer's training to advantage, and had seen through and reconstructed for his own information three of the tricks down to the last detail. Yet he said nothing. Civil engineer Rieger hardly ever said anything at all.

The Professor had meanwhile digressed from his recent argument in favour of dithyrambic exuberance on the following subject: "Didn't you all notice her? During the performance, I mean. I tell you, Mr. Rieger, what a woman! The most beautiful creature I ever saw. At the third table on the left—"

The conversation having reached this point, a silence ensued. The bee-keeper was by now completely wrapped up in his silent gloom. Poor fellow, who knows what imaginings were besetting him! His Titian-red bride took not the slightest notice of him, she did not glance at him once. She had been provoked (maybe by the Professor's speeches), she was in full sail, her bow high and erect, although not heaving with the waves. The bow of her future-bound vessel was, paradoxically, heaving all by itself.

The inn's wide-open doors admitted no coolness. The night continued very warm.

Not a drop of rain had fallen at the first stroke of lightning, and if a wind had arisen, it could not be felt indoors. Yet the blue flash outside was almost immediately followed by a violent clap of thunder. At that very moment a late customer entered the front room, occupied now only by the party at the table. He was a well-dressed gentleman, his face rather broad and smooth, with slightly slanting eyes. This became particularly evident after he had removed his hat, uncovering a highly-domed forehead. He asked politely and in a low voice whether he could still get, in spite of the advanced hour, something to eat, even if it were but some cheese and butter. The innkeeper's wife bounced obligingly to the counter and the customer sat down at a neighbouring table. He ordered only mineral water and apple juice to drink.

As it usually happens when one enters an inn at a late hour, where only a few people are still sitting together, one easily gets drawn into conversation. Meanwhile the talk had reverted again, by one accidental remark or another, to Kratki-Baschik. This topic seemed to hold some, even if incidental interest for the newcomer; it was at any rate evident that he followed the conversation in which now the Titian-dyed redhead also participated, after having observed the stranger for quite a while with interest and not very discreetly; one had to admit that she watched him quite openly. Before he knew it, he was involved in the conversation, the innkeeper's wife herself providing him with some explanation of the evening's happenings, not forgetting to mention the excellence of the presentation they all had seen. The new customer was just getting ready to answer her, when he was asked by the innkeeper to join them. He accepted and carried his glass to their table. The innkeeper's wife continued her praises of the Senior Secretary's artistry, mentioning also his name and position.

"Yes," said the newcomer. "I know him. An excellent dilettante."

"Pardon me, dilettante—," laughed the innkeeper's wife. "Had I but a fraction of his ability!"

"Yes, indeed," said the stranger. "He is very good, this Mr. Blahoutek, and as amateurs go, one of the very best."

"Is the gentleman perhaps himself in this line of business?" inquired the innkeeper interestedly.

"Yes, indeed," was the reply.

"And what, if I may ask, is the difference, I mean: what distinguishes a professional from an amateur like Mr. Blahoutek?"

"Well, a dilettante may, in general, perform quite outstanding tricks, even of his own invention, but, naturally, he lacks the technique that only the most advanced professional training can give, he lacks real artistry."

"Well, then: is the gentleman himself such an artist?"

The answer was in the affirmative.

"What a pity that the Senior Secretary took all of his possessions along!" cried the innkeeper. "Otherwise we could borrow one of his gadgets and the gentleman could oblige us with a beautiful piece of magic!"

"One does not always need gadgets," remarked the stranger in a casual tone of voice.

"Did you just now come from another restaurant here in the vicinity?" inquired the friendly Mrs. Blauensteiner.

"No, I was alone at home until now."

"Why!" exclaimed the lady. "Then you first went out as late as eleven o'clock?"

"Yes, I did," was the reply. By this time it dawned upon Dr. Döblinger, and this by way of his nose (the nose of a writer is one of his tools and possesses a technique that only the most advanced professional training can give). From the very moment the stranger sat down at their table, the author had been besieged by a vision of his own quiet, empty flat in the vicinity of the inn. So vivid and persistent was this vision that it nearly haunted him, appearing before his inner eye, accompanied by a very subtly piercing longing: the easy chairs, heavily shrouded against the dangerous attacks of moths, and a large wardrobe with mirrors, its tightly-closed doors hiding the rugs, yet emitting from time to time the faintest whiff of camphor and naphthalene into the relative coolness of the room.

It was the height of summer, there was no denying it.

This fragrance was everywhere, hovering in flats that had withdrawn into themselves and away from the hot and noisy street. The fragrance almost seemed to spread a gospel of gentle detachment, inviting one to withdraw deeper still.

The stranger, too, came from such a solitary flat. One could smell this loneliness.

Meanwhile two or three flashes of lightning had been seen, accompanied by thunder, though less intense than the first time; a short rain now descended, its splashing soon giving way to silence again. Yet coolness now wafted from the street.

Franz Blauensteiner, the innkeeper, was not one to give up an idea easily; tonight he had quite made up his mind to see for himself whether the unknown artist could really outdo the Senior Secretary, and yet, as he said, without equipment. So he proceeded to ask the gentleman what was needed for the performance of his trick. "It will probably be easiest for you to find some playing cards and a handful of nails, six to eight of them will do. The cards may just as well be old and dirty ones, they all fall to the floor in the end."

The requested items were brought. Suspense was mounting among the patrons. The stranger, sitting toward the end of the table and not very far from the panelled wall, handed the innkeeper and his wife the cards, casually requesting them to select one secretly, to keep it well in mind without removing it from the set, and to lay the whole pack of cards on the table in front of him.

This done, and the unknown customer having meanwhile paid his moderate bill, he seized the nails in his left hand, the cards in his right, and threw or rather hurled both simultaneously against the panelled wall. The flock of cards dispersed, falling and gliding everywhere, onto the table, into the laps of the onlookers, down to the floor, followed by a clatter of falling nails. The next moment the innkeeper's wife uttered a shriek: on the wall, directly across from her, hung, face toward the room and pierced by a nail, the card she and her husband had chosen by secret agreement: the ten of spades. A dead silence followed. The stranger smiled obligingly, reached for his hat, bowed slightly, and left the inn. The Titian-red bride now sat stiffly erect and stared with wide-open eyes, her bow heaving heavily in his wake, even after he had disappeared from sight.

Within a minute of the stranger's departure, however, an even more surprising event took place. The bee-keeper suddenly started up from his gloomy brooding and ran out of the room. He did not bother to pick up his hat.

As we were able to learn from himself at a later date, he had indeed succeeded in catching a last glimpse of the stranger in the street, and had overtaken him at a running pace. This had been the stranger's reply to his stammered address: "Young man, great art should not be studied with a purpose in mind; even less for the purpose of winning a girl over; purpose kills art. May you bear this in mind."

Well, for the time being we were all still sitting together, minus artist and bee-keeper, whose return was expected by everyone very shortly. Yet, he did not turn up. The first conjectures were brought forth along with attempts to console or rather appease the Titian-red bride, who was beginning to show distinct signs of the rage to which we all fall prey so easily when we glance off the fine, yet absolutely inexorable borderline of our dominion. "Of course he will come," said the Professor. "He will be here presently." Things did not, however, take quite as natural a course. Little by little the situation was getting out of hand, threatening to degenerate into a disgrace for the redhead. Civil engineer Rieger's eyes grew somber and sad, as they always did when somebody was caught in an embarrassing situation. Then, shortly after the Professor's words, the telephone rang. "It will be he," said Dr. Winkler. The innkeeper answered the call. It was he. The Titian-red bride disappeared into the booth. During their lengthy conversation not a word was said at the table; everything, including the Professor's pronouncements upon the natural course of human affairs, seemed to be hanging by a thread. The conversation went on forever. Finally she emerged. Her pallor escaped nobody's notice, nor did her altered looks: she was not a bit pretty now. She did not heave. Rather, her rage now burst the corset of respectability, she went to pieces before everybody's eyes. "What do you know," she cried—still by the booth, not even returned to the table. "That idiot has the nerve to tell me we are through, he never wants to see me again. . . ." Even the Professor could not get out his (though conceivably still possible) consolations, so he silently sank, smoothly shining head and all, below the surface of the conversation. The Titian-red bride left, not bothering about her bridegroom's hat. It was more a breaking with this circle (in which she was indeed never seen again) than leave-taking. After this the innkeeper tried again, unsuccessfully, to remove by hand the nail that still held the ten of spades. Everybody was pleasantly affected by this card on the wall. Finally Blauensteiner got a small pair of pliers. Now it worked. "It serves her right," said Elly Blauensteiner after the Titian-dyed redhead had left. "He will certainly come back to her again," reiterated the Professor, still submerged. "He will never come back to her," answered Rieger. His words, though few, were true.

During the next few days the ten of spades on the wall—which must have had something of a Menetekel about it and therefore was so often alluded to—this ten of spades was simply talked to death. This seems to be the way of all great art: it is gnawed by tiny teeth until it falls to pieces and can be argued away; it is the fate of miracles, reduced to a miniature scale. Art and miracles cannot be part of life; they would grow unbearable, only to end as hard clods of the beyond in this world, crushing everything. Late in the night, after the accursed playing card had finally disappeared from the wall, the innkeeper Franz Blauensteiner sat a long time in silence, staring straight in front of him, until he finally summed it up: "This one was, of course, a—a different magician's art." ■

Friedrich Dürrenmatt (1921–   )

THE TUNNEL

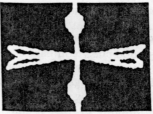

Translated from the German by
Carla Colter and Alison Scott

THE YOUNG MAN who boarded his usual train that Sunday afternoon was twenty-four years old and fat. He was fat in order to protect himself, for anything he perceived out of the ordinary terrified him. Indeed, this clarity of vision was probably the only real ability he possessed, and even this was a burden to him. Although his fat gave a general protection to his body, he found it necessary to stuff every sort of hole in his body through which the terrifying influences might reach him. He smoked cigars (Ormond Brazil 10). He wore a pair of sunglasses over his ordinary glasses. He even stuffed his ears with wads of cotton wool. At twenty-four he was still dependent on his parents, a consequence of rather nebulous studies at the University. And the University was two hours away from home by train. Departure time five-fifty. Arrival at seven twenty-seven.

And so this student, fat and twenty-four years old, boarded his usual Sunday train to attend a seminar the following day. The fact that he had already decided to skip class was irrelevant. As he left his home town the afternoon sun shone from a cloudless summer sky. It was pleasant weather for a trip he knew almost by heart. The train's route lay between the Alps and the Juras, past rich villages and towns, over a river and, after some twenty minutes further travel, into a little tunnel just beyond Burgdorf. The train was overcrowded and he had entered at one of the front cars. With considerable difficulty he worked his way toward the rear. Perspiring, and with two pairs of glasses, he offered an oafish appearance. All the travelers were sitting closely packed, some even on suitcases. All the second-class compartments were occupied, and only the first-class compartments were relatively empty. The young man fought through the melee of families and recruits, students and lovers, falling against this one or that one as the train swayed, stumbling against stomachs and breasts until he came to a seat in the last car. At last he had found space enough to have a bench to himself, a pleasant surprise, since third-class coaches are seldom divided into compartments with benches. Opposite him, playing a solitary game of chess, he noted a man even fatter than himself, and on the same bench, near the corridor, sat a red-haired girl reading a novel. The young man gratefully chose the window seat on the empty bench. He had just lit an Ormond Brazil 10 when the train entered the little tunnel. Of course he had traveled this stretch many times before, almost every Saturday and Sunday throughout the past year, but he had never found the opportunity to examine the tunnel closely. He had, in fact, been only vaguely aware of it. Several times he had intended to give it his full attention, but each time he had been thinking of other matters, and each time the brief plunge into darkness had passed unnoticed, so fast was the train and so brief its plunge into the darkness of the little tunnel.

And even this time he had not been thinking of the tunnel and so had forgotten to take off his sunglasses. Outside the tunnel the sun had been shining with all its force, flooding the hills and woods and the distant chain of the Juras with golden evening light. Even the little houses of the town through which they had just passed had seemed built of gold. This abrupt passage from light to darkness must then be the reason why the tunnel seemed so much longer than usual. He waited patiently in the dark compartment for the return to daylight. At any moment the first pale shimmer of daylight would gleam on his windowpane, widen as quickly as a flash of lightning, then close in powerfully with its full yellow brightness. Nevertheless, the darkness lasted. He took off his sunglasses. At about the same time the girl lit a cigarette. As her match flared orange he thought he detected a grim annoyance in her face. No doubt she resented the interruption in her perusal of her novel. He looked at his wrist watch. The luminous dial said six-ten.

He leaned back, settling himself in the corner between window and compartment wall, and directed his thoughts to the complications of his studies. No one really believed he was studying at all. He thought of the seminar he had to attend the next day, and which he would not attend. Each of his activities seemed a pretext designed to achieve order behind the façade of routine pursuits. Perhaps what he sought was not order itself, but only a semblance of order. The art of an actor who used his fat, his cigars and his cotton wool as make-up for a genteel comedy, while all the while he knew himself to be a part of some monstrous farce. When he next looked at his watch the time was six-fifteen. The train was still in the tunnel. He felt confused. At last the light bulbs flickered and the compartment brightened. The red-haired girl returned to her novel and the fat gentleman resumed his solitary chess game. The whole compartment now appeared reflected in the window. But outside, on the other side of the window, the tunnel was still there.

He stepped into the corridor in which a tall man was walking up and down restlessly. He observed the light raincoat and the black scarf around the gentleman's neck. Surely there was no need for a scarf in this weather? A black scarf? He peered into the other compartments in the rear coach. The passengers were reading their newspapers or chatting. Normal. He returned to his corner and sat down. The tunnel must come to an end any minute now. At any second? His wrist watch read six-twenty. He felt an obscure annoyance with himself for not having paid more attention to the tunnel on previous trips. They had been in the tunnel for a quarter of an hour now. And surely, allowing for the speed of the train, it must be one of the longest tunnels in Switzerland. Or perhaps he had taken the wrong train. But he could recall no other tunnel of such length and importance within twenty minutes of his home. On impulse he asked the fat chess player if the train were indeed bound for Zurich. The man confirmed this. The student ventured again that he hadn't known that there was such a long tunnel on this part of the journey. The chess player was more than a little annoyed to have his difficult considerations interrupted a second time. He replied testily that in Switzerland there were a great many tunnels, in fact, an extraordinary number of tunnels, that he was actually traveling in Switzerland for the first time, but that an affluence of tunnels was the first thing one noticed about Switzerland, and indeed, his statistical almanac confirmed the fact that no country possessed such a positive abundance of tunnels as Switzerland! And he added that now he must excuse himself; he was very sorry, really, but a most difficult chess problem in regard to the Nimzowitsch Defense occupied his mind and he could afford no further diversions. The last remark was polite, but firm. It was evident that no further conversation could be expected from the chess player and, in any event, he could be of little use, since the route was new to him.

At that moment the conductor appeared, and the student had high hopes that his ticket would be refused. The official was pale and scrawny. He gave an impression of nervousness as he remarked to the girl near the door that she would have to change trains at Olten. Although Olten was also a regular stop on the Zurich run, the young man did not give up hope of being on the wrong train, so complete was his conviction that he had mistaken trains in boarding. He didn't doubt that he would have to pay extra fare, but he accepted the expense with equanimity. The return to daylight would be cheap at the price. He therefore handed his ticket to the conductor and said that his destination was Zurich. He accomplished the speech without once removing the Ormond Brazil 10 from his mouth.

"But the gentleman is on the right train," replied the conductor as he inspected the ticket.

"But we're going through a tunnel!" The young man had spoken with considerable anger. He was determined to put an end to the confusion. The official replied that they had just passed Herzogenbuchsee and would soon approach Langenthal where the train was due at six-twenty. The young man looked at his watch. Six-twenty. But they had been traveling through the tunnel for the past twenty minutes, he persisted. The conductor raised his brows.

"This is the Zurich train," he said, now looking for the first time toward the window. "Six-twenty," he said again, uneasily. "We'll be in Olten soon. Arrival time six thirty-seven. We must have gone into some bad weather suddenly. A storm. Yes. That's why it's dark."

The gentleman with the Nimzowitsch Defense problem entered the conversation now. He had been holding out his ticket (and holding up his game) for some time, but the conductor had not yet noticed him. "Nonsense," he interjected. "Nonsense! We're traveling through a tunnel. I can see the rock clearly. Looks like granite. Switzerland has more tunnels than all the rest of the world put together. Read it in a statistical almanac."

The conductor relieved him of his ticket, and repeated pleadingly that this was truly the Zurich train. Unmollified, the young man demanded to speak to the Chief Conductor. The ticket collector now felt his dignity to have been abused. He directed the student to the front of the train, but reiterated huffily that the train was going to Zurich, that the time was now six twenty-five, that in twelve minutes time (according to the summer schedule) the train would arrive in Olten, and that the young man should have no further doubts on that point. *He* traveled this train at least twelve times a month.

Nevertheless the young scholar set off to find the Chief Conductor. Movement through the crowded train now seemed even more difficult than before. The train must be traveling exceedingly fast. In any event, it was making a frightful racket. He stuffed the wads of cotton a little more firmly into his ears, for he had loosened them in order to speak to the ticket collector. The passengers were behaving calmly. This train was no different from any other Sunday afternoon train, and no one appeared worried. In the second-class compartments he came upon an Englishman standing by the corridor window. "Simplon," [1] he was saying, as he tapped the pane with his pipe and beamed inanely.

Things were very much as usual in the dining car too. No seats were vacant, and neither waiters nor diners, occupied with Wiener schnitzel and rice, made any comment on the tunnel. But there, near the exit of the dining car, he recognized the red bag of the Chief Conductor.

"What can I do for you, sir?" The Chief Conductor was a tall man, quiet behind a carefully groomed black mustache and neat rimless glasses.

"We have been in a tunnel for twenty-five minutes."

The Conductor did not look toward the windows, as the young man might have expected, but turned to a nearby waiter. "Give me a packet of Ormond 10," he said. "I smoke the same brand as the gentleman here." The waiter, however, indicated that the brand was not in stock, and the young man, glad of an opportunity for further conversation, proffered a Brazil.

"Thank you," returned the Conductor. "In Olten I shall hardly have time to buy any. You are doing me a great favor. Smoking is a most important business. Will you come this way, please?"

Mystified, the young man followed him into the freight car ahead of the diner.

"The next car is the locomotive," offered the official. "This is the front of the train."

---

1. *Simplon,* a mountain pass in the Alps in Switzerland near the Italian border; site of the world's longest railroad tunnel.

A sickly yellow light burned amid the baggage. Most of the car lay in total darkness. The side doors were barred, as was the small window beside them, and through its irons the greater blackness of the tunnel seeped in. The trunks, many decorated with hotel stickers, the bicycles and the baby carriage that composed the cargo of the coach seemed haphazardly arranged. The Chief Conductor, an obviously precise man, hung his red bag on a nearby hook.

"What can I do for you?" he asked again, without, however, looking at the student. Instead, he began to enter neat columns in a book he had taken from his pocket.

"We have been in a tunnel since Burgdorf," answered the young man with determination. "There is no such enormous tunnel on this line. I know. I travel back and forth every week on this train."

The Chief Conductor continued to write. "Sir," he said, stepping close to his inquisitor, so close that their bodies almost touched, "sir, I have little to tell you. I have no idea how we got into this tunnel. I have no explanation for it. But I ask you to consider this. We are moving along on tracks: therefore this tunnel leads somewhere. We have no reason whatever to believe that anything is wrong with this tunnel, except, of course, that there seems to be no end to it." The Chief Conductor still held the unlit Ormond Brazil 10 between his lips. He had spoken extremely quietly, yet with such dignity and clarity, and with such assurance that his words were audible despite the increased noise of the baggage car.

"Then I must ask you to stop the train," said the young man impatiently. "I really don't understand you. If there's something wrong with this tunnel—and it seems you can't explain even its existence—then your duty is to stop this train at once."

"Stop the train?" returned the older man slowly. It seemed he had already thought of that, but, as he informed his companion, it was a serious matter to stop a train. With this, he shut the book and laid it in the red bag which was swaying to and fro on its hook. Then he carefully lit the Ormond 10. The young man offered to pull the emergency brake overhead, and was on the point of releasing the lever, when suddenly he staggered forward and was sent crashing against the wall. At the same moment, the baby carriage rolled toward him and several trunks slid by. The Chief Conductor swayed strangely and began to move, hands outstretched, through the freight car.

"We are going downhill!" he announced as he joined the young man now leaning against the wall. But the expected crash of hurtling train against granite tunnel did not occur. There was no shattering of telescoped coaches. Once again the train seemed to be running on a level. The door opened at the other end of the car. In the bright light of the diner, until the door swung to again, they could see the passengers merrily toasting one another's health.

"Come into the locomotive." At this point the Chief Conductor was peering thoughtfully, almost menacingly at the student. He opened the door nearby. As he did so a rush of tempestuous heat-laden air struck the pair with such force that they were driven back against the wall. At the same moment a frightful clatter resounded through the almost empty freight car.

"We'll have to climb over to the engine," he cried into the younger man's ear. Despite his shouting, his voice was hardly audible. He then disappeared through the right angle of the open doorway. The student followed cautiously in the direction of the swaying and brightly lit engine. He didn't know why he was climbing, but at this point determination had overcome reason. He found himself on a pitching platform between the two cars, and clung desperately to the iron rails on both sides. Although the terrific draft moderated but slightly as he inched his way up to the locomotive, he dreaded the wind less than the immediate nearness of the tunnel walls. They were hidden from him in the blackness, but were nevertheless frighteningly close. It was necessary to focus all his attention on the engine ahead, yet the pounding of the wheels and the hissing vibrating push of air against him gave him the feeling of careening, at the speed of a falling star, into a world of stone.

A board just wide enough to walk on crossed the gap between the cars and ran the length of the engine. Above and parallel to it, a curving metal rod served as railing. To reach the plank he would have to make a jump of nearly a yard. He braced himself, leaped, and pushed himself along the board. His progress was slow, since he had to press close to the outside of the engine to keep his foothold. It was not until he reached the long side of the engine and was fully exposed to the roaring hurricane of wind and to the menacing cliff walls now brilliantly illuminated by the engine lights that he began to realize his fear. But just then he was rescued by the Chief Conductor who pulled him through a small door into the engine. Exhausted, the young man lay against the wall. He was grateful for the sudden quiet. With the engine door shut, the steel walls of the giant locomotive deadened the noise almost completely.

"Well, we've lost the Ormond Brazil too," said the Conductor.

"It wasn't a very sensible idea to light one before starting the climb, but they break so easily in one's pocket. It's their unusual length."

The young man was delighted to converse normally again. The close and terrifying rock walls had reminded him uncomfortably of his everyday world, of its ever-similar days and years. The thought occurred to him that their boring similitude had perhaps been only a preparation for the present moment: that this was a moment of initiation, of truth, this departure from the surface of the earth and precipitous descent into the womb of the earth. He took another brown package from his right coat pocket and offered the Chief Conductor a new cigar. He took one himself, and carefully they lit their Brazils from the Conductor's lighter.

"I am very fond of these Ormonds," said the older man, "but one must pull very hard on them. Otherwise they go out so easily."

For some reason these words made the student suspicious. Was the Conductor as uncomfortable as he about the tunnel? For the tunnel still ran on interminably, and his mind persisted in the thought that surely the tunnel must stop, even as a dream can end, all of a sudden.

"Six-forty," he said, consulting his watch. "We should be in Olten now." Even as he spoke, he thought of the hills and woods radiant only a short while ago in the late golden sun. The thought could have been present in both their minds. Nevertheless, the two men stood and smoked and leaned against their wall.

"Keller is my name," announced the Conductor as he puffed at his Brazil.

The student refused to change the topic of conversation.

"The climb to the engine was very dangerous, didn't you think? At least it was for me. I'm not used to that sort of thing. Anyway, I'd like to know why you've brought me here."

"I don't know," said Keller. "I wanted time to consider."

"Time to consider?"

"Yes," returned the Chief Conductor. "That's right." And he went on smoking. Just then the engine reeled over at a still steeper angle.

"We could go into the engineer's cabin," suggested Keller. He did not, however, leave his position against the wall. Annoyed by his companion's indecisiveness, the young man stepped briskly along the corridor to the driver's cabin, then abruptly stopped.

"Empty!" he said to the Conductor who had now moved up behind him. "The driver's seat is empty!" They went into the cabin. It was swaying too, for the engine was still tearing through the tunnel at enormous speed, bearing the train along with it, as though the weight of the coaches behind no longer counted.

"Allow me," said the Chief Conductor. He pressed some levers and pulled the emergency brake. There was no change. "We tried to stop the engine earlier. As soon as we noticed the alteration in the tracks. It didn't stop then either."

"It certainly isn't stopping now," said the other. He pointed to the speed indicator. "A hundred. Has the engine ever done a hundred before?"

"Good heavens! It has never gone so fast. Sixty-five at the most."

"Exactly. And the speed is increasing. Now the speedometer says a hundred and five. We must be falling." He went up to the window, but he couldn't keep his balance. He was pressed with his face against the glass, so fantastic was their speed. "The engine driver?" he shouted as he stared at the rock masses streaking towards him in the glare of the arc lights, disappearing above him and below him on either side of the engineer's cabin.

"He jumped off," Keller yelled back. He was now sitting on the floor, his back against the controls.

"When?" The student pursued the matter obstinately. Keller hesitated a while. He decided to relight his Ormond, an awkward task, for his legs were then at the same height as his head while the train continued its roll to one side.

"Five minutes after the switch. No use thinking to save him. Freight carman abandoned the train too."

"And you?" asked the student.

"I am in charge of this train. I, too, have always lived without hope."

"Without hope," repeated the young man. By then he was lying on the glass pane, face pressed against glass. Glass and engine and human flesh were pressed together above the abyss. "Back in the compartment," he thought, "we had entered the tunnel, but we didn't know that even then everything was already lost. We didn't think that anything had changed, and yet the shaft of the depths had already received us, and we had entered our abyss."

"I'll have to go to the rear," shouted the Chief Conductor. "The coaches will be in a panic. Everyone will be trying to get to the rear of the train."

"That's true." The student thought of the chess player and of the red-haired girl with her novel. He handed Keller his remaining packages of Ormond Brazil. "Take them. You'll lose your cigar again when you climb over."

"Aren't you coming?" The Conductor was once more on his feet and with difficulty he had begun to clamber up the funnel of the corridor. The student gazed at the useless instruments, at the useless ridiculous levers and switches shining silver-like in the glare of the cabin lights.

"A hundred and thirty," he called. "I don't think you'll be able to get to the coaches above us at this speed."

"It's my duty," shouted Keller over his shoulder.

"Certainly," returned the young man. He didn't bother turning his head to watch the other's senseless efforts.

"At least I have to try," yelled the Conductor. He was already far over the head of the fat young man. He braced elbows and thighs against slippery walls and seemed, indeed, to be making some progress. But just then the engine took a further turn downward. It hurtled toward the interior of the earth, goal of all things, in its terrible plunge. Keller now was directly over his friend who lay face downward on the silver gleaming window at the bottom of the driver's cabin. His strength gave. Suddenly he fell, crashed against the control panel and came to rest on the window beside his companion.

"What are we to do?" he cried, clinging to the young man's shoulders and shouting into his ear. The very fact that it was now necessary to shout alarmed him. The noise of the onrushing walls had destroyed even the quiet of the engine.

The younger man lay motionless on the pane of glass which separated him from the depths below. His fat body and weighty flesh were of no further use to him, no protection now.

"What are we to do?" persisted the Chief Conductor.

"Nothing," came the merciless reply. Merciless, yet not without a certain ghostly cheerfulness. Now, for the first time, his glasses were gone and his eyes were wide open. Greedily he sucked in the abyss through those wide-open eyes. Glass and metal splinters from the shattered control panel now studded his body. And still he refused to tear his thirsting eyes from the deadly spectacle below. As the first crack widened in the window beneath them, a current of air whistled into the cabin. It seized his two wads of cotton wool and swept them upward like arrows into the corridor shaft overhead. He watched them briefly and spoke once more.

"Nothing. God let us fall. And now we'll come upon him." ■

Günter Eich [1] (1907–   )

THE STILTS-WALKER

Translated from the German by
Carolyn Bly

I MEET MANY PEOPLE, and there is hardly a one among them who is happy. But I am, because I have done what I wanted to do when I was a boy. I have the profession I always wanted: I am an agent for the Astrol Firm, producers and distributors of shoe polish.

This much accounts for the practical side of my work, but it is the higher things (which belong to every true calling—and to mine) that give me my unending happiness. How should I explain this to anyone who hasn't experienced it?

The casual observer fails to see the two facets of my occupation as a single entity. When I have been around to all the shops in a given town, and taken orders for the shoe polish, I return to my pickup. By then it has usually drawn more or less of a crowd —primarily children. It is not so much the wild-colored advertisements on the sides that attract them—there are many trucks of the kind to be seen—but I have to admit that the poison-

"The Stilts-Walker" by Günter Eich, translated by Carolyn Bly in NEW DIRECTIONS IN PROSE AND POETRY 18. Reprinted by permission of the translator.
1. *Günter Eich* (gœn'tér ıн).

green and purple of the Astrol Firm colors do seem to mesmerize people as a viper's eyes do a toad. No, it is the extraordinary build of the truck itself that stops everyone who catches sight of it. There are two ladders attached vertically to the sides, one to the left, the other to the right. They bend toward each other high over the top of the cab, towering up there in open space. Between them a greater-than-lifesize man's shoe (also poison-green) turns in a circle. From it hang huge purple laces like drapery tassels. If you pull these (and the children always do, soon enough) a phonograph inside the truck is set going. It plays a series of worn lively or sentimental records, followed by a few minutes of commercial. Its remarkable effectiveness lies in the fact the children suppose the mechanism is forbidden them; it is just this psychological device that catches them. When I approach the pickup myself, there are always some evildoers (actually my unwitting accomplices) who tumble off the ladders, purely out of bad conscience. The others watch me apprehensively, but I look right through them, open the doors at the back of the truck, climb in, and shut them behind me. I get dressed in the darkness inside.

I have to admit that even to this day when I am alone in the pickup, my heart sometimes misses a beat out of nervousness. I am tense to the point of tears—all for that instant when I must reopen the door. Perhaps it is the same with the actor in his dressing room, who prepares himself for his entrance. Be that as it may, mine is a much more profound and soul-searching onslaught than any cue to come onstage. But I always manage to pull myself together.

When I have got on the purple trousers (which are twice as long as my legs and therefore must be carefully caught up in folds) and the poison-green sandwich boards that carry the name *Astrol* on my back and breast, I take up the red stovepipe hat in my hand, open the doors, and come out head first.

I approach one of the ladders (regularly changing off between the two) and start climbing the rungs, at the same time unfastening the stilts that are hidden behind the ladder poles. When I have reached the top I let the extra lengths of trouser leg slip over the stilts, unrolling to their ends. Then I descend a few rungs until my fingers can get hold of the stilts-tops and my feet find the jutting stops. Then I push myself off from the truck and begin my jaunt through the streets—high over the heads of the jostling and bawling crowds.

I recall very plainly how as a child I first saw such a stilts-walker. Down the road he came with blowing coattails. At the same time, smoke was coming from the potato fields; I shall always associate him with the smell of the potato fires. My mother held me up in her arms, and looking at him, I was struck silent for the first time in my life. It was the most wonderful thing I had ever seen. The stilts-man leaned way down to me (it was amazing he could do it!) and when his beard was about to touch me he popped a chocolate into my mouth! With that chocolate, my heart was committed—to be just what he was. When I saw him again some years later he had lost none of his fascination. It became more and more obvious to me that there was nothing greater in the world than to be a stilts-walker.

Men fail to be happy because they give up their *real* goals; each practical difficulty, as it comes up, pushes them a little more off the path. Oh, I too have had difficulties and I have had to call on myself for a great deal of patience to overcome them —to take the setbacks as they came without despairing. The very process of walking on stilts, which I started in childhood, could have toppled me into the sands of despair. And merely to *manipulate* the stilts meant nothing; I had to win such mastery that the art of stilts-walking would no longer hold any secrets from me. This came before everything else: giving the impression of complete self-sufficiency, and finally, acquiring even a kind of dancer's grace which had to look effortless. Of course I still have a long way to go to reach that point, but I daresay I've not spared myself any trouble. Since I was six no day has passed without my devoting several hours to training. Even now I give three or four hours—quite apart from demonstrations— to the stilts, summer or wintertime regardless, regardless of rain, snow, slick ice, or mud—in big city traffic, in fields, in thickets; I ford rivers and cross glaciers and rockfalls. My stilts-assault on the Dufourspitze is of Alpine class. Even as a child I accustomed myself to sleeping on the stilts, backed up against a tree or a wall. I won matches against sprinters and galloping horses. On long journeys I proved endurance, on staircases and moving trucks, skill. Through various modifications I have perfected the conventional stilts model and I believe my present equipment to be unsurpassed. I design and make them myself and have three pairs in use: one with directional signals and horn for big city operation, one wooden pair for long distance travel, and the third of light metal for demonstrations.

But what are difficulties on the road compared to this other that an unappreciative world prepared for me? I won't speak of the mockery and humiliation I endured before reaching even the first milestone of my career—the staff room of the Astrol Works.

Here, however, where I thought myself so near my goal, a new obstacle arose that almost deflected me from my plans. I was informed that the firm was to stop using stilts-advertising. At first I thought this might work to my advantage anyway: perhaps they merely lacked a trained, rising generation. But the day I ventured to inquire in the advertising department I found to my horror that they had no intention whatever of recruiting stilts-walkers any more. They were considered obsolete.

I was stunned. All that week I agonized over a solution. Should I confess I was ruined—my career wiped out, all for lack of perception? Or, on the other hand, how might I, the last employed stilts-walker, persuade the directors that they had lightheadedly thrown overboard their greatest asset—everything that the world connected with their name? One idea after another came to me, all of which I rejected.

I read the biography of Demosthenes (might not a quick, fiery speech help?) but the stones under the tongue convinced me I was no orator. Should I write a letter to the management instead, and waken their better judgment with unimpugnable argument? No . . . the phrases I formed in my mind were feeble, totally incapable of conveying inspiration. I then saw that if anything could convince them it must be the stilts themselves.

I stole from the factory two green and purple enamel signs that read *Astrol,* fastened them to my breast and back with wires, and every day I stilts-walked after working hours through the streets. This had its results. After three or four days I was summoned by the management.

That indescribable moment, when I saw my goal, as though in blinding lightning, so near! I hurried feverishly across the factory lot, up the waxed and shining staircase to the offices. I forgot to knock and stood unannounced in the silence of those rooms I had never entered before. A displeased face, powdered pale, turned to stare at me. I supposed this ill-humor would be dispensed with if I mentioned my name—but a sharp voice taught me otherwise. Either this *nuisance,* as they called it, would come to an end or I should be dismissed at the first of the next month. I don't know how I found the door and the door-knob.

After I had made it across the landing and down the stairs I stopped dead in the vestibule and looked at the factory yard.

The window was open and a warm, wistful breeze blew from the allotment gardens.

I closed the window, went back upstairs, down the hall, and back into the offices—again without knocking. The girl was now working at her typewriter and I spoke quickly before she could look up.

"I will continue the *nuisance*," said I. "I will continue it even if I am fired. And I will continue it after I am fired."

The girl raised her eyebrows and said, "Wait just a moment please." She disappeared into the inner office and I waited quietly, while my very soul shook.

Just as quietly I greeted the director of the Astrol Firm a few seconds later. I expected excitement and harsh words, but to my surprise he spoke to me with almost paternal kindliness. I didn't trust my ears when he thanked me for my stilts-walking in the service of the firm. "I wish," he said, "that all our personnel at Astrol were inspired with the same spirit. But . . ." and here he stood up and leaned over the desk to inspect me more closely without coming around, "but haven't you considered that perhaps you are more of a drawback to us than a help when you—you must pardon me—when you go around representing Astrol in your patched trousers and tinny signs back and front, and that wire around your hips?"

I felt myself redden—of course he was right! I said, "I will change that."

"Change it? The firm has no money for that."

"Oh I didn't mean that the firm should change it," I said in amazement. "*I* will do it. I will not be a disgrace to the firm. I shan't get on the stilts again until you are satisfied with my trousers—that I promise! Besides, I have already saved toward a new suit. I will buy red trousers and a green jacket—you are completely right!"

He stared a little, murmuring, "Good! good!" Then he gave me his hand across the desk top and I shook it. "We are in agreement then."

"Thank you," I repeated. He nodded and I turned to go.

"Just one thing," he said. "Exactly why are you doing this?"

I didn't understand the question. What could he mean? Did he expect that I worked days for the firm and walked on stilts in the evenings for my own sake? There are people nowadays, it must be acknowledged, who do think of salesmanship and stilts-walking as independent of one another; but just as the business would be a low thing without the symbolical elevation by stilts, so the stilts-walking would be a mere hovering about in insubstantial space without the attachment to practicality. The one is nothing without the other—only thus does the world keep in harmony!

I beg to be excused for my happiness; I don't wish it only for myself: I should like to share it with others, and now and then I think I do. At twilight I go stilts-walking through the streets of some small city. With the easy play of my arms and my tireless steps, I feel the pale sickle-shaped moon and the night clouds drawing close. And under the stilts I sense the wonderful earth, that sphere circling in the universe. On my back and breast are the shining letters *ASTROL*. Unflagging little footsteps follow me and I hear the excited breathing and disconnected words like music, of someone enraptured. When the first lantern is lighted, I lean far down and glance into the hot fiery face of a child. He is studying me, and in his eyes I see the new flame of the inspiration that will never die out.

So it is, once in a while. . . .

Hans Magnus Enzensberger
(1929–   )

FOR A SENIOR COLLEGE TEXTBOOK

Translated from the German by
Eva Hesse

don't read odes, boy, timetables
are more exact. unroll the sea-charts
before it is too late. be on your guard. don't sing.
the day will come when they paste upon the door
5 new blacklists and brand their mark on those who answer no.
learn to pass unrecognized, to change quarters,
identity and face: you'll need to more than i did.
become adept at minor treason,
the sordid daily escape. the encyclicals
10 will do to make a fire, manifestos
to wrap up butter and salt
for the defenceless. anger and endurance
are necessary to blow into the lungs of power
the deadly powder, ground fine
15 by such as you, who have learnt much
and are fastidious in their ways.

Johann Wolfgang von Goethe [1]
(1749–1832)

THE ERL-KING

Translated from the German by
Sir Walter Scott

The Erl-King, or Erlkönig *(elf-king) in German, is a goblin who inhabits the Black Forest and works evil for human beings, especially children.*

O who rides by night thro' the woodland so wild?
It is the fond father embracing his child;
And close the boy nestles within his loved arm,
To hold himself fast, and to keep himself warm.

5 "O father, see yonder! see yonder!" he says;
"My boy, upon what dost thou fearfully gaze?"
"O, 'tis the Erl-King with his crown and his shroud."
"No, my son, it is but a dark wreath of the cloud."

THE ERL-KING SPEAKS
"O come and go with me, thou loveliest child;
10 By many a gay sport shall thy time be beguiled;
My mother keeps for thee full many a fair toy,
And many a fine flower shall she pluck for my boy."

---

1. *Johann Wolfgang von Goethe* (yō'hän wŭlf'gäng von gœ'tə).

"O father, my father, and did you not hear
The Erl-King whisper so low in my ear?"
15 "Be still, my heart's darling—my child, be at ease;
It was but the wild blast as it sung thro' the trees."

ERL-KING
"O wilt thou go with me, thou loveliest boy?
My daughter shall tend thee with care and with joy;
She shall bear thee so lightly thro' wet and thro' wild,
20 And press thee, and kiss thee, and sing to my child."

"O father, my father, and saw you not plain
The Erl-King's pale daughter glide past thro' the rain?"
"O yes, my loved treasure, I knew it full soon;
It was the grey willow that danced to the moon."

ERL-KING
25 "O come and go with me, no longer delay,
Or else, silly child, I will drag thee away."
"O father! O father! now, now, keep your hold,
The Erl-King has seized me—his grasp is so cold!"

Sore trembled the father; he spurr'd thro' the wild,
30 Clasping close to his bosom his shuddering child;
He reaches his dwelling in doubt and in dread,
But, clasp'd to his bosom, the infant was dead.

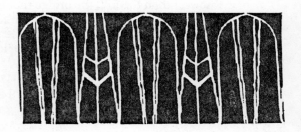

MIGNON

Translated from the German by
Thomas Carlyle

Mignon is a character in Goethe's novel Wilhelm Meister's
Apprenticeship. *She is a young Italian girl who is in love
with Wilhelm, who has rescued her from servitude to a cruel
master. But Wilhelm feels only compassion towards her. She
is consumed with a longing to return to her homeland and
finally dies.*

    Knowest thou the land where citron-apples bloom,
    And oranges like gold in leafy gloom,
    A gentle wind from deep blue heaven blows,
    The myrtle thick, and high the laurel grows?
5 Knowest thou it then?
                  'Tis there! 'Tis there!
    O my true loved one, thou with me must go!

    Knowest thou the house, its porch with pillars tall,
    The rooms do glitter, glitters bright the hall,
    And marble statues stand, and look each one:
10 What's this, poor child, to thee they've done?
    Knowest thou it then?
                  'Tis there! 'Tis there!
    O my protector, thou with me must go!

    Knowest thou the hill, the bridge that hangs on clouds,
    The mules in mist grope o'er the torrent loud,
15 In caves lay coiled the dragon's ancient brood,
    The crag leaps down, and over it the flood:
    Knowest thou it then?
                  'Tis there! 'Tis there!
    Our way runs; O my father, wilt thou go?

PROMETHEUS

Translated from the German by
Walter Kaufman

The Titan Prometheus appears in Greek myth as the champion of man. One story even credits him with the creation of the human race, forming man out of the mud.

Cover your heavens, Jove,
with misty clouds
and practice, like a boy
beheading thistles,
5 on oaks and mountain peaks!
My earth you must leave me
still standing,
and my cottage, which you did not build,
and my hearth
10 whose warmth
you envy me.

I know nothing poorer
under the sun than you gods!
Wretchedly you nourish
15 your majesty
on sacrificial tolls
and flimsy prayers,
and would starve if children
and beggars were not
20 hopeful fools.

"Prometheus" from TWENTY GERMAN POETS, ed. and trans. by Walter Kaufman. Copyright © 1962 by Random House, Inc. Reprinted by permission of the publisher.

When I was a child,
not knowing my way,
I turned my erring eyes
sunward, as if above there were
25 an ear to hear my lamentation,
a heart like mine
to care for the distressed.

Who helped me
against the Titans' wanton insolence?
30 Who rescued me from death,
from slavery?
Have you not done all this yourself,
my holy glowing heart?
And young and good, you glowed,
35 betrayed, with thanks for rescue
to him who slept above.

I honor you? For what?
Have you ever eased the suffering
of the oppressed?
40 Have you ever stilled the tears
of the frightened?
Was I not welded to manhood
by almighty Time
and eternal Fate,
45 my masters and yours?

Did you fancy perchance
that I should hate life
and fly to the desert
because not all
50 my blossom dreams ripened?

Here I sit, forming men
in my own image,
a race to be like me,
to suffer, to weep,
55 to delight and to rejoice,
and to defy you,
as I do.

Günter Grass[1] (1927–   )

PLACED AMID OLD MEN

Translated from the German by
Michael Hamburger

How at ninety they still lie
and put off their dying
till it's a legend.

Into the mottled hands
5   of old men who rise early
the world was laid.

Their many times folded power
and the folds of old skin
despise what is smooth.

10 Placed amid old men, we
bite our nails till they're spare,
we make no new growth.

Hard, wise and kind
they last ascetically
15   and soon will outlive us.

From NEW POEMS by Günter Grass, originally published by Hermann
Luchterhand Verlag GmbH in Germany under the title *Ausgefragt*, copyright © 1967 by Hermann Luchterhand Verlag GmbH; English translation © 1968 by Harcourt, Brace & World, Inc. and reprinted with the
permission of Harcourt, Brace & World, Inc., Hermann Luchterhand
Verlag GmbH, and Penguin Books Ltd.
1. *Günter Grass* (gœn'tèr gräs).

POWERLESS, WITH A GUITAR

Translated from the German by

Michael Hamburger

We read napalm and imagine napalm.
Since we cannot imagine napalm
we read about napalm until
by napalm we can imagine more.
5 Now we protest against napalm.
    After breakfast, silent,
    we see in photographs what napalm can do.
    We show each other coarse screen prints
    and say: there you are, napalm.
10   They do that with napalm.
    Soon there'll be cheap picture books
    with better photographs
    which will show more clearly
    what napalm can do.
15 We bite our nails and write protests.
    But, we read, there are
    worse things than napalm.
    Quickly we protest against worse things.
    Our well-founded protests, which at any time
20   we may compose fold stamp, mount up.
    Impotence, tried out on rubber façades.
    Impotence puts records on: impotent songs.
    Powerless, with a guitar.—
    But outside, finely meshed
25 and composed, power has its way.

From NEW POEMS by Günter Grass, originally published by Hermann
Luchterhand Verlag GmbH in Germany under the title *Ausgefragt*, copyright © 1967 by Hermann Luchterhand Verlag GmbH; English translation © 1968 by Harcourt, Brace & World, Inc. and reprinted with the
permission of Harcourt, Brace & World, Inc., Hermann Luchterhand
Verlag GmbH, and Penguin Books Ltd.

DO SOMETHING

Translated from the German by
Michael Hamburger

We can't just look on.
Even if we can't stop anything
we must say what we think.
(Do something. Do something.
5 Anything. Do something, then.)
Indignation, annoyance, rage looked for their adjectives.
Indignation called itself righteous.
Soon people spoke of everyday annoyance.
Rage fell into impotence: impotent rage.
10 I speak of the protest poem
and against the protest poem.
(Once I saw recruits taking the oath
unswear it behind their backs with crossed fingers.)
Impotently I protest against impotent protests.
15 What I mean is Easter, silence and peace marches.
What I mean is the hundred good names
underneath seven true sentences.
What I mean is guitars and similar
protest instruments conducive to records.
20 I speak of the wooden sword and the missing tooth,
of the protest poem.

From NEW POEMS by Günter Grass, originally published by Hermann
Luchterhand Verlag GmbH in Germany under the title *Ausgefragt*, copyright © 1967 by Hermann Luchterhand Verlag GmbH; English translation © 1968 by Harcourt, Brace & World, Inc. and reprinted with the
permission of Harcourt, Brace & World, Inc., Hermann Luchterhand
Verlag GmbH, and Penguin Books Ltd.

Just as steel has its booms, so poetry has its booms.
Rearmament opens markets for anti-war poems.
The cost of production is low.
25 Take an eighth of righteous indignation,
two eighths of everyday annoyance
and five eighths—to heighten that flavour—of impotent rage.
For medium-sized feelings against the war
are cheaply obtained
30 and have been shopsoiled ever since Troy.
(Do something. Do something.
Anything. Do something, then.)

One lets off steam: already righteous indignation goes up
        in smoke.
The small everyday annoyance makes the safety valves hiss.
35 Impotent rage discharges itself, fills a balloon with gas,
this rises, rises, grows smaller and smaller, is gone.
Are poems breathing exercises?
If that is their function,—and prosaic
as my grandfather, I ask what their function is—
40 then poetry is therapy.
Is a poem a weapon?
Some, too heavily armed, can hardly walk.
They have to use their dissatisfaction with circumstances
as a vehicle:
45 they reach their destination, they can hit the mark:
first the weekly paper, then the anthology:
The napalm metaphor and its permutations
in the protest poem of the 'sixties.
I mean poems that are tracts.
50 Righteous indignation enumerates terrors and miseries.
Everyday annoyance discovers the rhyme for no bread.
Impotent rage sets people talking breathlessly about itself.
(Do something. Do something . . .)
There are laws of leverage.
55 But they hold it against the stone
that it will not budge.
Next day the helpless style of well-founded protest
acts as a bait for the well-aimed style of smooth refutation.
Since in the cause they are always right
60 but all too easily slip up over details
the signatories tacitly half-dissociate themselves
from the authors and from their protests.
(Not only burglars buy gloves.)

What remains is: resilient misunderstandings
65 quote one another. Erroneous corrections
learn from guinea pigs
how to breed so that no one keeps track.

The stone takes pity and acts
as though it had been moved:
70 while indignation, annoyance and rage interrupt one another,
the specialists in power
appear smiling in front of the public. They make well-informed
          speeches
about the price demanded for freedom:
about napalm and its deterrent effects;
75 about well-founded protests and understandable rage.
All this is permitted.
Since power respects only power
impotent protest is allowed to carry on
until, because the noise is disturbing,
80 protest is no longer allowed.—
But we despise power.
We are not powerful, we keep assuring each other.
Without power we enjoy our impotence.
We do not want power; but power has us.—
85 Now righteous indignation feels misunderstood.
Our everyday annoyance ends in silent marches
that have first been announced and permitted.
Our impotent rage runs around in circles.
This provokes the equally righteous indignation
90 of angered policemen:
impotent rage becomes aggressive.
The fist grows into a head
and thinks in terms of low blows hooks to the liver
          knuckle-hard.
(Do something. Do something . . .)
95 All this becomes institutionalized, and by power
is caressed beaten subsidized.
Already the stone that was to be moved
gathers moss, unmoved.
Can we go on like that?—Yes, in a circle.
100 What shall we do?—Not anything.
How express our rage?—I know a recipe:
Strike nails into the sound barrier.
Behead dandelions and candles.
Assert yourselves on the couch.

105   We still feel rage.
      Already we're hoarse all over.
      We're against everything, vainly.
      What else can we do now?
      How shall we express our rage?
110 Do something. Do something.
      We must do something or other,
      do something, do it.
         Come on, then, quickly protest.
         That fellow won't join our protest.
115   Come on, then, quickly sign.
      You've always been against it.
      Those who don't sign are for it.
    Lovely is rage in the paddock,
    before it is fed.
120 For a long time impotence ran around in the rain,
    but now it is drying its socks.
    Rage and safety valves, about them a song;
    Impotence, your needle's eye is a song.
      Because I can't do anything,
125   because I can't do anything
      I'm full of rage, I'm full of rage.
      Do something, then. Do something.
      Anything. Do something, then.
      We must do something or other,
130   does no good, does no good,
      we must do something or other,
      do something, do it.
    Silently march in protest.
    Have done it once, have done it.
135 Write a poem, then.
    Have written it, have done it.
    Cook some brawn. Pig's head brawn:
    let impotence jell, rage quiver in sympathy.
    I know a recipe; who'll follow it cooking?

FOLDING CHAIRS

Translated from the German by

Michael Hamburger

How sad these changes are.
People unscrew the name plates from the doors,
take the saucepan of cabbage
and heat it up again, in a different place.

5 What sort of furniture is this
that advertises departure?
People take up their folding chairs
and emigrate.

Ships laden with homesickness and the urge to vomit
10 carry patented seating contraptions
and unpatented owners
to and fro.

Now on both sides of the great ocean
there are folding chairs;
15 how sad these changes are.

From SELECTED POEMS by Günter Grass, translated by Michael Hamburger, copyright © 1966 by Martin Secker and Warburg Limited. Originally published in GLEISDREIECK by Hermann Luchterhand Verlag GmbH. Reprinted by permission of Harcourt, Brace & World, Inc., and Martin Secker & Warburg Limited.

IN THE EGG

Translated from the German by
Michael Hamburger

We live in the egg.
We have covered the inside wall
of the shell with dirty drawings
and the Christian names of our enemies.
5 We are being hatched.

Whoever is hatching us
is hatching our pencils as well.
Set free from the egg one day,
at once we shall draw a picture
10 of whoever is hatching us.

We assume that we're being hatched.
We imagine some good-natured fowl
and write school essays
about the colour and breed
15 of the hen that is hatching us.

When shall we break the shell?
Our prophets inside the egg
for a middling salary argue
about the period of incubation.
20 They posit a day called X.

Out of boredom and genuine need
we have invented incubators.
We are much concerned about our offspring inside the egg.
We should be glad to recommend our patent
25 to her who looks after us.

But we have a roof over our heads.
Senile chicks,
polyglot embryos
chatter all day
30 and even discuss their dreams.

And what if we're not being hatched?
If this shell will never break?
If our horizon is only that
of our scribbles, and always will be?
35 We hope that we're being hatched.

Even if we only talk of hatching
there remains the fear that someone
outside our shell will feel hungry
and crack us into the frying pan with a pinch of salt.—
40 What shall we do then, my brethren inside the egg?

Gerhart Hauptmann (1862–1946)

FLAGMAN THIEL

*Translated from the German by
Adele S. Seltzer*

I

EVERY SUNDAY Thiel,[1] the flagman, was to be seen sitting in a pew in the church at Neu Zittau. If he was absent, you might be sure he was on Sunday duty or else—as happened twice in the course of ten years—at home ill in bed. Once a great lump of coal from the tender of a passing locomotive had struck his leg and sent him rolling into the ditch at the bottom of the embankment. The second time the trouble was a wine bottle that had come flying from an express and had hit him in the middle of his chest. Nothing but these two mishaps had ever succeeded in keeping Thiel from church the instant he was off duty.

The first five years he had had to come alone to Neu Zittau from Schön-Schornstein, a small collection of homes on the Spree. Then, one fine day, he appeared in the company of a delicate, sickly-looking woman. The people thought she ill-suited his herculean build. And on a later Sunday afternoon, at the altar of the church, he solemnly gave her his hand and pledged his troth.

So, for two years, the delicate young creature sat beside him in the pew. For two years her fine, hollow-cheeked face bent over the ancient hymnal beside his weather-tanned face.

"Flagman Thiel" by Gerhart Hauptmann, from GREAT GERMAN SHORT NOVELS AND STORIES, ed. by Victor Lang. Copyright 1952 by Random House, Inc. Reprinted courtesy of the publisher.
1. *Thiel* (tēl).

And suddenly the flagman was to be seen sitting alone, as of old.

On one of the preceding weekdays the bell had tolled for the dead. That was all.

Scarcely any change, so the people declared, was to be observed in the flagman. The brass buttons of his clean Sunday uniform were as brightly polished as before, his red hair as sleekly pomaded and as neatly parted, military fashion. Only he held his broad, hairy neck a little bent, and sang more eagerly, and listened to the sermon more devoutly. The general opinion was that his wife's death had not hit him very hard. A view that was strengthened when in the course of the year he married again. The second wife was a strong, stout milkmaid from Altegrund.

Even the pastor felt free to express his doubts when Thiel came to announce his engagement.

"So soon again? You really want to marry so soon again?"

"I can't keep my house running, sir, with the wife who's gone."

"To be sure. But I mean—aren't you in a bit of a hurry?"

"It's on account of the boy."

Thiel's wife had died in childbirth. The boy had lived and been named Tobias.

"Yes, yes, to be sure, the boy," said the pastor, with a gesture clearly revealing that he had not thought of the infant until that moment. "That throws a different light on the matter. What have you been doing with him until now while you are at work?"

Thiel explained that he left Tobias in the care of an old woman. Once she had nearly let him get burned, and another time had let him roll from her lap to the floor. Fortunately the child had not been badly hurt—only a big surface bruise. Such a state of things could not continue, the flagman said, especially as the child, being delicate, required particular attention. For that reason and also because he had sworn to his wife on her deathbed that he would always take exceedingly good care of the child, he had decided to marry again.

The people found absolutely nothing to cavil with in the new couple that now visited the church regularly on Sundays. The milkmaid seemed to have been made for the flagman. She was but a few inches shorter than he and exceeded him in girth, while her features were just as coarsely molded as his, though, in contrast, they lacked soul.

If Thiel had cherished the desire for an inveterate worker and paragon of a housewife in his second wife, then his hopes were surprisingly fulfilled. However, without knowing it, he had purchased three other qualities, too, a hard, domineering disposition, quarrelsomeness, and brutal passion.

Within half a year the whole place knew who was lord and master in the flagman's little house. Thiel became the object of general pity. It was a piece of good luck for the "creature," the exercised husbands said, that she had got such a gentle lamb as Thiel for a husband. With other men she wouldn't come off so easy, she'd receive some hard knocks. An animal like that had to be managed—with blows, if need be—a good sound thrashing to make her behave herself.

But Thiel, despite his sinewy arms, was not the man to thrash his wife. What got the people so annoyed seemed to cause him no perturbation. As a rule, he let his wife's endless sermonizings pass without a word, and when he did occasionally make a response, the slow drag of his speech and the quiet coolness of his tone contrasted oddly with her high-pitched bawling.

The outside world seemed scarcely to touch him. It was as though he carried something within him that heavily overbalanced all of the evil it brought by good.

Nevertheless, for all his phlegm, there were occasions on which he would not allow things to pass—when little Toby was concerned. Then his childlike goodness, his yieldingness took on a dash of determination that even so untamed a temperament as Lena's did not dare to oppose.

The moments, however, in which he revealed this side of his character became rarer and rarer, and finally ceased completely. During the first year of his marriage he had shown a certain suffering resistance to Lena's tyranny. In the second year this also ceased completely. After a quarrel he no longer left for his work with his earlier indifference in case he had not previously placated her. Often he even stooped to beg her to be kind again. His solitary post in the heart of the Brandenburg pine forest was no longer, as it had been, the place where he would rather be than anywhere else on earth. The quiet devout thoughts of his dead wife were crossed by thoughts of the living wife. It was not with repugnance, as in the first months of his marriage, that he trod the homeward way, but often with passionate haste, after having counted the hours and minutes till the time of his release.

He who had been united to his first wife by a more spiritual love fell into his second wife's grip through the power of crude impulses. He became almost wholly dependent upon her.

At times he experienced pangs of conscience at this turn, and resorted to a number of unusual devices to bring about a change. For one thing, he declared his hut and his beat to be holy ground, dedicated exclusively to the shades of the dead. And he actually succeeded by all sorts of pretexts in preventing Lena from accompanying him there. He hoped he should always be able to keep her off. The very number of his hut and the direction in which it lay were still unknown to her.

Thus, by conscientiously dividing the time at his disposal between the living and the dead, Thiel actually succeeded in soothing his conscience.

Often, to be sure, especially in moments of solitary devotion, when he felt the tie between him and his dead wife deeply and warmly, he beheld his present condition in the light of truth, and he experienced disgust.

If he was doing day duty, his spiritual intercourse with her was limited to dear recollections of their life together. But in the dark, when a snowstorm raged among the pines and along the embankment, his hut at midnight, by the light of his lantern, became a chapel.

With a faded photograph of the departed before him on the table, and the hymnal and the Bible turned open, he alternately read and sang the whole night long, interrupted only at intervals by the trains rushing past. He would attain a state of ecstasy in which he had visions of his wife standing there in person.

In its remoteness this post, which Thiel had held for ten years, contributed to the intensification of his mystic inclinations. To the north, east, south and west, it was separated by a walk of at least three quarters of an hour from the nearest habitation. It lay in the very heart of the forest. But there was a grade crossing there, and Thiel's duty was to lower and raise the gates.

In the summer days passed, in the winter weeks without a single person except other railroad workers setting foot on Thiel's beat. Almost the only changes in the solitude came from the weather and the periodic mutations of the seasons. It was not difficult to recall the events—besides the two mishaps to his body—that had broken into the regular course of the hours of service.

Four years previous the imperial special bearing the Kaiser to Breslau had gone dashing by. Once on a winter's night an express had run over a stag. And once on a hot summer's day, as Thiel was making an inspection of his beat, he had found a corked bottle of wine. It was scorching hot to the touch, and Thiel had esteemed its contents because when he uncorked it a geyser spouted out, showing that the stuff was well fermented. Thiel had laid the bottle on the edge of a pond in the woods to cool off. Somehow it had disappeared from the spot, and even after the passage of years Thiel never thought of that bottle without a pang of regret.

A bit of diversion was provided by a spring behind the hut. From time to time men at work on the road bed or on the telegraph lines came for a drink, and stayed, of course, to talk a while. Sometimes the forest ranger would also come when he was thirsty.

Tobias developed slowly. It was not until he was two years old that he learned to walk and talk. For his father he displayed unusual affection, and as he grew more understanding Thiel's old love for his child was re-awakened. Accordingly Lena's love for the child decreased, turning into unmistakable dislike when the next year a baby boy was born to her, too.

After that bad times began for Tobias. In his father's absence he was particularly made to suffer. He had to dedicate his feeble powers unrewarded to the service of the little cry-baby. He became more and more exhausted. His head grew too large round, and his fiery red hair with the chalky face beneath, on top of his wretched little body made an unlovely and pitiful impression. When the backward mite was seen dragging himself down to the Spree with his baby brother bursting with health in his arms, curses were muttered behind the windows of the cottages. But no one ever ventured to utter the curses in the open.

Thiel, who was most of all concerned, seemed to have no eyes for what was going on, and refused to understand the hints of well-meaning neighbors.

II

ONCE Thiel returned from night duty at seven o'clock of a June morning. Directly Lena had greeted him, she burst into her usual complaining.

A few weeks before notice had been given that they could no longer cultivate the piece of land which they rented for planting potatoes for their own use, and no other land had been found to replace it. Though everything pertaining to the land was part of

Lena's duty, Thiel none the less had to listen to a hundred iterations that he would be to blame if they had to buy ten sacks of potatoes for dear money. Thiel merely muttered a word or two. Paying slight attention to Lena's tirade, he went straight over to Tobias's bed, which he shared with the boy on nights when he was off duty.

He sat down and watched the sleeping child with an anxious expression on his good face. For a while he contented himself with chasing away the persistent flies, then he woke him up. A touching joy lighted up the boy's blue, deep-set eyes. He snatched for his father's hand, and a pitiful smile drew the corners of his mouth. Thiel helped him put on his few bits of clothing. Suddenly a shadow chased across his face. He noticed that his son's right cheek was slightly swollen and bore finger marks designed white on red.

At breakfast Lena brought up the same subject again, pursuing it with even more vigor. Thiel cut her off by telling her that the railroad inspector had given him for nothing the use of a stretch of land alongside the tracks not far from his hut, probably because it was too distant for the inspector to use for himself.

Lena was incredulous, then gradually her doubts melted away and she became noticeably good-humored. How big was the lot? How good was the soil? She plied him with questions. And when she learned that there were actually two dwarf fruit trees on the land, she fairly lost her head. At length the questions were all asked, and as the shopkeeper's bell, which could be heard in every house in the place, kept ringing incessantly, Lena ran forth to ferret out the latest news.

While she remained in the dark shop crowded with wares, Thiel occupied himself at home with Tobias, who sat on his knee playing with pine cones that his father had brought from the woods.

"What do you want to be when you grow up?" asked Thiel. The stereotyped question was invariably answered by the equally stereotyped reply, "Railroad inspector." It was not asked in fun. The flagman's dreams actually soared so high. It was in all seriousness that he cherished the hope that with God's help Tobias would become something extraordinary. The instant "railroad inspector" left the child's bloodless lips, Thiel's face brightened, fairly radiated bliss.

"Go play now, Tobias," he said soon afterward, lighting his pipe with a shaving kindled at the hearth fire. The boy showing shy pleasure went out.

Thiel undressed and got into bed. For a long while he lay staring up at the low, cracked ceiling. Finally he fell asleep and woke up shortly before twelve o'clock. While Lena in her noisy fashion prepared the midday meal, he dressed and went out on the street to fetch Tobias, whom he found scratching plaster out of a hole in the wall and stuffing it into his mouth. Thiel led him by the hand past the eight houses that constituted the hamlet down to the Spree. The stream lay dark and glassy between sparsely foliaged poplars. Thiel sat down on a block of granite close to the water's edge.

Every fair day the villagers were accustomed to see him on this spot. The children were devoted to him. They called him Father Thiel. He taught them games that he remembered from his own childhood, reserving, however, the best of his memories for Tobias. He whittled him arrows that flew farther than those of the other boys, he carved him willow pipes, and even deigned to sing ditties in his rusty bass, and tap the beat with the horn handle of his knife against the bark of a tree.

The people thought him silly. They blamed him. They could not understand how he could go to so much trouble for the little brats. Though they should have been richly content, seeing that the children were well taken care of when in his charge. Besides, Thiel did more than play with them. He took up serious things, too. He heard the older ones recite their lessons, helped them study their Bible and hymn verses, and spelled out c-a-t and d-o-g with the younger ones.

After the midday meal Thiel rested again a while, drank a cup of coffee, and began to prepare for work. It took him a lot of time, as for everything he did. Each move had been regulated for years.

The objects carefully spread out on the walnut dresser went into his various pockets always in the same order—knife, notebook, comb, a horse's tooth, an old watch in a case, and a small book wrapped in red paper. The last was handled with especial care. During the night it lay under Thiel's pillow, and by day was carried in his breast pocket. On a label pasted on the cover was written in Thiel's awkward yet flourished hand, "Savings Account of Tobias Thiel."

The clock on the wall with the long pendulum and sickly yellow face indicated a quarter to five when Thiel left. A small boat, his own property, ferried him across the Spree. Arrived at the further side, he stood still a moment and listened back in the direction he had come from. Then he turned into a broad path through the woods and within a few moments reached the depths of the deep-booming pine forest, its mass of needles like a dark green undulating sea.

The moist layers of needles and moss made a carpet as inaudible to the tread as felt. Thiel made his way without looking up, now past the rusty brown columns of the older trees, now between the thickly-enmeshed younger growth, and farther on across broad stretches of nursery, over-shadowed by a few tall slim pines for the protection of the young saplings. A transparent bluish haze rising from the earth laden with mingled fragrances blurred the forms of the trees. A heavy, drab sky hung low over the tops. Flocks of cawing crows seemed to bathe in the gray of the atmosphere. Black puddles filled the depressions in the path and cast a still drearier reflection of a dreary nature.

"Fearful weather," thought Thiel when he roused out of deep reflection and looked up.

Suddenly his thoughts were deflected. A dim feeling came to him that he must have forgotten something. And surely enough, when he searched his pockets, he discovered that he had not brought along the sandwich that he required on account of the long hours on duty. For a while he stood undecided. Then turned and hurried back.

In a short while he reached the Spree, rowed himself across in a few powerful strokes, and without delay, perspiring from every pore, ascended the gradual slope of the village street. The shopkeeper's old, mangy poodle lay in the middle of the road. On the tarred board fence around a cottager's yard perched a hooded crow. It spread its feathers, shook itself, nodded, uttered an ear-splitting caw, caw, and with a slapping sound of its wings rose in the air and let the wind drive it in the direction of the forest.

Nothing was to be seen of the villagers—about twenty fishermen and lumbermen with their families.

The stillness was broken—by a high-pitched voice. The flagman involuntarily stopped. A volley of violent, jangling tones assailed his ears. It seemed to come from the open dormer window of a low house that he knew only too well.

Treading as silently as possible, he glided nearer. Now he quite clearly recognized his wife's voice. Only a few steps more, and he could understand almost everything she said.

"You horrid little beast, you! Is the poor baby to scream its belly inside out from hunger? What? Just you wait—just you wait. I'll teach you to mind. You'll never forget."

For a few moments there was silence. Then a sound could be

heard like the beating out of clothes. And the next instant another hailstorm of abuse was let loose.

"You miserable little puppy, you! Do you think I'll let my own child die of hunger because of a mean little thing like you?— Shut your mouth!" A slight whimper had been audible. "If you don't shut your mouth, I'll give you something that'll keep you going a whole week."

The whimpering did not subside.

The flagman felt his heart pounding in irregular beats. He began to tremble slightly. His glance fastened on the ground as though his mind were wandering, and again and again his coarse, hard hand went up to his freckled forehead to brush back a dank strand of hair. For a second he was about to give way. He stood shaken by a convulsion that swelled his muscles and drew his fingers into a clenched ball. The convulsion subsided. He was left in a state of dull exhaustion.

With unsteady steps he entered the narrow, brick-paved vestibule and slowly, wearily mounted the creaking wooden stairs.

"Pugh, pugh, pugh!" You could hear how with every sign of scorn and fury someone spat out three times in succession. "You horrid, mean, sneaking, cowardly, low-down good-for-nothing!" The epithets followed one another in crescendo, the voice that uttered them breaking several times from strain. "You want to hit my boy, do you? You ugly little brat you, don't you dare to hit the poor helpless child on its mouth. What's that? Huh? If I wanted to soil my hands on you, I'd—"

At that moment the door to the living room was opened, and the rest of the sentence remained unspoken on the frightened woman's tongue. She was livid with passion, her lips twitched evilly. Her right hand raised in the air sank and grasped the saucepan with milk in it. She tried to pour some into the baby's bottle, but desisted as the larger part of the milk flowed down the outside of the bottle on to the table. She clutched at various objects without being able to hold them any length of time. Finally she recovered herself sufficiently to address her husband with violence. What did he mean by coming home at this unusual hour? Was he thinking of spying on her? That would be too much. This last was directly followed by the asseveration that she had a clear conscience and need not lower her eyes before any one.

Thiel scarcely heard what she said. He gave a hasty look at Toby, who was crying aloud, and for a few moments he had to restrain forcibly a something dreadful rising within him. Then the old phlegm spread over his taut features, and at the same time a furtive, lustful light came into his eyes. His glance played over his wife's heavy limbs while she, with averted face, bustled about still making an effort to be composed. Her full, half-bared breasts swelled with excitement and threatened to burst her corset. Her drawn-up skirts accentuated the width of her broad hips. A force seemed to emanate from the woman, indomitable, inescapable. Thiel felt himself powerless to cope with it. Tightly, like a cobweb, yet firmly as a mesh of steel, it laid itself around him, chaining him down, robbing him of his strength. In this condition he was incapable of saying a word to her, much less a harsh word.

Thus it was that Tobias, bathed in tears, cowering in a corner, saw his father go over to the oven bench without looking round at him, pick up the forgotten sandwich, hold it out to Lena by way of the only explanation, give a short, distraught nod of his head in good-by, and disappear.

III

THIEL made all possible haste back to his solitary post in the woods. Even so he was a quarter of an hour late. The assistant who relieved him, a consumptive, the victim of the unavoidably rapid changes in temperature to which the work subjected one, was waiting prepared to leave on the sanded little platform of the hut, on which the number, black on white, gleamed from a distance between the tree trunks.

The two men shook hands, exchanged a few brief reports, and parted, the one disappearing within the hut, the other taking the continuation of the road by which Thiel had come. His convulsive cough sounded further and further away among the trees, until finally the one human sound in the solitude fell silent.

Thiel as always, after his fashion, set about preparing the small square room for the night. He worked mechanically, his mind occupied with the impression of the past hour.

First he laid his supper on the narrow, brown-painted table beside one of the windows like slits through which the stretch of track could be conveniently viewed. Next he kindled a fire in the small, rusty stove and placed a pot of cold water on top. After that he straightened out his utensils, a shovel, a spade, a wrench and a few other things, and then cleaned his lantern and filled it with fresh oil.

Scarcely were his arrangements completed when the signal rang shrilly, three times, and three times again, to announce that a train from the direction of Breslau was pulling out of the near station. Thiel showed no hurry, allowing a few minutes to pass before emerging from the hut with flag and cartridge case in his hand. And it was with a lazy, dragging shuffle that he walked along the narrow strip of sand to the crossing, about sixty feet away. Though there was scarcely any traffic along the road at that point, still he conscientiously let down and raised the gates before and after the passage of each train.

This operation now concluded, he leaned idly on one of the black-and-white barred anchor-posts.

The tracks cut in a straight line right and left into the green forest stretching beyond the reach of the eye. On each side the mass of needles stood apart to leave, as it were, an avenue free for the reddish-brown graveled embankment. The black tracks running parallel looked like the strands of a huge iron net drawn together to a point on the horizon in the extreme south and north.

The wind had risen, it drove light waves of mist along the edge of the forest into the distance. A humming came from the telegraph poles alongside the tracks. On the wires that stretched from pole to pole like the sustaining cords spun by a huge spider perched swarms of chirping birds. A woodpecker flew with a laugh over Thiel's head. The man did not so much as look up.

The sun hanging from under the edge of vast masses of clouds and about to sink into the dark-green sea of treetops poured streams of purple over the forest. The pillared arcades of the pine trunks on the yon side of the embankment took fire as from within and glowed like metal. The tracks, too, began to glow, turning into the semblance of fiery snakes. They were the first to pale. The glow, leaving the ground, slowly ascended upward, resigning first the bodies of the trees, then the lower tops to the cold light of dissolution. For a while a reddish sheen lingered on the extreme crowns.

Silently and solemnly was the exalted drama enacted.

The flagman still stood at the gates motionless. At length he made a step forward. A dark point on the horizon where the tracks joined, became more than a point. Increasing from second to second it yet seemed to stand still. Then of a sudden it acquired movement, and drew nearer. A vibrating and humming went through the tracks, a rhythmic clang, a muted thunder. It grew louder and louder until at length it sounded not unlike the hoof beats of a storming cavalry regiment. From a distance the air pulsated intermittently with a panting and a blustering. Then suddenly the serenity of the forest snapped. A mad uproar filled the welkin, the tracks curved, the earth shook —a blast of air, a cloud of dust and steam and smoke—and the snorting monster had gone by.

The noises waned as they had waxed. The exhalations thinned away. Shrunken to a point again the train vanished in the distance, and the old solemn hush again settled upon this corner of the forest.

"Minna," whispered the flagman, as if coming out of a dream.

He returned to the hut, where he brewed himself some weak coffee, then sat down, sipping from time to time and all the while staring at a dirty piece of newspaper that he had picked up on his round.

Gradually a curious unrest came upon him. Attributing it to the heat from the stove, he tore off his coat and waistcoat. That proving to be of no help, he got up, took a spade from a corner, and went out to the lot that the inspector had presented to him.

It was a narrow strip of soil, overgrown with weeds. The blossoms on the two fruit trees were like snowy white foam. Thiel calmed down, a quiet content possessed him.

To work now.

The spade cut into the earth with a crunch. The wet clods flew and crumbled as they fell.

For a long while he dug uninterruptedly. Then he paused and said to himself audibly, shaking his head gravely:

"No, no, it won't do. No, it won't do."

The thought had suddenly struck him that Lena would be coming there often to look after the lot, and his accustomed life would be seriously disturbed. At one blow pleasure in the possession of the bit of ground turned into distaste. Hastily, as if he had been about to do wrong, he ripped the spade out of the earth and carried it back to the hut.

Again he sank into gloomy reflections. Almost without knowing why, he could not endure the prospect of Lena's presence for whole days at a stretch while he was on duty. Much as he might try he could not reconcile himself to the idea. It seemed to him he had something valuable to defend, against someone who was attempting to violate his holiest sanctuary. Involuntarily his muscles tautened in a slight cramp, and a short, defiant laugh escaped him.

The sound of his own laughter was alarming. He looked about and lost the thread of his thoughts. Finding it again he went back to the same dismal broodings.

Then suddenly a heavy black curtain was torn apart, his eyes so long befogged had now a clear view. He had the sensation of awakening from a deathlike sleep that had lasted two years. With an incredulous shake of the head he contemplated all the awful things he must have been guilty of in that condition. The long-suffering of his child, which the impressions of the earlier afternoon should only have confirmed, now were clearly revealed to his soul. Pity and penitence overcame him, and also great shame that all this long while he had lived in disgraceful resignation, never taking the dear, helpless child's part, not even finding the strength to admit how much the child suffered.

From the self-tormenting contemplation of his sins of omission a great tiredness came over him. He fell asleep, bent over the table with his forehead resting on his hand.

For a long while he lay like that, and several times uttered the name Minna in a choked voice.

A rushing and roaring filled his ears, as of great masses of water. He tore his eyes open and looked about. Darkness enveloped him. His limbs gave way, the sweat of terror oozed from every pore, his pulse beat irregularly, his face was wet with tears.

He wanted to look toward the door, but in the inky darkness did not know which way to turn. He rose reeling. And still terror possessed him. The woods outside boomed like the ocean, the wind drove rain and sleet against the panes. Thiel groped about helplessly. For a moment he felt himself to be drowning. Then suddenly there was a dazzling bluish flare, as of drops of supernatural light falling down into the earth's atmosphere to be instantly extinguished by it.

The moment sufficed to restore the flagman to reason. He fumbled for his lantern and found it. At the same instant the thunder awoke on the farthest edge of the heavens over Brandenburg. At first a dull, restrained rumble, it rolled nearer in surging metallic waves, until overhead it discharged itself in great peals, menacing roars that shook the earth to its foundations.

The window panes clattered. Thiel lighted the lantern, and his first glance after he regained self-control was at the clock. In a bare five minutes the express was due. Thinking he had failed to hear the signal, he made for the crossing as quickly as the dark and the storm permitted. Just as he was letting down the gates the signal rang—the sound was scattered by the wind in all directions.

The pine trees bent over, their branches scraped against each other with uncanny creakings and squeakings. For a few moments the moon was visible, a pale yellow chalice amid the torn clouds. By its light could be seen the wind's mauling of the black treetops. The foliage of the birches along the embankment waved and fluttered like ghostly horses' tails. Beneath them lay the rails gleaming wet, absorbing the pale moonlight in spots here and there.

Thiel tore the cap from his head. The rain soothed him. It ran down his face mingled with tears.

His brain was in a ferment with confused recollections of his dream. Tobias seemed to be undergoing maltreatment, and such horrible maltreatment that the mere thought of it stopped his heart. Another vision was clearer, of his dead wife. She had come from somewhere along the railroad tracks. She had looked very ill and was wearing rags for clothes. Without looking round she passed the hut, and then—here his memory became vague—she had great difficulty somehow in proceeding, she even collapsed several times.

Thiel pondered. And then he knew that she was in flight. No doubt of it. Else why those anxious backward glances as she dragged herself forward with her legs giving way under her? Oh, those awful looks of hers!

But there was something that she was carrying, wrapped in cloths, something limp, bloody, pale. And the way she looked down on it reminded him of a past scene.

A dying woman who kept her gaze fixed on her newborn babe with an expression of the deepest pain, intolerable torture. It was an expression he could no more forget than that he had a father and a mother.

Where had she gone? He did not know. But one thing was clear in his soul: she had withdrawn from him, disregarded him, dragged herself further and further away into the dark, stormy night. "Minna, Minna," he had cried, and the sound of his own cry awakened him.

Two round red lights like the staring eyes of a huge monster penetrated the dark. A bloody sheen glided in advance, transforming the drops of rain in its course into drops of blood. A veritable rain of blood seemed to descend from heaven.

Horror fell upon Thiel, mounting and mounting as the train drew nearer. Dream and reality fused into one. He still saw the woman wandering down the tracks. His hand wavered toward the cartridge case, as if to stop the speeding train. Fortunately it was too late. Lights flared before his eyes, the train had rushed past.

The remainder of the night there was little peace for Thiel. He felt a great urgency to be at home, a great longing to see little Toby, from whom, it seemed to him, he had been separated for years. Several times, in his growing anxiety over the child's condition he was tempted to quit duty.

To shorten the hours until his release he determined as soon as day dawned to walk his beat. So, with a cane in one hand and a large iron wrench in the other, he went out into the dirty gray twilight and stepped along on the spine of a rail, halting every now and then to tighten a bolt with the wrench or to hammer at one of the fishplates that held the rails together.

The wind and rain had stopped, fragments of a pale blue sky became visible between rifts in the banked clouds. The monotonous tap-tap of his soles on the hard metal and the sleepy drip-drop from the wet trees gradually calmed Thiel.

At six o'clock he was relieved. Without delay he started home.

It was a glorious Sunday morning. The clouds had broken and drifted beyond the horizon. The sun, gleaming like a great blood-red gem, poured veritable masses of light upon the forest. Through the network of the branches the beams shot in sharp straight lines casting a glow upon islets of lacy ferns and here and there turning silvery-grey patches on the ground into bits of coral. The tops of the trees, the trunks, the grass shed fire like dew. The world seemed to lie under a deluge of light. And the freshness of the air penetrated to the very core of one's being.

Even in Thiel's brain the fantasies of the night could not but grow pale. And when he entered the room where little Toby was lying in bed with the sun shining on him and more color in his cheeks than usual, they disappeared completely.

To be sure, in the course of the day Lena thought she noticed something odd about him. At church instead of looking in the book he observed her sidewise, and in the middle of the day, when Toby was supposed as usual to carry the baby out on the street, he took it from the boy's arms and laid it in her lap. Otherwise there was nothing conspicuously different about him.

Having no chance to take a nap and as he was to do day duty that week, he went to bed early, at nine o'clock. Exactly as he was about to fall asleep, his wife told him that she intended to accompany him the next morning to dig the lot and plant potatoes.

Thiel winced. He awoke completely, but kept his eyes shut.

Lena went on. If the potatoes were to amount to anything, she said, it was high time to do the planting. And she would have to take the children along because it would probably occupy her the entire day.

Thiel muttered a few unintelligible words, to which she paid no attention. She had turned her back and by the light of a tallow candle was occupied with unfastening her corset and letting down her skirts. Suddenly, without herself knowing why, she turned round and beheld her husband's ashen face distorted by a play of passions. He had raised himself partly, supporting himself by his hands on the edge of the bed, his burning eyes fastened upon her.

"Thiel!" cried the woman, half in anger, half in fear.

Like a somnambulist who hears his name called, Thiel came out of his daze. He stammered something, threw his head back on the pillow, and pulled the quilt over his ears.

Lena was the first to get up the next morning. She went about noiselessly, making the necessary preparations for the excursion. The baby was put into the perambulator, then Tobias was awakened and dressed. He smiled when he was told where he was going.

When everything was ready and even the coffee was made and set on the table, Thiel awoke. His first sensation on seeing the arrangements was of displeasure. He wanted to protest, but the proper opening refused to frame itself. Besides, what arguments could he advance that would weigh with Lena? And there was his child's little face beaming with joy, growing happier and happier each instant, until Thiel, from the sight of his delight in the approaching excursion, could not think of opposing it.

Nevertheless, on the way through the woods, as he pushed the baby carriage with difficulty through the deep soil, Thiel was not free from anxiety.

Tobias gathered flowers and laid them in the carriage. He was happier than almost any time his father had seen him. In his little brown plush cap he hopped about among the ferns and tried, helplessly to be sure, to catch the glassy-winged dragon flies that darted above them.

As soon as they reached the spot, Lena made a survey. She threw the sack of seed potatoes on the grassy edge of a small grove of birches, kneeled down, and let the darkish soil run between her fingers.

Thiel watched her eagerly.

"Well," he said, "how is it?"

"Every bit as good as the corner on the Spree."

A burden fell from the flagman. He contentedly scratched the stubble on his face. He had feared she would be dissatisfied.

After hastily devouring a thick slice of bread the woman tossed aside head cloth and jacket, and began to spade up the earth with the speed and endurance of a machine. At regular intervals she straightened up and took several deep breaths. But the pauses were never for long, except when she had to suckle the baby, which she did quickly, with panting, perspiring breasts.

After a while the flagman called to her from the platform in front of the hut:

"I must inspect the beat. I'm taking Tobias with me."

"What!" she screamed back. "Nonsense! Who'll stay with the baby? You'll come here," she shouted still louder.

But the flagman as if not hearing walked off with Toby. For a moment she considered whether she should not run after the two, then desisted because of the loss of time.

Thiel walked down the tracks with his son. The boy was quite excited, everything was so new and strange. Those narrow black rails warmed by the sun—he could not comprehend what they could be meant for. And he kept up an incessant stream of funny questions. What struck him as strangest of all was the resonance of the telegraph poles.

Thiel knew the sound of each pole on his beat so well that with closed eyes he could tell at exactly what spot he stood. And now he stopped several times, holding Tobias by the hand, to listen to the wonderful tones that came from the wood like sonorous chorals from inside a church. The pole at the extreme south end made a particularly full, beautiful sound. It was a mingling of tones that seemed to come without pausing for breath.

Tobias ran round the weathered post to see if he could not through some hole discover the originators of the lovely music. His father listening sank into a devout mood, as in church. He distinguished a voice that reminded him of his dead wife, and fancied it was a choir of blessed spirits, her voice mingling with the others. A deep emotion, a great yearning brought the tears to his eyes.

Tobias asked to be allowed to gather the flowers in the field alongside the tracks. Thiel as always let the child have his way.

Fragments of the blue sky seemed to have dropped on to the meadow, so thickly was it strewn with small, blue blossoms.

Like colored pennants the butterflies fluttered and floated among the shining white trunks of the birches. The delicate green foliage gave forth a soft rustle.

Tobias plucked flowers. His father watched him meditatively. Occasionally the flagman raised his eyes and searched between the leaves for a glimpse of the sky, which held the golden sunlight like a huge, spotless bowl.

"Father," said the child, pointing to a brown squirrel which with small scratching sounds was darting up a solitary pine tree, "Father, is that the good Lord?"

"Silly boy," was all that Thiel could find to reply as bits of loosened bark fell from the trunk of the tree to his feet.

Lena was still digging when Thiel and Tobias returned. She had already spaded up half the plot!

The trains passed at intervals. Each time they rushed by Tobias watched with mouth agape. Even his stepmother was amused by the funny faces he made.

The midday meal, consisting of potatoes and a remnant of roast pork, was consumed inside the hut. Lena was in good spirits. Even Thiel seemed ready to resign himself to the inevitable with good grace. While they ate, he entertained his wife by telling her various things connected with his work. Could she, for instance, imagine that there were forty-six screws in one rail, and more like that.

By mealtime the spading had been done, and in the afternoon Lena was going to sow the potatoes. This time, insisting that Tobias must look after the baby, she took him along.

"Watch out!" Thiel called after her, suddenly gripped by concern. "Watch out that he doesn't go too close to the tracks."

A shrug of Lena's shoulders was her only answer.

The signal rang for the Silesian express. Scarcely had Thiel taken his place in readiness at the gates when the approaching rumble became audible. Within a fraction of a minute he could see the train. On it came, the black funnel spitting steam in countless puffs, one chasing upward after the other. There! One —two—three milk-white geysers gushing up straight as candles —the engine whistling. Three times in succession, short, shrill, alarming.

"They're putting on the brakes," Thiel said to himself. "I wonder why."

He stepped out beyond the gates to look down the tracks, mechanically pulling the red flag from its case and holding it straight in front of him.

Good heavens! Had he been blind? God, O God, what was that? There—between the rails.

"Stop!" he screamed with every atom of breath in his lungs.

Too late. A dark mass had gone down under the train and was being tossed between the wheels like a rubber ball.

Only a few seconds more and with a grating and squeaking of the brakes, the train came to a standstill.

Instantly the lonely stretch became a scene of animation. The conductor and brakeman ran along the gravel path beside the tracks back to the rear end. From every window curious faces peered. And then the crowd that had gathered in the rear formed into a cluster, and moved forward.

Thiel panted. He had to hold on to something not to sink to the ground like a slaughtered steer.

How's that? Were they actually waving to him?

"No!"

A scream came from the spot where the accident had occurred, followed by a howling as from an animal. Who was that? Lena? It was not her voice, yet—

A man came hurrying down the tracks.

"Flagman!"

"What's the matter?"

"An accident."

The messenger shrank before the strange expression in the flagman's eyes. His cap hung on the side of his head, his red hair stood straight up.

"He's still alive. Maybe something can be done."

A rattle in the flagman's throat was the only answer.

"Come quickly—quickly."

With a tremendous effort Thiel pulled himself together. His slack muscles tautened, he drew himself to his full height, his face was empty and dead.

He followed the man at a run, oblivious of the pale, frightened faces at the windows. A young woman looked out, a traveling salesman with a fez on his head, a young couple apparently on their honeymoon. What were they to him? The contents of those rattling, thumping boxes on wheels had never concerned him. His ears were filled with Lena's lamentations.

Yellow dots swam before his eyes, countless yellow dots like fireflies. He shrank back, he stood still. From out of the dance of fireflies it came toward him, pale, limp, bloody—a forehead beaten black and blue, blue lips with dark blood trickling from them. Tobias!

Thiel said nothing. His face went a dirty white. He grinned as if out of his senses. At length he bent over, he felt the limp, dead limbs heavy in his arms. The red flag went round them.

He started to leave.

Where?

"To the railroad doctor, to the railroad doctor," came from all sides.

"We'll take him," called the baggage-master, and turned to prepare a couch of coats and books in his car. "Well?"

Thiel made no move to let go of the boy. They urged him. In vain. The baggage-master had a stretcher handed out from the car and ordered a man to remain with the father. Time was precious. The conductor's whistle shrilled. Coins rained from the windows.

Lena raved like a madwoman. "The poor woman," they said in the coaches, "the poor, poor mother."

The conductor whistled several times, the engine blew a signal, sent white clouds hissing up from its cylinders, and stretched its sinews of iron. In a few seconds, the mail express, with floating flags of smoke, was dashing with redoubled speed through the forest.

The flagman, whose mood had altered, laid the half-dead child on the stretcher.

There he lay with his racked tiny body. Every now and then a long wheeze raised the bony chest, which was visible under the tattered shirt. The little arms and legs, broken not only at the joints, assumed the most unnatural positions. The heel of one small foot was twisted to the front, the arms hung over the sides of the stretcher.

Lena kept up a continuous whimper. Every trace of her former insolence had disappeared. Over and over again she repeated a story to exonerate herself.

Thiel seemed not to notice her. With an expression of awful anxiety he kept his eyes riveted on the child.

A hush had fallen, a deadly hush. The tracks rested hot and black on the glaring gravel. The noon had stifled the wind, and the forest stood motionless, as if carved in stone.

In muffled voices the two men took counsel. The quickest way to reach Friedrichshagen would be to go back to the neighboring station in the direction of Breslau, because the next train, a fast commutation, did not stop at the station that was nearer to Friedrichshagen.

Thiel seemed to consider if he should go along. At the time there was no one there who understood the duties of the position, so with a mute motion of his head he indicated to his wife that she should take hold of the stretcher. She did not dare to refuse though she was concerned about having to leave the baby behind.

Thiel accompanied the cortège of two to the end of his beat, then stood still and looked after them long. Suddenly he clapped his hand to his forehead with a blow that resounded afar. It might wake him up, he thought. Because this was a dream like the one he had had yesterday. No use. Reeling rather than walking he reached his hut. There he fell face downward on the floor. His cap flew into a corner, his carefully kept watch fell from his pocket, the case sprang open, the glass broke. An iron fist seemed to be clamped on his neck, so tight that he could not move no matter how he moaned and groaned and tried to free himself. His forehead was cold, his throat parched.

The ringing of the signal roused him. Under the influence of those three repeated sounds the attack abated. Thiel could rise and do his duty. To be sure, his feet were heavy as lead, and the stretch of rails circled about him like the spokes of an enormous wheel with his head for its axis. But at least he could stand up a while.

The commutation train approached. Tobias must be in it. The nearer it drew the more the pictures before Thiel's eyes blurred. Finally all he saw was the mutilated boy with the bloody mouth. Then darkness fell.

After a while he awoke from the swoon. He found himself lying in the hot sun close to the gates. He rose, shook the sand from his clothes and spat it from his mouth. His head cleared a bit, he could think more quietly.

In the hut he immediately picked his watch up from the floor and laid it on the table. It was still going. For two hours he counted the seconds, then the minutes, while representing to himself what was happening to Tobias. Now Lena was arriving with him, now she stood in front of the doctor. The doctor observed the boy and felt him all over, and shook his head.

"Bad, very bad—but perhaps—who can tell?"

He made a more thorough examination.

"No," he then said, "no, it's all over."

"All over, all over," groaned the flagman. But then he drew himself up, raised his unconsciously clenched fist, rolled his eyes to the ceiling, and shouted as if the narrow little room must burst with the sound of his voice. "He must live, he must. I tell you, he must live."

He flung open the door of the hut—the red glow of evening fell through—and ran rather than walked to the gates. Here he stood still seemingly bewildered. Then suddenly spreading his arms he went to the middle of the roadbed, as if to stop something that was coming from the same direction as the commutation. His wide-open eyes made the impression of blindness. While stepping backward to make way for something, a stream of half-intelligible words came from between his gritted teeth.

"Listen. Don't go. Listen, listen. Don't go. Stay here. Give him back to me. He's beaten black and blue. Yes, yes. All right. I'll beat her black and blue, too. Do you hear? Stay. Give him back to me."

Something seemed to move past him, because he turned and made as if to follow.

"Minna, Minna,"—his voice was weepy like a small child's—"Minna, listen. Give him back to me. I will—" He groped in the air as if to catch and hold someone fast. "My little wife—yes, yes—and I'll—and I'll beat her—so she's black and blue, too—I'll beat her, too—with the hatchet—you see?—with the kitchen hatchet—I'll beat her with the kitchen hatchet. And that'll be the end of her. And then—yes, yes—with the hatchet—yes, with the kitchen hatchet—black blood."

Foam gathered on his lips, his glassy eyeballs rolled incessantly.

A gentle breath of the evening blew steadily over the forest, a rosy cloud mass hung in the western sky.

He had followed the invisible something about a hundred paces when he stood still, apparently having lost courage. With fearful dread in his eyes, he stretched out his arms, pleading, adjuring. He strained his eyes, shaded them with his hand, as if to discern the inessential being in the far distance. Finally his head sank, and the tense expression of his face changed into apathy. He turned and dragged himself the way he had come.

The sunlight laid its final glow over the forest, then was extinguished. The trunks of the pines rose among the tops like pale, decayed bones, and the tops weighed upon them like greyish black layers of mold. The hammering of a woodpecker penetrated the silence. Up above one last dilatory pink cloud traversed the steely blue of the sky. The breath of the wind turned dankly cold as if blowing from a cellar.

The flagman shivered. Everything was new and strange. He did not know what he was walking on, or what was about him. A squirrel hopped along the roadbed. Thiel pondered. He had to think of the Lord. But why? "The Lord is hopping along the tracks, the Lord is hopping along the tracks." He said it several times as if to get at something associated with it. He interrupted himself. A ray of illumination fell upon his brain. "Good heavens! That's madness." He forgot everything else and turned upon this new enemy. He tried to order his thoughts. In vain. They'd come and go and ramble away and shoot off at a tangent. He caught himself in the absurdest fancies, and shuddered at the consciousness of his impotence.

The sound of a child crying came from the birch grove nearby. It was the signal for madness. Almost against his will he had to hurry to the spot where the baby, whom everybody had neglected, was crying and kicking on the unblanketed floor of its carriage.

What did he mean to do? What had driven him there? The questions were submerged in a whirling eddy of thoughts and emotions.

"The Lord is hopping along the tracks." Now he knew. Tobias —she had murdered him—Lena—the child had been entrusted to her care. "Stepmother! Beast of a mother!" he hissed between clenched teeth. "And her brat lives."

A red mist enveloped his senses. Two baby eyes penetrated through it. He felt something soft, fleshy between his fingers. He heard gurgling, whistling sounds, mingled with hoarse cries that came from he did not know whom.

Then something fell upon his brain like hot drops of sealing wax, and his spirit was cleared as from a cataleptic trance. Aroused to consciousness, he caught the quiver in the air that was the final reverberation of the signal, and in a trice he realized what he had been about to do. His hand relaxed its grip on the throat, under which the infant had writhed and squirmed. It gasped for breath, then began to cough and bawl.

"It's alive. Thank the Lord, it's alive."

He let it lie and hastened to the crossing. Dark clouds of smoke rolled in the distance, the wind drove them to the ground. He distinguished the panting of an engine that sounded like the intermittent, tortured breathing of a giant.

The stretch was shrouded in a cold twilight. But after a while the clouds of smoke parted, and Thiel recognized the train as being the freight that was returning with open empty cars and bringing home the men who had been working on the roadbed during the day. It had ample running time to stop at each station to drop or pick up the men.

Quite a distance from Thiel's hut the brakes began to be put on, and a loud clanking and clanging and rattling and screeching tore the silence before the train came to a standstill with a single shrill, long-drawn whistle.

About fifty men and women were in the different cars. Nearly all of them stood, some of the men with bared heads. There was a mystifying air of solemnity about them. When they caught sight of the flagman, a whispering began among them, and the old men drew their pipes from between their yellow teeth and held them respectfully in their hands. Here and there a woman would turn to blow her nose.

The conductor descended and advanced toward Thiel. The workmen saw him solemnly shake the flagman's hand, and then saw Thiel with slow steps almost military in their stiffness go back to the rear. None of them dared to address him, though they all knew him.

From the rear wagon they were lifting little Toby.

He was dead.

Lena followed. Her face was a bluish white, brown rings underlined her eyes.

Thiel did not so much as cast a glance at her. She, however, was shocked at sight of her husband. His cheeks were hollow, his eyelashes and beard were plastered, his hair, it seemed to her, was gone grayer. Traces of dried tears all over his face. And an unsteady light in his eyes that made her shudder.

The stretcher had been brought back for transporting the body home.

For a while there was gruesome silence. Thiel lost himself in black depths of awful thoughts. Darkness deepened. A herd of deer started to cross the embankment. The stag stood still between the rails and turned his agile neck curiously. The engine whistled. He and the rest of the herd disappeared in a flash.

At the moment that the train was about to start Thiel collapsed. The train stood still, and counsel was held as to what had now best be done. Since every effort they made to bring the flagman back to his senses proved futile, they decided to let the child's body lie in the hut temporarily, and use the stretcher for conveying the flagman instead. Two men carried the stretcher, Lena followed, pushing the baby carriage, sobbing the whole way, the tears running down her cheeks.

The great purplish ball of the moon shone low between the trunks of the pine trees. As it rose it paled and diminished in size until finally it hung high in the heavens like a swinging lamp, and cast a pale sheen over the forest, through every chink and cranny of the foliage, painting the faces of the processionists a livid white.

Cautiously but sturdily they made their way through the close second growth, then past broad nurseries with the larger trees scattered among the younger ones. Here the pale light seemed to have collected itself in great dark bowls.

Occasionally a rattle came from the unconscious man's throat, and occasionally he raved. Several times he clenched his fists and tried to raise himself, his eyes all the time remaining closed. Getting him across the Spree was difficult, and a return trip had to be made to fetch Lena and the baby.

As they ascended the slight eminence on which the hamlet was situated, they met a few of the inhabitants, who forthwith spread the news of the misfortune. The whole colony came running.

Among her gossips Lena broke into fresh lamentations.

Thiel was with difficulty carried up the narrow stairway of his home and put to bed. And the men returned immediately to bring little Toby's body back.

Some of the old, experienced people advised cold compresses. Lena carried out their prescription eagerly, properly, dropping cloths into icy cold spring water and renewing them as soon as the unconscious man's burning forehead had heated them. Anxiously she observed his breathing. It seemed to come more regularly and to continue to improve each minute.

However, the day's excitement had told upon her, and she decided to try to get a little sleep. No use! Whether she held her eyes open or shut, she kept seeing the events of the past hours. The baby slept. Contrary to her wont, she had not paid much attention to it. Altogether she had turned into a different person. Not a trace of her former arrogance. The sick man with the colorless face shining with sweat dominated her even in sleep.

A cloud passed, obscuring the moon and throwing the room into complete darkness. Lena heard nothing but her husband's heavy though regular breathing. She felt creepy in the dark and considered whether she should not rise and kindle a light. But as she attempted to get up, a leaden weight on her limbs pulled her back, her lids drooped, she fell asleep.

Some time later the men returning with the boy's body found the front door wide open. Surprised at this, they mounted and found the upstairs door also open. They called the woman by her name. No answer. They struck a match. The flare of it revealed awful havoc.

"Murder, murder!"

Lena lay in her blood, her face unrecognizable, her skull broken open.

"He murdered his wife, he murdered his wife!"

They ran about witless. Neighbors came. One bumped against the cradle.

"Good heavens!" He shrank back, ashen pale, his eyes fixed in a horrified stare. The baby lay with its throat cut.

The flagman had disappeared. The search made for him that night proved fruitless. The next morning, however, the man who replaced him found him on the tracks at the spot where little Toby had been run over, holding the shaggy brown cap in his arm and caressing it as if it were a living thing.

The block signaler, apprised of his discovery, telegraphed for help. Several men tried with kindly inducements to lure Thiel from the tracks. He was not to be budged. The express then due had to be stopped, and it was only by the united efforts of the entire crew and the use of force that the man, who had begun to rave fearfully, could be removed from the railroad. They had to bind his hands and feet, and the policeman summoned to the spot guarded his transportation the whole way to Berlin, where he was examined in the jail and the next day was sent to a free psychopathic ward. He never let go of the shaggy brown cap. He watched over it with jealous tenderness. ■

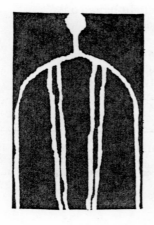

Heinrich Heine [1] (1797–1856)

THE MESSAGE

Translated from the German by
Louis Untermeyer

My page, arise, and quickly mount
    The horse of swiftest stride;
And breathlessly, through wood and field,
    To Duncan's palace ride.

5 Wait softly in the stable there
    Until you are espied;
Then ask, "Which one of Duncan's girls
    Is going to be a bride?"

And if they say, "The dark-haired one,"
10   Then rush home like the blast.
But if they say, "The light-haired one,"
    You need not ride so fast.

But in the village buy a rope,
    A rope with toughened strands.
15 Then ride back slowly, speak no word,
    And place it in my hands.

From THE POEMS OF HEINRICH HEINE, revised edition, translated by Louis Untermeyer, copyright, 1923, by Harcourt, Brace & World, Inc.; renewed, 1951, by Louis Untermeyer. Reprinted by permission of the publishers.
1. *Heinrich Heine* (hīn′riн hī′nə).

THE LORELEY

Translated from the German by

Aaron Kramer

The Loreley was a water-nymph inhabiting the Rhine, who lured sailors to their destruction.

I cannot explain the sadness
That's fallen on my breast.
An old, old fable haunts me,
And will not let me rest.

5 The air grows cool in the twilight,
And softly the Rhine flows on;
The peak of a mountain sparkles
Beneath the setting sun.

More lovely than a vision,
10 A girl sits high up there;
Her golden jewelry glistens,
She combs her golden hair.

With a comb of gold she combs it,
And sings an evensong;
15 The wonderful melody reaches
A boat, as it sails along.

The boatman hears, with an anguish
More wild than was ever known;
He's blind to the rocks around him;
20 His eyes are for her alone.

—At last the waves devoured
The boat, and the boatman's cry;
And this she did with her singing,
The golden Loreley.

"The Loreley" by Heinrich Heine, translated by Aaron Kramer from THE POETRY AND PROSE OF HEINRICH HEINE, selected and edited with an introduction by Frederic Ewen. Copyright 1948 by The Citadel Press. Reprinted by permission of The Citadel Press, Inc.

MY SONGS, YOU SAY

Translated from the German by

Louis Untermeyer

My songs, you say, are poisoned.
　　How else, love, could it be?
You have, with deadly magic,
　　Poured poison into me.

5 My songs, you say, are poisoned.
　　And well I know it, too.
I carry a thousand serpents
　　And, love, among them—you.

WHEN I AM WITH MY OWN

Translated from the German by

Louis Untermeyer

When I am with my own adored,
　　Oh, then my heart beats high;
I am as rich as any lord;
　　The world is mine to buy!

5 But every time I leave her, then
　　My wealth, that seemed secure,
Is spent; and I am once again
　　The poorest of the poor.

From THE POEMS OF HEINRICH HEINE, revised edition, translated by Louis Untermeyer, copyright, 1923, by Harcourt, Brace & World, Inc.; renewed, 1951, by Louis Untermeyer. Reprinted by permission of the publishers.

ANNO 1829

Translated from the German by

Aaron Kramer

Give me a fine wide plain, where I
May comfortably bleed to death!
Within this crowded world of trade
Oh do not let me gasp for breath!

5 They banquet well, they guzzle well,
Enjoy the blessings of the mole—
And show a generosity
No smaller than the poor-box hole.

They're always puffing on cigars.
10 Their hands in trouser-pockets rest;
And their digestion is first-rate—
Would they were easy to digest!

The spices that have made them rich
Are sold and savored everywhere;
15 And yet a rotten crawfish-smell,
Despite all spicing, fills the air.

O, that I saw gigantic wrong,
Unspeakable and bloody crime;—
But not this well-fed rectitude,
20 That always pays its bills on time!

To Lapland, or to Africa,
Or Pomerania—I would fly!
No matter to what distant land;
Take me along, you clouds on high!

25 Take me along!—They do not hear—
The clouds on high are wise indeed!
When voyaging above this town,
They hurry past with troubled speed.

"Anno 1829" by Heinrich Heine, translated by Aaron Kramer from THE POETRY AND PROSE OF HEINRICH HEINE, selected and edited with an introduction by Frederic Ewen. Copyright 1948 by The Citadel Press. Reprinted by permission of The Citadel Press, Inc.

Heine 131

ANNO 1839

Translated from the German by

Aaron Kramer

Germany, distant love of mine!
When I remember you, I pine.
Gay France is dull—this flippant folk
Bears down my spirit like a yoke.

5 In witty Paris nothing rules
But Mind. O little bells of fools,
O bells of faith!—How dear, how sweet
You sound above the German street!

Courteous men! Yet I reply
10 To their *"Bonjour"* with jaundiced eye.
The rudest treatment I was given
In Germany, now seems like Heaven.

These smiling women! never still,
Forever churning—like a mill.
15 I'll take the German girls instead.
They never talk when they're in bed.

And here in France our whole life seems
To spin around, like frenzied dreams.
At home all things are in a groove,
20 As though nailed down—they scarcely move.

From far away I seem to hear
Night-watchman bugles, soft and clear;
Night-watchman songs are sweetly ringing,
And far-off nightingales are singing.

25 At home, in Schilda's oaken grove,
How well the poet thrived! I wove
My tender-hearted verses there,
Of moonlight and of violet-air.

"Anno 1839" by Heinrich Heine, translated by Aaron Kramer from THE POETRY AND PROSE OF HEINRICH HEINE, selected and edited with an introduction by Frederic Ewen. Copyright 1948 by The Citadel Press. Reprinted by permission of The Citadel Press, Inc.

THE SILESIAN WEAVERS

Translated from the German by

Aaron Kramer

In 1844 the weavers of Silesia revolted against unbelievably harsh working conditions. Although they realized their revolt would be doomed to failure, the weavers nevertheless proceeded with it as a sign of protest.

In gloomy eyes there wells no tear.
Grinding their teeth, they are sitting here:
"Germany, your shroud's on our loom;
And in it we weave the threefold doom.
5   We weave; we weave.

"Doomed be the God who was deaf to our prayer
In Winter's cold and hunger's despair.
All in vain we hoped and bided;
He only mocked us, hoaxed, derided—
10   We weave; we weave.

"Doomed be the king, the rich man's king,
Who would not be moved by our suffering,
Who tore the last coin out of our hands,
And let us be shot by his blood-thirsty bands—
15   We weave; we weave.

"Doomed be the fatherland, false name,
Where nothing thrives but disgrace and shame,
Where flowers are crushed before they unfold,
Where the worm is quickened by rot and mold—
20   We weave; we weave.

"The loom is creaking, the shuttle flies;
Not night nor day do we close our eyes.
Old Germany, your shroud's on our loom,
And in it we weave the threefold doom;
25   We weave; we weave."

A WARNING

Translated from the German by

Louis Untermeyer

You will print such books as these?
      Then you're lost, my friend, that's certain.
      If you wish for gold and honor,
Write more humbly; bend your knees.

5 Yes, you must have lost your senses,
      Thus to speak before the people,
      Thus to dare to talk of preachers
And of potentates and princes.

Friend, you're doomed, so it appears;
10   For the princes have long arms,
      And the preachers have long tongues,
And the masses have long ears!

IT GOES OUT

Translated from the German by
Louis Untermeyer

The curtain falls; the play is done;
Ladies and gentlemen, one by one,
Go home at last. How was the play?
I heard applause as I came away.
5 A much-respected audience
Praised the author beyond a doubt;
But now that they have all gone hence
The house is silent, the lights are out.

But wait! A sound is heard within,
10 Feeble but fairly near the stage;
Perhaps the string of a violin
Has suddenly broken down with age.
Peevishly in the dark parterre
The restless rats run here and there,
15 And the place reeks of rancid oil.

All things grow musty; all things spoil.
The last lamp tries to stem the rout;
Then, with a sputter and sigh of doubt,
The light (that was my soul) goes out.

DÜSSELDORF

Translated from the German by
Aaron Kramer

Düsseldorf lies on the east bank of the Rhine in what was once the territory of the Palatinate. Its ruler, the Prince Elector, was one of the body of German princes who chose from among themselves the Holy Roman Emperor. In 1805 the city became the capital of the Grand Duchy of Berg, created by Napoleon and bestowed on Joachim Murat, a brilliant cavalry officer.

THE TOWN OF DÜSSELDORF IS VERY BEAUTIFUL, and if you think of it when you are far away and happen to have been born there, you are strangely affected. I was born there, and I feel as if I had to go home at once. When I say *home,* I mean the Bolkerstrasse, and the house where I was born. The house will some day be famous, and I have told the old woman who now owns it under no circumstances to sell it. The whole house would now hardly fetch as much as the tips which elegant green-veiled English ladies will give the maid when she shows them the room where I first saw the light of day, and the henhouse where my father used to lock me up for stealing grapes, and the brown door on which my mother taught me to write letters with chalk. Heavens, Madame, if ever I turn out to be a famous writer, it will have cost my poor mother trouble enough to make me one.

But at present my fame is still sleeping in the marble quarries of Carrara. The paper laurel wreath with which they have crowned my brow has not yet spread its fragrance throughout the world, and when elegant green-veiled English ladies come to

Düsseldorf, they do not so much as look at the famous house, but go straight to the market-place to inspect the colossal, black equestrian statue standing in the middle of it. It is said that this statue represents the Prince Elector Jan Wilhelm.[1] He wears black armor, and has a long flowing wig. As a boy I was told that the artist, while casting this statue, observed with horror that there was not metal enough, and so all the citizens came running with their silver spoons to help him complete the casting. And I used to stand for hours before the statue, racking my brains with the question: How many silver spoons can be contained within it; and how many apple tarts can be bought with all that silver? For apple tarts were then my passion.— Now it is love, truth, freedom, and cray-fish soup. Indeed, close to the Elector's statue at the corner of the theater there generally stood a comical-looking, bow-legged fellow, with a white apron and a basket of piping-hot apple tarts which he hawked in an irresistible falsetto: "Apple tarts, fresh from the oven! Sweet-smelling apple tarts!" As a matter of fact, when the Tempter tried to seduce me in my riper years, he spoke with the very same alluring falsetto, and I should never have stayed at Signora Julietta's for twelve full hours, if she had not used that sweet, savory apple-tart voice on me. To tell the truth, apple tarts would never have attracted me so much, had not bandy-legged Herman covered them so mysteriously with his white apron—and it was this white apron—but I am digressing. I was speaking of the equestrian statue, with so many silver spoons inside it, and not a spoonful of soup—the statue which represents the Elector Jan Wilhelm.

They say he was a decent sort of fellow, a great lover of art, and even very talented. He founded the art gallery at Düsseldorf, and in the observatory there you can still see an extraordinary and ingenious collapsible goblet made of wood, which he carved in his leisure hours—of which he had twenty-four every day.

In those days princes were not so care-ridden as they are now. Their crowns grew firmly on their heads, and at night they pulled night-caps over them, and slept peacefully. And the people slept peacefully at their feet, and on awaking each morning they said: "Good morning, father!" And the prince replied: "Good morning, my dear children!"

---

1. *this statue . . . the Prince Elector Jan Wilhelm.* The Flemish sculptor Gabriel Grupello (1649–1716) executed the equestrian statue of Jan Wilhelm II (1658–1716).

But suddenly all this changed. One morning, when we awoke at Düsseldorf and were about to say, "Good morning, father!", our father was gone. The whole town was in a state of numb bewilderment and in a funereal mood; and the people stole silently to the market-place and read the long announcement on the door of the town hall. The weather was dreary, and yet Kilian, the emaciated tailor, was standing in his nankeen jacket, which he generally wore in the house, and his blue woolen stockings hung down so that his bare little legs looked out mournfully, and his thin lips quivered while he muttered to himself the words of the proclamation. An old pensioned soldier of the Palatinate read in a somewhat louder voice, and now and then a bright tear dropped on his honest, grizzled moustache. I stood beside him and wept too, and asked him why we were weeping. He replied: "The Elector wishes to thank you." Then he began reading again, and when he came to the words, "for your proved loyalty," and "we release you from your allegiance," he wept even more bitterly. It is odd to see an old man in a faded uniform and with a scarred soldier's face bursting into tears. While we were reading, the electoral coat-of-arms was taken down from the town hall; and everything assumed as bleak an aspect as if people were awaiting an eclipse of the sun. The town councillors went about with a languid, discharged sort of gait, and even the all-powerful bailiff looked as if he no longer had orders to give and stood so calm and indifferent, although crazy Aloysius was again standing on one leg and rattling out the names of the French generals, grimacing idiotically, while the drunken cripple Gumpertz rolled in the gutter and sang, "Ça ira,[2] ça ira!"

But I went home sobbing, "The Elector wishes to thank you." My mother could do nothing; I knew what I knew, and refused to be comforted. I went to bed weeping, and that night I dreamt that the world had come to an end. The beautiful flower gardens and green meadows there were rolled up and put away like rugs; the town bailiff climbed up a high ladder and took down the sun; tailor Kilian stood by and said to himself, "I must go home and put on my best clothes, for I am dead and I'm going to be buried this very day." And it grew darker and darker. A few stars glimmered fitfully, and even these fell down like yellow leaves in autumn. Gradually everyone disappeared, and I, poor child, wandered about disconsolately, till at last I stood by a row of willows on a desolate farm, and saw a man who was

---

2. Ça ira (sä' ē rä'), "It will go on," from a song of the French Revolution.

turning up the earth with a spade, and by his side stood a hideous, malicious woman, with something in her apron that resembled a severed head. It was the moon! She laid it with anxious care into the open grave; and behind me stood the old pensioned soldier of the Palatine who sobbed and spelled out the words, "The Elector wishes to thank you."

When I awoke, the sun was shining through my window as usual. In the streets, drums were beaten, and when I entered our parlor and bade my father "Good morning" (he was in his white dressing-gown), I heard the nimble-footed barber telling my father in all details, while he was doing his hair, that today the new Archduke Joachim would be crowned in the town hall, that he belonged to a very good family, that he was married to Emperor Napoleon's sister,[3] and was himself a man of address, wore his beautiful black hair in curls, and was shortly to make his entry and could not fail to please all the ladies. Meanwhile the drumming continued in the streets. I went to the door and saw the French troops marching in—that glorious, gay nation, which has marched through the world with song and triumph, —the cheerfully serious faces of the grenadiers, the bear-skin caps, the tricolor cockades, the gleaming bayonets, the *voltigeurs*,[4] jubilant and full of *point d'honneur*,[5] and the all-powerful, silver-laced drum-major, who could throw his gold-knobbed baton as high as the second story, and his glances as far as the third—where pretty girls sat at the windows. I was overjoyed at the prospect of having soldiers quartered with us—my mother was not—and I hurried to the market place. There everything was changed, as if the whole world had been freshly painted. There was a new coat of arms on the town hall; the iron railings of the balcony were hung with embroidered velvet; French grenadiers stood guard; the old councillors had put on fresh faces and wore their Sunday best and looked at one another in French and said, *"bon jour."* Ladies were peering from every window, curious citizens and smart soldiers filled the square, and we boys clambered up the huge horse of the Elector and looked down on the motley crowds in the market place.

Our neighbor's boy Pitter and lanky Kurz nearly broke their necks on this occasion; though this would have proved no misfortune, for Pitter afterward ran away from home, enlisted,

---

3. *Archduke Joachim . . . Emperor Napoleon's sister.* Joachim Murat married Caroline, Napoleon's youngest sister, in 1800. **4.** *voltigeurs* (vol′ ti jėrz′), riflemen. **5.** *point d'honneur* (pwän′ dô ner′), pride.

deserted, and was shot dead in Mayence; Kurz, on the other hand, later began making geographical explorations into other people's pockets, was chosen an active member of a public treadmill, broke the iron ties which bound him to that institution and to his country, crossed the waters in safety, and died in London from wearing too tight a necktie which knotted of itself when an official of the crown pulled away the plank on which he happened to be standing.

Lanky Kurz told us that there was no school today on account of the coronation. We waited a long while for things to start. At last the balcony of the town hall was filled with gaily-dressed gentlemen, flags and trumpets, and the Burgomaster, in his famous red coat, made a speech, somewhat extenuated like India rubber or a knitted nightcap into which a stone has been thrown—not, however, the philosopher's stone. A few of the phrases I could catch distinctly, for example, that they meant to make us all happy; and when he finished, the trumpets blew, the flags fluttered, the drums were beaten, and there were shouts of *"Vivat!"* and I also shouted *"Vivat!"*, at the same time holding on fast to the old Elector. And I had need of a firm hold, for I was getting quite dizzy and began to think that people were standing on their heads, because the world was turning; and the Elector with his wig seemed to nod and whisper, "Hold tight!" And it was only the sound of the cannon being fired on the ramparts that brought me to my senses, and I slowly dismounted from the Elector's horse.

On my way home, I again saw crazy Aloysius dancing on one leg, while he rattled out the names of the French generals; and the cripple Gumpertz wallowing drunk in the gutter, roaring, *"Ça ira, ça ira."* And I said to my mother, "They want to make us all happy; that is why there is no school today."   ■

LONDON

Translated from the German by
Aaron Kramer

I HAVE SEEN the greatest wonder which the world can show to the astonished mind. I have seen it, and am more astonished than ever. Still vivid in my memory remains the stone forest of houses, and amid them the rushing stream of living human faces, with all their motley passions and all their terrible and restless impulses of love, of hunger, of hatred.

I am speaking of London.

Send a philosopher to London, but, not on your life, a poet! Send a philosopher there and stand him at a corner of Cheapside,[1] and he will learn more there than from all the books of the last Leipzig fair. As the human waves roar around him, a sea of new thoughts will rise before him, and the Eternal Spirit which hovers upon its waters will breathe upon him. The most hidden secrets of the social order will suddenly be revealed to him. He will hear the pulse of the world beat audibly, and see it visibly—for if London is the right hand of the world, its active, mighty right hand, then we may regard the street which leads from the Exchange to Downing Street as the world's radial artery.

But send no poet to London! This downright earnestness in all things, this colossal uniformity, this machine-like movement, this moroseness even in pleasure, this exaggerated London—smothers the imagination and rends the heart. And should you ever send a German poet there, a dreamer, who stands staring at every single thing—say, a ragged beggar-woman, or a resplendent goldsmith's shop—why then, things will go badly with him, and he will be jostled on all sides, and

"London" by Heinrich Heine, translated by Aaron Kramer from THE POETRY AND PROSE OF HEINRICH HEINE, selected and edited with an introduction by Frederic Ewen. Copyright 1948 by The Citadel Press. Reprinted by permission of The Citadel Press, Inc.
1. *Cheapside,* an overcrowded district in London.

even knocked down with a mild "God damn!" God damn! that damned pushing! I soon perceived that these Londoners have much to do. They live on a grand scale, and though food and clothing are dearer there than with us, they must still be better fed and clothed than we are. As behooves gentility, they also have enormous debts, yet sometimes in a boastful mood, they squander their guineas, pay other nations to fight for their pleasure, whose respective kings they give a handsome *douceur* [2] into the bargain. Therefore, John Bull must work day and night to obtain money for such expenses; day and night he must tax his brain to invent new machines, and he sits and reckons in the sweat of his brow, and rushes and scurries without looking about him, from the docks to the Exchange, and from the Exchange to the Strand. Hence it is quite understandable, when a poor German poet stands in his way at the corner of Cheapside gazing into an art-dealer's window he should knock him aside somewhat unceremoniously. "God damn!"

The picture at which I was gaping at the corner of Cheapside was that of the crossing of the Beresina by the French. [3]

When, jolted out of my preoccupation, I looked again on the roaring street, where a motley throng of men, women, children, horses, stagecoaches, and with them a funeral procession, whirled, groaned, and creaked along, it seemed to me as though all of London were a Beresina Bridge, where everyone presses on in mad haste to save his little scrap of life, where the arrogant rider tramples down the poor pedestrian; where he who falls to the ground is lost forever; where even the best friends rush by, indifferently, over the corpses of their comrades; and thousands of exhausted and bleeding creatures clutch in vain at the planks of the bridge, and plunge into the icy pit of death.

How much more cheerful and homelike it is in our dear Germany! With what dreamy coziness, with what Sabbatical quiet things glide along here! Calmly the watch is changed; uniforms and houses gleam in the quiet sunshine, swallows flit over the flagstones, fat court-councillors' wives smile from the windows, while in the echoing streets there is room enough for the dogs to sniff at one another properly, and for men to stand at ease and discourse on the theater, and bow low—very, very

---

2. *douceur* (dü sèr'), a tip. 3. *the crossing of the Beresina by the French.* The Beresina is a river in western Russia crossed by Napoleon in 1812 during his retreat.

low!—when some little aristocratic scoundrel or vice-scoundrel, with colored little ribbons on his shabby little coat, or some court-marshal-lowbrain, powdered and gilded, prances by, graciously returning the greeting.

I had made up my mind in advance not to be astonished at that hugeness of London of which I had heard so much. But I had as little success as the poor schoolboy who had made up his mind not to feel the whipping he was about to receive. The fact was that he expected to receive the usual blows with the usual cane in the usual way on the back; whereas he received a most unusually severe thrashing in an unusual place with a slender switch. I anticipated great palaces, and saw nothing but small houses. But their very uniformity and their infinite number are wonderfully impressive.

· · · · ·

THE STRANGER who wanders through the great streets of London and does not chance right into the quarters in which the common people live, sees little or nothing of the dire misery there. Only here and there, at the entrance of some dark alley, a ragged woman stands mutely with a suckling babe at her exhausted breast, and begs with her eyes. Perhaps if those eyes are still beautiful, one glances into them and shrinks back at the world of wretchedness to be found here. The common beggars are all old people, generally blackamoors, who stand at the corners of the streets clearing pathways—a very necessary thing in muddy London—and ask for coppers in return. It is only in the dark night that Poverty, with her fellows, Vice and Crime, glides from her lair. She shuns the daylight all the more carefully, since her wretchedness contrasts so glaringly with the pride of wealth which struts about everywhere. Only hunger drives her sometimes from her dark alley at midday, and then she stares with eloquent, mute, beseeching eyes at the rich merchant who hurries past, busy, jingling his coins, or at the idle lord, who, like a surfeited god, rides by on his high horse, now and then glancing with an aristocratically blasé air at the crowds below—as if they were a swarm of ants, or a herd of baser creatures whose joys and sorrows had nothing in common with his feelings. For above this mass of humanity which clings close to the earth, England's nobility soars, like beings of higher order, and regards its little island as a temporary lodging, Italy as its summer garden, Paris as its social salon, and the whole wide world as its property. These nobles sweep along, without cark or care, and their gold is a talisman which makes their wildest wishes come true.

Poor poverty! How agonizing must your hunger be, when others wallow in arrogant surfeit! And when a man, with indifferent hand, throws a crust into your lap, how bitter must be the tears with which you wet it! You drink poison with your own tears. You are surely right when you ally yourself with Vice and Crime. Outlawed criminals often have more humanity in their hearts than those cold, irreproachable citizens of virtue, in whose bloodless hearts the power of doing evil is quenched—as well as the power of doing good. And even Vice is not always Vice. I have seen women on whose cheeks red vice was painted, but in whose hearts dwelt heavenly purity. I have seen women —would I saw them again!—

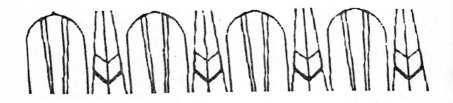

Herman Hesse [1] (1877–1962)

WITHIN AND WITHOUT

Translated from the German by
T. K. Brown

THERE WAS ONCE a man by the name of Frederick; he devoted himself to intellectual pursuits and had a wide range of knowledge. But not all knowledge was the same to him, nor was any thought as good as any other: he loved a certain type of thinking, and disdained and abominated the others. What he loved and revered was logic—that so admirable method—and, in general, what he called "science."

"Twice two is four," he used to say. "This I believe; and man must do his thinking on the basis of this truth."

He was not unaware, to be sure, that there were other sorts of thinking and knowledge; but they were not "science," and he held a low opinion of them. Although a freethinker, he was not intolerant of religion. Religion was founded on a tacit agreement among scientists. For several centuries their science had embraced nearly everything that existed on earth and was worth knowing, with the exception of one single province: the human soul. It had become a sort of custom, as time went on, to leave this to religion, and to tolerate its speculations on the soul, though without taking them seriously. Thus Frederick too was tolerant toward religion; but everything he recognized as superstition was profoundly odious and repugnant to him. Alien, uncultured, and retarded peoples might occupy them-

---

"Within and Without" by Herman Hesse, translated by T. K. Brown from THE WORLD'S BEST edited by Whit Burnett. Reprinted by permission of Whit Burnett.
1. *Hesse* (hes′ə).

selves with it; in remote antiquity there might have been mystical or magical thinking; but since the birth of science and logic there was no longer any sense in making use of these outmoded and dubious tools.

So he said and so he thought; and when traces of superstition came to his attention he became angry and felt as if he had been touched by something hostile.

It angered him most of all, however, if he found such traces among his own sort, among educated men who were conversant with the principles of scientific thinking. And nothing was more painful and intolerable to him than that scandalous notion which lately he had sometimes heard expressed and discussed even by men of great culture—that absurd idea that "scientific thinking" was possibly not a supreme, timeless, eternal, foreordained, and unassailable mode of thought, but merely one of many, a transient way of thinking, not impervious to change and downfall. This irreverent, destructive, poisonous notion was abroad—even Frederick could not deny it; it had cropped up here and there as a result of the distress throughout the world brought about by war, revolution, and hunger, like a warning, like a white hand's ghostly writing on a white wall.

The more Frederick suffered from the fact that this idea existed and could so deeply distress him, the more passionately he assailed it and those whom he suspected of secretly believing in it. So far only a very few from among the truly educated had openly and frankly professed their belief in this new doctrine, a doctrine that seemed destined, should it gain in circulation and power, to destroy all spiritual values on earth and call forth chaos. Well, matters had not reached that point yet, and the scattered individuals who openly embraced the idea were still so few in number that they could be considered oddities and crotchety, peculiar fellows. But a drop of the poison, an emanation of that idea, could be perceived first on this side, then on that. Among the people and the half-educated no end of new doctrines could be found anyway, esoteric doctrines, sects, and discipleships; the world was full of them; everywhere one could scent out superstition, mysticism, spiritualistic cults, and other mysterious forces, which it was really necessary to combat, but to which science, as if from a private feeling of weakness, had for the present given free rein.

One day Frederick went to the house of one of his friends, with whom he had often studied. It so happened that he had not seen this friend for some time. While he was climbing the stairs of the house he tried to recall when and where it was that he had last been in his friend's company; but much as he could pride himself on his good memory for other things he could not remember. Because of this he fell imperceptibly into a certain vexation and ill humor, from which, as he stood before his friend's door, he was obliged forcibly to free himself.

Hardly had he greeted Erwin, his friend, when he noticed on his genial countenance a certain, as it were forbearing, smile, which it seemed to him he had never seen there before. And hardly had he seen this smile, which despite its friendliness he at once felt to be somehow mocking or hostile, when he immediately remembered what he had just been searching his memory for in vain—his last previous meeting with Erwin. He remembered that they had parted then without having quarreled, to be sure, but yet with a sense of inner discord and dissatisfaction, because Erwin, as it had seemed to him, had given far too little support to his attacks at that time on the realm of superstition.

It was strange. How could he have forgotten that entirely? And now he also knew that this was his only reason for not having sought out his friend for so long, merely this dissatisfaction, and that he had known this all the time, although he had invented for himself a host of other excuses for his repeated postponement of this visit.

Now they confronted one another; and it seemed to Frederick as if the little rift of that day had meantime tremendously widened. He felt that in this moment something was lacking between him and Erwin that had always been there before, an aura of solidarity, of spontaneous understanding—indeed, even of affection. Instead of these there was a vacuum. They greeted each other; spoke of the weather, their acquaintances, their health; and—God knows why!—with every word Frederick had the disquieting sensation that he was not quite understanding his friend, that his friend did not really know him, that his words were missing their mark, that they could find no common ground for a real conversation. Moreover Erwin still had that friendly smile on his face, which Frederick was beginning almost to hate.

During a pause in the laborious conversation Frederick looked about the studio he knew so well and saw, pinned loosely on the wall, a sheet of paper. This sight moved him strangely and awakened ancient memories; for he recalled that, long ago in their student years, this had been a habit of Erwin's, a way he sometimes chose of keeping a thinker's saying or a poet's verse fresh in his mind. He stood up and went to the wall to read the paper.

There, in Erwin's beautiful script, he read the words: "Nothing is without, nothing is within; for what is without is within."

Blanching, he stood motionless for a moment. There it was! There he stood face to face with what he feared! At another time he would have let this leaf of paper pass, would have tolerated it charitably as a whim, as a harmless foible to which anyone was entitled, perhaps as a trifling sentimentality calling for indulgence. But now it was different. He felt that these words had not been set down for the sake of a fleeting poetic mood; it was not a vagary that Erwin had returned after so many years to a practice of his youth. What stood written here, as an avowal of his friend's concern at the moment, was mysticism! Erwin was unfaithful!

Slowly he turned to face him, whose smile was again radiant.

"Explain this to me!" he demanded.

Erwin nodded, brimming with friendliness.

"Haven't you ever read this saying?"

"Certainly!" Frederick cried. "Of course I know it. It's mysticism, it's Gnosticism.[2] It may be poetic, but—well, anyway, explain the saying to me, and why it's hanging on your wall!"

"Gladly," Erwin said. "The saying is a first introduction to an epistemology [3] that I've been going into lately, and which has already brought me much happiness."

Frederick restrained his temper. He asked, "A new epistemology? Is there such a thing? And what is it called?"

"Oh," Erwin answered, "it's only new to me. It's already very old and venerable. It's called magic."

The word had been uttered. Profoundly astonished and startled by so candid a confession, Frederick, with a shudder, felt that he was confronted eye to eye with the arch-enemy, in the person of his friend. He did not know whether he was nearer rage or tears; the bitter feeling of irreparable loss possessed him. For a long time he remained silent.

Then, with a pretended decision in his voice, he began, "So now you want to become a magician?"

"Yes," Erwin replied unhesitatingly.

"A sort of sorcerer's apprentice, eh?"

"Certainly."

---

2. *Gnosticism,* the belief of various sects during the first six centuries after Christ, which attempted to reconcile the doctrines of Christianity with Greek thought and which viewed reality as a series of divine emanations. 3. *epistemology,* a branch of philosophy which inquires into the nature and limits of knowledge; a theory of knowledge.

A clock could be heard ticking in the adjoining room, it was so quiet.

Then Frederick said, "This means, you know, that you are abandoning all fellowship with serious science, and hence all fellowship with me."

"I hope that is not so," Erwin answered. "But if that's the way it has to be, what else can I do?"

"What else can you do?" Frederick burst out. "Why, break, break once and for all with this childishness, this wretched and contemptible belief in magic! That's what else you can do, if you want to keep my respect."

Erwin smiled a little, although he too no longer seemed cheerful.

"You speak as if," he said, so gently that through his quiet words Frederick's angry voice still seemed to be echoing about the room, "you speak as if that lay within my will, as if I had a choice, Frederick. That is not the case. I have no choice. It was not I that chose magic: magic chose me."

Frederick sighed deeply. "Then goodby," he said wearily, and stood up, without offering to shake hands.

"Not like that!" Erwin cried out. "No, you must not go from me like that. Pretend that one of us is lying on his deathbed— and that is so!—and that we must say farewell."

"But which of us, Erwin, is dying?"

"Today it is probably I, my friend. Whoever wishes to be born anew must be prepared to die."

Once more Frederick went up to the sheet of paper and read the saying about within and without.

"Very well," he said finally. "You are right, it won't do any good to part in anger. I'll do what you wish; I'll pretend that one of us is dying. Before I go I want to make a last request of you."

"I'm glad," Erwin said. "Tell me, what kindness can I show you on our leavetaking?"

"I repeat my first question, and this is also my request: explain this saying to me, as well as you can."

Erwin reflected a moment and then spoke:

"Nothing is without, nothing is within. You know the religious meaning of this: God is everywhere. He is in the spirit, and also in nature. All is divine, because God is all. Formerly this was called pantheism. Then the philosophic meaning: we are used to divorcing the within from the without in our thinking, but this is not necessary. Our spirit is capable of withdrawing behind the limits we have set for it, into the beyond. Beyond the pair of antitheses of which our world consists a new and different knowledge begins. . . . But, my dear friend, I must confess to you—since my thinking has changed there are no longer any unambiguous words and sayings for me: every word has tens and hundreds of meanings. And here what you fear begins—magic."

Frederick wrinkled his brow and was about to interrupt, but Erwin looked at him disarmingly and continued, speaking more distinctly, "Let me give you an example. Take something of mine along with you, any object, and examine it a little from time to time. Soon the principle of the within and the without will reveal one of its many means to you."

He glanced about the room, took a small clay figurine from a wall shelf, and gave it to Frederick, saying:

"Take this with you as my parting gift. When this thing that I am now placing in your hands ceases to be outside you and is within you, come to me again! But if it remains outside you, the way it is now, forever, then this parting of yours from me shall also be forever!"

Frederick wanted to say a great deal more; but Erwin took his hand, pressed it, and bade him farewell with an expression that permitted no further conversation.

Frederick left; descended the stairs (how prodigiously long ago he had climbed them!); went through the streets to his home, the little earthen figure in his hand, perplexed and sick of heart. In front of his house he stopped, shook the fist fiercely for a moment in which he was clutching the figurine, and felt a great urge to smash the ridiculous thing to the ground. He did not do so; he bit his lip and entered the house. Never before had he been so agitated, so tormented by conflicting emotions.

He looked for a place for his friend's gift, and put the figure on top of a bookcase. For the time being it stayed there.

Occasionally, as the days went by, he looked at it, brooding on it and on its origins, and pondering the meaning that this foolish thing was to have for him. It was a small figure of a man or a god or an idol, with two faces, like the Roman god Janus,[4] modeled rather crudely of clay and covered with a burnt and somewhat cracked glaze. The little image looked coarse and insignificant; certainly it was not Roman or Greek workmanship; more likely it was the work of some backward, primitive race in Africa or the South Seas. The two faces, which were exactly alike, bore an apathetic, indolent faintly grinning smile

---

4. *Janus*, the Roman god who was the guardian of doors and gates, represented with two faces.

—it was downright ugly the way the little gnome squandered his stupid smile.

Frederick could not get used to the figure. It was totally unpleasant and offensive to him, it got in his way, it disturbed him. The very next day he took it down and put it on the stove, and a few days later moved it to a cupboard. Again and again it got in the path of his vision, as if it were forcing itself upon him; it laughed at him coldly and dull-wittedly, put on airs, demanded attention. After a few weeks he put it in the anteroom, between the photographs of Italy and the trivial little souvenirs which no one ever looked at. Now at least he saw the idol only when he was entering or leaving, and then he passed it quickly, without examining it more closely. But here too the thing still bothered him, though he did not admit this to himself.

With this shard, this two-faced monstrosity, vexation and torment had entered his life.

One day, months later, he returned from a short trip—he undertook such excursions now from time to time, as if something were driving him restlessly about; he entered his house, went through the anteroom, was greeted by the maid, and read the letters waiting for him. But he was ill at ease, as if he had forgotten something important; no book tempted him, no chair was comfortable. He began to rack his mind—what was the cause of this? Had he neglected something important? Eaten something unsettling? In reflecting it occurred to him that this disturbing feeling had come over him as he had entered the apartment. He returned to the anteroom and involuntarily his first glance sought the clay figure.

A strange fright went through him when he did not see the idol. It had disappeared. It was missing. Had it walked away on its little crockery legs? Flown away? By magic?

Frederick pulled himself together, and smiled at his nervousness. Then he began quietly to search the whole room. When he found nothing he called the maid. She came, was embarrassed, and admitted at once that she had dropped the thing while cleaning up.

"Where is it?"

It was not there any more. It had seemed so solid, that little thing; she had often had it in her hands; and yet it had shattered to a hundred little pieces and splinters, and could not be fixed. She had taken the fragments to a glazier, who had simply laughed at her; and then she had thrown them away.

Frederick dismissed the maid. He smiled. That was perfectly

all right with him. He did not feel bad about the idol, God knows. The abomination was gone; now he would have peace. If only he had knocked the thing to pieces that very first day! What he had suffered in all this time! How sluggishly, strangely, craftily, evilly, satanically that idol had smiled at him! Well, now that it was gone he could admit it to himself: he had feared it, truly and sincerely feared it, this earthen god. Was it not the emblem and symbol of everything that was repugnant and intolerable to him, everything that he had recognized all along as pernicious, inimical, and worthy of suppression—an emblem of all superstitions, all darkness, all coercion of conscience and spirit? Did it not represent that ghastly power that one sometimes felt raging in the bowels of the earth, that distant earthquake, that approaching extinction of culture, that looming chaos? Had not this contemptible figure robbed him of his best friend—nay, not merely robbed, but made of the friend an enemy? Well, now the thing was gone. Vanished. Smashed to pieces. Done for. It was good so; it was much better than if he had destroyed it himself.

So he thought, or said. And he went about his affairs as before.

But it was like a curse. Now, just when he had got more or less used to that ridiculous figure, just when the sight of it in its usual place on the anteroom table had gradually become a bit familiar and unimportant to him, now its absence began to torment him! Yes, he missed it every time he went through that room; all he could see there was the empty spot where it had formerly stood, and emptiness emanated from the spot and filled the room with strangeness.

Bad days and worse nights began for Frederick. He could no longer go through the anteroom without thinking of the idol with the two faces, missing it, and feeling that his thoughts were tethered to it. This became an agonizing compulsion for him. And it was not by any means simply on the occasions when he went through that room that he was gripped by this compulsion—ah, no. Just as emptiness and desolation radiated from the now empty spot on the anteroom table, so this compulsive idea radiated within him, gradually crowded all else aside, rankling and filling him with emptiness and strangeness.

Again and again he pictured the figure with utmost distinctness, just to make it clear to himself how preposterous it was to grieve its loss. He could see it in all its stupid ugliness and barbarity, with its vacuous yet crafty smile, with its two faces—indeed, as if under duress, full of hatred and with his mouth drawn awry, he found himself attempting to reproduce that smile. The question pestered him whether the two faces were really exactly alike. Had not one of them, perhaps only because of a little roughness or a crack in the glaze, had a somewhat different expression? Something quizzical? Something sphinx-like? And how peculiar the color of that glaze had been! Green, and blue, and gray, but also red, were in it—a glaze that he now kept finding often in other objects, in a window's reflection of the sun or in the mirrorings of a wet pavement.

He brooded a great deal on this glaze, at night too. It also struck him what a strange, foreign, ill-sounding, unfamiliar, almost malignant word "glaze" was. He analyzed the word, and once he even reversed the order of its letters. Then it read "ezalg." Now where the devil did this word get its sound from? He knew this word "ezalg," certainly he knew it; moreover, it was an unfriendly and bad word, a word with ugly and disturbing connotations. For a long while he tormented himself with this question. Finally he hit upon it: "ezalg" reminded him of a book that he had bought and read many years ago on a trip, and that had dismayed, plagued, and yet secretly fascinated him; it had been entitled *Princess Ezalka*. It was like a curse: everything connected with the figurine—the glaze, the blue, the green, the smile—signified hostility, tormenting and poisoning him. And how very peculiarly *he,* Erwin, his erstwhile friend, had smiled as he had given the idol into his hand! How very peculiarly, how very significantly, how very hostily.

Frederick resisted manfully—and on many days not without success—the compulsive trend of his thoughts. He sensed the danger clearly: he did not want to go insane! No, it were better to die. Reason was necessary, life was not. And it occurred to him that perhaps *this* was magic, that Erwin, with the aid of that figure, had in some way enchanted him, and that he should fall as a sacrifice, as the defender of reason and science against these dismal powers. But if this were so, if he could even conceive of that as possible, then there *was* such a thing as magic, then there *was* sorcery. No, it were better to die!

A doctor recommended walks and baths; and sometimes, in search of amusement, he spent an evening at an inn. But it helped very little. He cursed Erwin; he cursed himself.

One night, as he often did now, he retired early and lay restlessly awake in bed, unable to sleep. He felt unwell and uneasy. He wanted to meditate; he wanted to find solace, wanted to speak sentences of some sort to himself, good sentences, comforting, reassuring ones, something with the straightforward serenity and lucidity of the sentence, "Twice two is four." Nothing came to mind; but, in a state almost of lightheadedness, he mumbled sounds and syllables to himself. Gradually words formed on his lips, and several times, without being sensible of its meaning, he said the same short sentence to himself, which had somehow taken form in him. He muttered it to himself, as if it might stupefy him, as if he might grope his way along it, as along a parapet, to the sleep that eluded him on the narrow, narrow path that skirted the abyss.

But suddenly, when he spoke somewhat louder, the words he was mumbling penetrated his consciousness. He knew them: they were, "Yes, now you are within me!" And instantly he knew. He knew what they meant—that they referred to the clay idol and that now, in this gray night hour, he had accurately and exactly fulfilled the prophecy Erwin had made on that unearthly day, that now the figure, which he had held contemptuously in his fingers then, was no longer outside him but within him! "For what is without is within."

Bounding up in a leap, he felt as if transfused with ice and fire. The world reeled about him, the planets stared at him insanely. He threw on some clothes, put on the light, left his house and ran in the middle of the night to Erwin's. There he saw a light burning in the studio window he knew so well; the door to the house was unlocked: everything seemed to be awaiting him. He rushed up the stairs. He walked unsteadily into Erwin's study, supported himself with trembling hands on the table. Erwin sat by the lamp, in its gentle light, contemplative, smiling.

Graciously Erwin arose. "You have come. That is good."

"Have you been expecting me?" Frederick whispered.

"I have been expecting you, as you know, from the moment you left here, taking my little gift with you. Has what I said then happened?"

"It has happened," Frederick said. "The idol is within me. I can't bear it any longer."

"Can I help you?" Erwin asked.

"I don't know. Do as you will. Tell me more of your magic! Tell me how the idol can get out of me again."

Erwin placed his hand on his friend's shoulder. He led him to an armchair and pressed him down in it. Then he spoke cordially to Frederick, smiling in an almost brotherly tone of voice:

"The idol will come out of you again. Have trust in me. Have trust in yourself. You have learned to believe in it. Now learn to love it! It is within you, but it is still dead, it is still a phantom

to you. Awaken it, speak to it, question it! For it is you yourself!
Do not hate it any longer, do not fear it, do not torment it—how
you have tormented this poor idol, who was yet you yourself!
How you have tormented yourself!"

"Is this the way to magic?" Frederick asked. He sat deep in
the chair, as if he had grown older, and his voice was low.

"This is the way," Erwin replied, "and perhaps you have
already taken the most difficult step. You have found by experience: the without can become the within. You have been beyond the pair of antitheses. It seemed hell to you; learn, my
friend, it is heaven! For it is heaven that awaits you. Behold,
this is magic: to interchange the without and the within, not by
compulsion, not in anguish, as you have done it, but freely,
voluntarily. Summon up the past, summon up the future: both
are in you! Until today you have been the slave of the within.
Learn to be its master. That is magic." ■

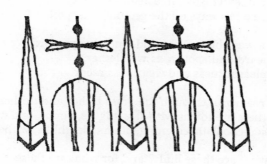

Hugo von Hofmannsthal
(1874–1929)

BALLAD OF OUTER LIFE

Translated from the German by
Walter Kaufman

And children grow up slowly with deep eyes,
that know of nothing; they grow up and toil
and die, and all men walk their ways.

And bitter fruit grow sweet, drop to the soil
5 at night, exhausted, like dead birds,
and lie a few days on the ground and spoil.

And always blows the wind, and always words
are heard and spoken as we blether,
and pleasantness and weariness recur.

10 And roads run through the grass hither and thither,
and there are towns with streetlights, ponds, and trees,
and some look threatening, others, deathlike, wither.

For what are these built? and for what are these
endlessly many? and no two the same?
15 Why always laughter, weeping, and decease?

What good to us is all this and these games,
when we are great, alone eternally,
and wandering never pursue any aims?

What good is it to have seen much such folly?
20 And yet he says much that says "evening,"
a word from which meaning and melancholy

issue like honey out of hollow combs.

THE TWO

Translated from the German by

Walter Kaufman

She bore the goblet in her hand—
her chin and mouth firm as its band—
her stride so weightless and so still
that not a drop would ever spill.

5 So weightless and so firm his hand:
he rode a young horse for his pleasure
and, looking like incarnate leisure,
compelled it; trembling it must stand.

But when he should take from her hand
10 the goblet that she lifted up,
the two were quivering so much
that each hand missed the other's touch,
and heavy grew the weightless cup
till dark wine rolled upon the sand.

Heinz Huber (1922–   )

THE NEW APARTMENT

Translated from the German by
Christopher Holme

THE OTHER EVENING we were invited round to the Messemers. Marx Messemer is a colleague of mine at the works, and a most gratifying friendship has grown up in course of time between our two families. Without wishing to overestimate our importance, I do believe that the function we fulfill through modest social gatherings like this is of some significance. It is the development of a form of society, of a social type even, which is adapted to our changed environment. When we began, there was no social intercourse and no society. Our grandparents were dead, our parents had made a mess of things, and those who had made rather less of a mess were not our parents. A zero-point situation, as the literary periodicals called it. I think I can say that we coped with this situation rather well. We read the literary periodicals and we looked for a profession and found one. We began to earn money and began also to invite one another out, and today we constitute a kind of new social grouping, one which is beginning to develop a style of its own, and which once more commands every respect.

To return to the Messemers, it is not long since they moved into a new apartment. Our place, too, is new but we have been in it rather longer. The Messemers have had theirs done up completely new, and we were keen to see how it would look.

The fact is that I think a lot of Marx Messemer. Or let's say that I admire him, at least up to a certain point. What I admire

"The New Apartment" by Heinz Huber, translated by Christopher Holme. Reprinted by permission of the translator.

above all is the reliability of his judgment, his taste, his modernity. With him everything is exactly right, while with me there's always something just short of perfection. In our home the new tea service always has two cups broken and the tea table is still one of the old kidney-shaped kind. Somehow we just don't manage to replace it with a more modern piece, though we know perfectly well what we want—long and narrow, in reddish-brown wood. It would go so well with our sand-colored chair covers. And then a pigeon-blue carpet—but we'll never achieve them. At least not for the present.

The Messemers on the other hand—as we walked in at their door, from our feet to the horizon of the far-distant baseboard there stretched a fine pile surface in graphite gray. At the vanishing point of the perspective lines, in front of a bare wall, a strange-looking branch projected from a large glass vase, standing on the ground. Echoes of surrealism, I thought to myself, early Chirico.[1] Perhaps Messemer himself was unconscious of them. He says he understands nothing about art, says he's a rationalist, a technician, a man of his hands (no doubt, so are we all) but he quite simply has it, that unerring sense of style, that infallible modernity.

A well-marked characteristic of our particular circle is that we have no feelings of mutual rivalry. Everyone is conscious of his own worth, even as I am, and so I have no reason to envy Marx Messemer. Yet when I saw his work table I was seized by a spasm of envy. There stood not, as might have been expected, a breathtakingly lovely, elegantly simple, wickedly expensive writing desk, Scandinavian of course and made by hand (he could have afforded it after all, just as I could) but no, not a bit of it. There stood a slab of raw deal, massive, of unusual size, in its natural whiteness, not polished but planed, and on it his typewriter. That's Marx Messemer all over. He's an expert in cool jazz, and that's what his whole flat is like—cool jazz converted into armchairs, carpets, lamps (or rather light-fittings), and pictures.

For a long time we were all devotees of the theory that pictures had played out their part as adornments to a room, and our craze was all for empty walls. That was of course an extreme fad, and we soon moved away from it. Nothing could be more foreign to our outlook than snobbery. We aim to have principles, but we try also to modify them. So the Messemers

---

1. *Chirico* (kē′rē kô), Giorgio di, Italian surrealist painter born in 1888.

once more had a picture on the wall, placed asymmetrically on a very daring wallpaper, one picture only, but that an original. I stood in front of it and was annoyed with myself. I too have pictures on the wall, but prints, fastened to it with drawing pins. To this day I have somehow just not managed at least to have them framed, though I'm always meaning to.

For Messemer such things are no problem and that's what impresses me so much about him. Exact improvisation, cool jazz, precision of living style.

We stood about informally, informally chatting on the graphite-gray carpet, holding beautifully-shaped glasses in our hands —brandy and soda. Whisky and soda, that's high society, at our social level it would be snobbery, and snobbish is the one thing we're not. We have a well-defined sense of what is appropriate. We're middle-class (I don't mean bourgeois, of course) and we know what's fitting for us. Brandy and soda.

Besides on social occasions like these we're generally moderate with the drink—hence the soda. The only one who drank neat brandy on this particular evening was Fräulein Kliesing who'd also been asked, and is anyhow for my taste a little bit eccentric, yes, decidedly eccentric. It's something I'm not so keen on, and I have trained myself little by little to a certain tolerance, till now I really rather like Fräulein Kliesing. We all have our faults.

There was a slight *contretemps* [2] as we were all arranging ourselves up at the sitting end. Fräulein Kliesing lowered herself into the Messemers' new armchair but immediately shot up again as if she had sat on a pin; her salmon-pink dress, she said, clashed horribly with the raspberry pink of the chair cover, and she was right, too. What made it worse was that this "shocking" pink of the cover was chosen with great finesse to contrast with the equally shocking emerald green of the wallpaper behind it. I should never have dared anything like that, but Messemer does dare and, you see, he brings it off.

In any case harmony was restored when Fräulein Kliesing transferred her salmon-colored dress to the clear gray of the couch while my wife's sky-blue contrasted correctly with the raspberry-pink chair. We're not esthetes, let this be clearly stated, but technicians, men of our hands. Yet just for that very reason it disturbs us if something of this kind, or indeed anything at all, is not quite in key.

---

2. *contretemps* (kôn′trə tän′), an embarrassing occurrence. [*French*]

In my home it is the sofa cushions which are wrong. Not that they're actually in bad taste, but they have come together rather by chance, not so carefully matched with one another and with their surroundings as at the Messemers. But that can easily be changed.

We take such a matter no more seriously than it deserves and the color problem of Fräulein Kliesing and the armchair did not occupy us for long. We were now talking about the Messemers' new apartment in general.

"How did you find this place to begin with?" "Well, we really did have rather a stroke of luck," said Kay, Messemer's delicious wife. "We hunted for ages, but there was always something. Extra conversion costs, and so on. You know the story. Then finally someone we knew, who had some connection with this property, told us there might be a possibility here. Only we should have to do it up ourselves. I didn't want to at first, but Marx thought . . ."

"I was for it straight away," said Marx. "But you can't imagine what it looked like in here when I first came to see the place. I could never have dreamed that anything like it existed nowadays."

Messemer took his time, lit his pipe, poured himself another brandy and soda, and then told the story of the apartment, and we sat in the new armchairs on the graphite-gray carpet, drank brandy and soda, and listened—although, to be candid, we were not all that interested. But what should one talk about? We neither can nor do we want to make fashionable conversation, and our common professional affairs, well, there's a tacit agreement that on such social occasions they are not discussed. Or should we have talked about Marcel Proust? [3] One doesn't talk about Proust, with us you might say Proust is taken for granted, just like our love for our wives. To speak about the one would be sentimentality, about the other snobbery, betraying in either case a faulty sense of style. Rather the Messemers' new apartment than that. Besides which, he tells a good story, even though he does overdo it a bit at times.

"When I first saw this room," he began, "it wasn't being lived in any longer, but the furniture was still here. I couldn't imagine how any human creature could have found room to exist here among all the furniture. I could see nothing but furniture. That's to say, at first I didn't even see that, the windows were

---

3. *Marcel Proust* (1871–1922), French novelist who introduced psychological analysis as an element in fiction.

curtained, the room dark. It was only when the woman with the keys turned on the light that solid ground began to be distinguishable in the darkness. The source of the gloomy light was a low-hanging lampshade, above shot silk and dust, below long, rectangular plate-glass pendants and cobwebs. All this close down over a broad table top, stains and dust here too, losing themselves in the half-darkness behind. At the sides, chair backs reared themselves, and over the nearest of them there hung an old-fashioned woman's hat. Behind it serried ranks of bookshelves, cupboards, whatnots, a sofa in the darkness, deeper still in the darkness an endless vista of grand piano, piles of books on the piano, dust on the books, scarcely room to move between them, not so much a living room as a second-hand furniture dealer's warehouse. Or a stage set for *The Madwoman of Chaillot*—if it had been written by Ionesco."

In descriptions like these Messemer is unbeatable. When he's up to his style, his descriptions range themselves one on another like the colored flags which a conjuror pulls out of his mouth on a never-ending string, gay and effortless. Fräulein Kliesing stared at Messemer in open-mouthed admiration. Moreover her admiration was so to speak sexless, for on the one hand Messemer had his delicious wife, and on the other Fräulein Kliesing had a man friend of her own. So nothing of that sort. We don't much go in for erotic disturbance, any more than we go in for illness.

Messemer was in full swing. "A nineteenth-century lumber room. The sloughed-off body-case of an old-fashioned insect. The flat had belonged to a professor's widow. I think he was a painter or something of the sort, but nothing distinguished. Later I found in the cellar a few rolls of painted canvas, landscape sketches and portrait studies. They were so stiff and brittle that the paint came off in layers when I unrolled them. I can even say the painting was not at all bad, for my taste."

"A bit academic surely," said Fräulein Kliesing.

"I wouldn't say that, not altogether. At any rate, the life led by the professor's widow was no longer very academic. Between ourselves, the woman in charge of the flat told me that the old lady, having no more room among all this furniture and old lumber, had moved into the cubbyhole next door. . . ."

"Where we now have our built-in wardrobe and shoe closet," Kay put in.

". . . and there behind a cupboard arranged herself a sort of berth on which most of her last days were spent. Once, she said, the old lady did not appear for four days, so that in the house it was thought something must have happened to her and the police were sent for to break open the door. But the old lady had only been lying behind her cupboard and staring at the wall. There was nothing else the matter with her. She was in fact very old, an old lady with whalebone and crumbling lace about her neck, contemplating in the gloom the professor's half-finished oil paintings on the wall, perhaps thinking of her honeymoon journey to Florence or perhaps of nothing at all, just fading away, slowly dying. . . ."

Messemer left his story in the air as if, having served him for a felicitous piece of description, he no longer had any further use for it. Now it was his wife's turn.

"And the dirt in the rooms, after all the old rags had been removed, you can't imagine. The wallpaper hung in tatters, covered with dust, or had been fastened back with drawing pins; the ceiling was black with soot and cobwebs, with huge cracks in it—we had to strip all the plaster off, right to the laths —and the whole floor had to be replaned it was so dirty. At first we thought of varnishing it. . . ."

"Matte or glossy?" asked my wife.

"Matte of course, I imagine?" said Fräulein Kliesing.

"Probably glossy," answered Kay. "But then we liked this velour carpeting so much that we decided to close-carpet the whole room instead, although that worked out a good deal more expensive."

"In the long run it's worth it, though," said Fräulein Kliesing. "When you have a floor varnished, you still have to have it waxed after a time, and then after two or three years the varnish must be renewed, while a good carpet lasts for years." Fräulein Kliesing, who had a charming little flat of her own, was quite an expert in such matters.

The nice thing about our circle is that we never work a subject to death; we're interested in everything, so that our talk never gets boring. Without meaning to, we have developed a very pleasant style of social intercourse; neither stiff conventionality nor amorphous bohemianism, but a free and open, sober modernity. We keep clear of fashionable and tepid conversation just as carefully as we do those night-long discussions which go round and round in circles. One must avoid exaggeration at all costs.

We turned again to the previous history of the Messemers' apartment.

"It wasn't altogether easy to get hold of this apartment," said Messemer. "In this room here as I've said lived the professor's widow, and she had finally died. But that was far from making it possible for us to move in, for in the second room, where our dining recess now is, there lived a second old lady who didn't die and who obstinately refused to go into an old people's home, although it was really more necessary for her than for her companion. The two women had been friends when years before they had taken this apartment. It was then new of course. But time—day after day so cramped together, ill, poor, a bit odd, the two of them—time dissipated their friendship. In the end they had the connecting door between the two rooms nailed up, and the great tiled stove which heated both rooms was no longer kept going. Instead each one put a small iron stove in her room. Up there behind the new wallpaper you can still see the hole which had to be made for the stovepipes."

"Really!" said Fräulein Kliesing. "Let's hope we don't all get like that one day."

"The professor's widow died simply of old age, but as for the one in the other room, she was certainly a bit dotty," Messemer said.

"About birdseed," his wife added. "Yes, birdseed. There can be no other explanation. Who would like another drink?"

We allowed our glasses to be refilled with brandy and soda, and Messemer continued, although his story, interesting as it was, for my taste was already going on rather too long.

"This one, in contrast to the other, had almost no furniture. Her walls, doors, and windowframes were stuck all over with nails and hooks of all shapes and sizes—for clothes, for towels, for bits of string with nothing attached to them any more, for key labels, dishcloths, oven rakes, and spotted photographs of babies long since grown up. A great deal of this stuff we later found, when we were able to get into the room, under the great heap of birdseed. The woman must have lived the whole time with a regular mountain of birdseed in the room—it took up a quarter of the floor space. Just simply poured out on the floor knee high. The house people told us how she had the window practically always open and the birds flew in and out the whole time, summer and winter. The birds come hopping around the room even now, though it's quite a while since the mountain of birdseed was removed. And we found the oddest things under the birdseed: medicine bottles, bits of stuff, old illustrated papers, prospectuses of bathing resorts, a glove, and a whole collection of varicolored powders each carefully folded up in paper—all buried under the birdseed."

"How ghastly!" said Fräulein Kliesing.

"Well," said Messemer, "the whole thing could almost have been called tragic. So far as can be discovered, the husband of the birdseed crone got lost in the Third Reich. And he wasn't even politically active. They said he had passed on something or other to someone else, or that sort of thing. Probably the whole thing was a mistake. In any case the husband never came back. It was his wife, then, who later on had this room and the heap of birdseed. The place was really not fit for human habitation, but she simply refused to move into the old people's home. What was more, she couldn't pay the rent any longer."

I had a feeling that Messemer now had really gone a bit too far, for an ordinary party.

Kay threw him a glance and told the rest of the story herself. "After the death of the professor's widow the birdseed woman became the principal tenant of the apartment. So first of all we had ourselves put down as nominal sub-tenants of the room that was now free, so that we should have a prior claim on the whole apartment if the birdseed woman should go. And besides that we paid the landlord the arrears of rent of the two old women. Then we had a word with the tenants of the other flats in the building, and wrote to the relations of the birdseed woman and got a place for her in an old people's home. And then we organized the removal for her and undertook the sale of those things she couldn't take with her into the home—it wasn't much in any case. Finally, after we had so taken her in hand and arranged everything for her, she presumably could see no further reason for holding out and moved to the old people's home where she has since settled down quite contentedly. We had the whole apartment transferred to us as principal tenants and could now begin to do it up. What we made of it you can see for yourselves. You wouldn't believe it was the same place if you'd seen the rooms before, when the two old women still lived here."

"It's really a delightful apartment," said Fräulein Kliesing. "I'm quite enthusiastic over the way you've done it. You couldn't possibly tell it was an old one."

"No, you hardly could," said Kay smiling, "only in the one room we simply cannot altogether get rid of the birdseed. Every so often I find myself sweeping a handful of it out of cracks in the floor. I thought it would be better once we had a vacuum cleaner, but we have got one now and it's just as bad. Perhaps we shall simply have to cover the floor with linoleum."

"I shouldn't have linoleum," said my wife. "It shows every footmark."

"No, I'm against linoleum, too," said Fräulein Kliesing. "I find that linoleum has more or less had its day."

Of course we didn't spend the whole evening talking about carpets and built-in cupboards. After Messemer had once more proved his power to hold an audience, for which I so envy him, he played us his newest cool jazz records. Then we discussed the question whether illnesses have physical or mental causes, and finally Messemer gave an account of the World Exhibition in Brussels. Again he was very entertaining, on top of his subject, sparkling like the outer skin of the Atomium [4] itself with metallic phrases. All in all, the evening, as always at the Messemers, was most enjoyable.

At about one o'clock we took our leave and went home. We had to take a taxi because we have no car. The Messemers of course have a car, but we for some reason or other haven't achieved one yet. But I'm quite confident we shall have one next year or the year after—provided that nothing comes in between, which I think rather improbable.

We've got plenty of time yet to get ourselves properly fixed up.

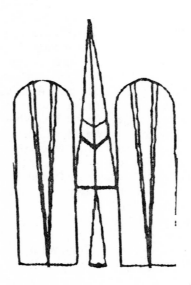

4. *the Atomium,* a 334-foot-high metal replica of an atomic structure, the symbol of the 1958 Brussels World's Fair.

Franz Kafka (1883–1924)

AN OLD MANUSCRIPT

Translated from the German

IT LOOKS as if much had been neglected in our country's system of defense. We have not concerned ourselves with it until now and have gone about our daily work; but things that have been happening recently begin to trouble us.

I have a cobbler's workshop in the square that lies before the Emperor's palace. Scarcely have I taken my shutters down, at the first glimmer of dawn, when I see armed soldiers already posted in the mouth of every street opening on the square. But these soldiers are not ours, they are obviously nomads from the North. In some way that is incomprehensible to me they have pushed right into the capital, although it is a long way from the frontier. At any rate, here they are; it seems that every morning there are more of them.

As is their nature, they camp under the open sky, for they abominate dwelling houses. They busy themselves sharpening swords, whittling arrows and practicing horsemanship. This peaceful square, which was always kept so scrupulously clean, they have made literally into a stable. We do try every now and then to run out of our shops and clear away at least the worst of the filth, but this happens less and less often, for the labor is in vain and brings us besides into danger of falling under the hoofs of the wild horses or of being crippled with lashes from the whips.

Speech with the nomads is impossible. They do not know our language, indeed they hardly have a language of their own. They communicate with each other much as jackdaws do. A screeching as of jackdaws is always in our ears. Our way of living and our institutions they neither understand nor care to understand. And so they are unwilling to make sense even out of our sign language. You can gesture at them till you dislocate your jaws and your wrists and still they will not have understood you and will never understand. They often make grimaces; then the whites of their eyes turn up and foam gathers on their lips, but they do not mean anything by that, not even a threat; they do it because it is their nature to do it. Whatever they need, they take. You cannot call it taking by force. They grab at something and you simply stand aside and leave them to it.

From my stock, too, they have taken many good articles. But I cannot complain when I see how the butcher, for instance, suffers across the street. As soon as he brings in any meat the nomads snatch it all from him and gobble it up. Even their horses devour flesh; often enough a horseman and his horse are lying side by side, both of them gnawing at the same joint, one at either end. The butcher is nervous and does not dare to stop his deliveries of meat. We understand that, however, and subscribe money to keep him going. If the nomads got no meat, who knows what they might think of doing; who knows anyhow what they may think of, even though they get meat every day.

Not long ago the butcher thought he might at least spare himself the trouble of slaughtering, and so one morning he brought along a live ox. But he will never dare to do that again. I lay for a whole hour flat on the floor at the back of my workshop with my head muffled in all the clothes and rugs and pillows I had, simply to keep from hearing the bellowing of that ox, which the nomads were leaping on from all sides, tearing morsels out of its living flesh with their teeth. It had been quiet for a long time before I risked coming out; they were lying overcome round the remains of the carcass like drunkards round a wine cask.

This was the occasion when I fancied I actually saw the Emperor himself at a window of the palace; usually he never enters these outer rooms but spends all his time in the inner-most garden; yet on this occasion he was standing, or so at least it seemed to me, at one of the windows, watching with bent head the ongoings before his residence.

"What is going to happen?" we all ask ourselves. "How long can we endure this burden and torment? The Emperor's palace has drawn the nomads here but does not know how to drive them away again. The gate stays shut; the guards, who used to be always marching out and in with ceremony, keep close behind barred windows. It is left to us artisans and tradesmen to save our country; but we are not equal to such a task; nor have we ever claimed to be capable of it. This is a misunder-standing of some kind; and it will be the ruin of us." ■

Eric Kästner (1899–   )

LEGEND NOT QUITE HOUSEBROKEN

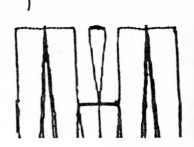

Translated from the German by
Walter Kaufman

Last year's Christmas Eve at five
Santa Claus did not arrive.
God dispensed with his old substitute,
feeling he himself ought to be calling.
5 Breaking custom, he stooped to commute
and, arriving, found the world appalling.

But he felt he must not make a fuss:
after all, he had created us.
And he went (well guarded by detectives,
10 Pinkerton's whom no firm supersedes,
men who followed him to all objectives)
through the towns, did nothing but good deeds.

God was liberal and did not ration,
and he gave, to give an illustration,
15 steam engines to sons of politicians,
and to those whose fathers earned enough,
boats and cars with up-to-date transmissions.
Prices he ignored, gave first-rate stuff.

God's funds were sufficient, and the racket
20 did not stop till through the surtax bracket.
Suddenly, a gap began to yawn;
and his bank informed him: Do not spend
any more, account is overdrawn.
So the present-giving had to end.

25 God is good. And knows it. So he sighed
and presumably felt mortified.
He consented to an interview
with three journalists who heard him tell—
they were of a socialistic hue—
30 that this world was the best possible.

And the poor need not forego a thing
if their numbers were not towering.
The reporters nodded embarrassed, and then
God took them to the golden door.
35 They asked: Will you come soon again?
But he replied: No, nevermore.

THE OTHER POSSIBILITY

Translated from the German by
Walter Kaufman

If we had won the war with waving
of flags and roaring, if we had,
then Germany would be past saving,
then Germany would have gone mad.

5 One would attempt to make us tame
like savage tribes that one might mention.
We'd leave the sidewalk if a sergeant came
and stand attention.

If we had won the war of late
10 we'd be a proud and headstrong state
and press in bed in our dreams
our hands to our trouser seams.

Women must bear, each woman serves
a child a year. Or calaboose.
15 The state needs children as preserves,
and it swills blood like berry juice.

If we had won the war, I bet
that heaven would be national,
the clergy would wear epaulets,
20 God be a German general.

Trenches would take the place of borders.
No moon, insignia instead.
An emperor would issue orders.
We'd have a helmet and no head.

25 If we had won, then everyone
would be a soldier; the entire
land would be run by goon and gun,
and all around would be barbed wire.

On order, women would throw twins,
30 for men cost hardly more than stone,
and above all one cannot win
a war with guns alone.

Then reason would be kept in fetters,
accused and always on the spot.
35 And wars would come like operettas.
If we had won the last war—but
we were in luck and we did not.

Alfred Lichtenstein
(1889–1914)

RETURN OF THE VILLAGE LAD

Translated from the German by
Michael Hamburger

When I was young the world was a little pond
Grandmother and red roof, the lowing
Of oxen and a bush made up of trees.
And all around was the great green meadow.

5 Lovely it was, this dreaming-into-the-distance,
This being nothing at all but air and wind
And bird-call and fairy-tale book.
Far off the fabulous iron serpent whistled—

Thomas Mann (1875–1955)

TRISTAN

*Translated from the German by
H. T. Lowe-Porter*

EINFRIED,[1] THE SANATORIUM. A long, white, rectilinear building with a side wing, set in a spacious garden pleasingly equipped with grottoes, bowers, and little park pavilions. Behind its slate roofs the mountains tower heavenwards, evergreen, massy, cleft with wooded ravines.

Now as then Dr. Leander directs the establishment. He wears a two-pronged black beard as curly and wiry as horsehair stuffing; his spectacle-lenses are thick, and glitter; he has the look of a man whom science has cooled and hardened and filled with silent, forbearing pessimism. And with this beard, these lenses, this look, and in his short, reserved, preoccupied way, he holds his patients in his spell: holds those sufferers who, too weak to be laws unto themselves, put themselves into his hands that his severity may be a shield unto them.

As for Fräulein von Osterloh, hers it is to preside with unwearying zeal over the housekeeping. Ah, what activity! How she plies, now here, now there, now upstairs, now down, from one end of the building to the other! She is queen in kitchen and storerooms, she mounts the shelves of the linen presses, she marshals the domestic staff; she ordains the bill of fare, to the end that the table shall be economical, hygienic, attractive,

1. *Einfried* (īn'frēd).

appetizing, and all these in the highest degree; she keeps house diligently, furiously; and her exceeding capacity conceals a constant reproach to the world of men, to no one of whom has it yet occurred to lead her to the altar. But ever on her cheeks there glows, in two round, carmine spots, the unquenchable hope of one day becoming Frau Dr. Leander.

Ozone, and stirless, stirless air! Einfried, whatever Dr. Leander's rivals and detractors may choose to say about it, can be most warmly recommended for lung patients. And not only these, but patients of all sorts, gentlemen, ladies, even children, come to stop here. Dr. Leander's skill is challenged in many different fields. Sufferers from gastric disorders come, like Frau Magistrate Spatz—she has ear trouble into the bargain—people with defective hearts, paralytics, rheumatics, nervous sufferers of all kinds and degrees. A diabetic general here consumes his daily bread amid continual grumblings. There are several gentlemen with gaunt, fleshless faces who fling their legs about in that uncontrollable way that bodes no good. There is an elderly lady, a Frau Pastor Höhlenrauch, who has brought fourteen children into the world and is now incapable of a single thought, yet has not thereby attained to any peace of mind, but must go roving spectre-like all day long up and down through the house, on the arm of her private attendant, as she has been doing this year past.

Sometimes a death takes place among the "severe cases," those who lie in their chambers, never appearing at meals or in the reception rooms. When this happens no one knows of it, not even the person sleeping next door. In the silence of the night the waxen guest is put away and life at Einfried goes tranquilly on, with its massage, its electric treatment, douches, baths; with its exercises, its steaming and inhaling, in rooms especially equipped with all the triumphs of modern therapeutic.

Yes, a deal happens hereabouts—the institution is in a flourishing way. When new guests arrive, at the entrance to the side wing, the porter sounds the great gong; when there are departures, Dr. Leander, together with Fräulein von Osterloh, conducts the traveller in due form to the waiting carriage. All sorts and kinds of people have received hospitality at Einfried. Even an author is here stealing time from God Almighty—a queer sort of man, with a name like some kind of mineral or precious stone.

Lastly there is, besides Dr. Leander, another physician, who takes care of the slight cases and the hopeless ones. But he bears the name of Müller and is not worth mentioning.

At the beginning of January a businessman named Klöterjahn [2]—of the firm of A. C. Klöterjahn & Co.—brought his wife to Einfried. The porter rang the gong, and Fräulein von Osterloh received the guests from a distance in the drawing-room on the ground floor, which, like nearly all the fine old mansion, was furnished in wonderfully pure Empire style.[3] Dr. Leander appeared straightway. He made his best bow, and a preliminary conversation ensued, for the better information of both sides.

Beyond the windows lay the wintry garden, the flowerbeds covered with straw, the grottoes snowed under, the little temples forlorn. Two porters were dragging in the guests' trunks from the carriage drawn up before the wrought-iron gate—for there was no drive up to the house.

"Be careful, Gabriele, *doucement*,[4] *doucement*, my angel, keep your mouth closed," Herr Klöterjahn had said as he led his wife through the garden; and nobody could look at her without tenderheartedly echoing the caution—though, to be sure, Herr Klöterjahn might quite as well have uttered it all in his own language.

The coachman who had driven the pair from the station to the sanatorium was an uncouth man, and insensitive; yet he sat with his tongue between his teeth as the husband lifted down his wife. The very horses, steaming in the frosty air, seemed to follow the procedure with their eyeballs rolled back in their heads out of sheer concern for so much tenderness and fragile charm.

The young wife's trouble was her trachea; it was expressly so set down in the letter Herr Klöterjahn had sent from the shores of the Baltic to announce their impending arrival to the director of Einfried—the trachea, and not the lungs, thank God! But it is a question whether, if it had been the lungs, the new patient could have looked any more pure and ethereal, any remoter from the concerns of this world, than she did now as she leaned back pale and weary in her chaste white-enamelled armchair, beside her robust husband, and listened to the conversation.

Her beautiful white hands, bare save for the simple wedding ring, rested in her lap, among the folds of a dark, heavy cloth skirt; she wore a close-fitting waist of silver-grey with a stiff

---

2. *Klöterjahn* (klœ′tér yän′). **3.** *Empire* (om pēr′) *style*, the style of architecture, furniture, etc. which developed in France during and immediately after the period of French Empire (c1800–1830). **4.** *doucement* (düs′mỗn), gently. [*French*]

collar—it had an all-over pattern of arabesques in high-pile velvet. But these warm, heavy materials only served to bring out the unspeakable delicacy, sweetness, and languor of the little head, to make it look more than ever touching, exquisite, and unearthly. Her light-brown hair was drawn smoothly back and gathered in a knot low on her neck, but near the right temple a single lock fell loose and curling, not far from the place where an odd little vein branched across one well-marked eyebrow, pale blue and sickly amid all that pure, well-nigh transparent spotlessness. That little blue vein above the eye dominated quite painfully the whole fine oval of the face. When she spoke, it stood out still more; yes, even when she smiled— and lent her expression a touch of strain, if not actually of distress, that stirred vague fear in the beholder. And yet she spoke, and she smiled: spoke frankly and pleasantly in her rather husky voice, with a smile in her eyes—though they again were sometimes a little difficult and showed a tendency to avoid a direct gaze. And the corners of her eyes, both sides the base of the slender little nose, were deeply shadowed. She smiled with her mouth too, her beautiful wide mouth, whose lips were so pale and yet seemed to flash—perhaps because their contours were so exceedingly pure and well-cut. Sometimes she cleared her throat, then carried her handkerchief to her mouth and afterwards looked at it.

"Don't clear your throat like that, Gabriele," said Herr Klöterjahn. "You know, darling, Dr. Hinzpeter expressly forbade it, and what we have to do is to exercise self-control, my angel. As I said, it is the trachea," he repeated. "Honestly, when it began, I thought it was the lungs, and it gave me a scare, I do assure you. But it isn't the lungs—we don't mean to let ourselves in for that, do we, Gabriele, my love, eh? Ha ha!"

"Surely not," said Dr. Leander, and glittered at her with his eyeglasses.

Whereupon Herr Klöterjahn ordered coffee, coffee and rolls; and the speaking way he had of sounding the c far back in his throat and exploding the b in "butter" must have made any soul alive hungry to hear it.

His order was filled; and rooms were assigned to him and his wife, and they took possession with their things.

And Dr. Leander took over the case himself, without calling in Dr. Müller.

The population of Einfried took unusual interest in the fair new patient; Herr Klöterjahn, used as he was to see homage paid her, received it all with great satisfaction. The diabetic general, when he first saw her, stopped grumbling a minute; the gentlemen with the fleshless faces smiled and did their best to keep their legs in order; as for Frau Magistrate Spatz, she made her her oldest friend on the spot. Yes, she made an impression, this woman who bore Herr Klöterjahn's name! A writer who had been sojourning a few weeks in Einfried, a queer sort he was, with a name like some precious stone or other, positively coloured up when she passed him in the corridor, stopped stock-still and stood there as though rooted to the ground, long after she had disappeared.

Before two days were out, the whole little population knew her history. She came originally from Bremen, as one could tell by certain pleasant small twists in her pronunciation; and it had been in Bremen that, two years gone by, she had bestowed her hand upon Herr Klöterjahn, a successful business man, and become his life partner. She had followed him to his native town on the Baltic coast, where she had presented him, some ten months before the time of which we write, and under circumstances of the greatest difficulty and danger, with a child, a particularly well-formed and vigorous son and heir. But since that terrible hour she had never fully recovered her strength—granting, that is, that she had ever had any. She had not been long up, still extremely weak, with extremely impoverished vitality, when one day after coughing she brought up a little blood—oh, not much, an insignificant quantity in fact; but it would **have been** much better to be none at all; and the suspicious **thing** was, that the same trifling but disquieting incident recurred after another short while. Well, of course, there were things to be done, and Dr. Hinzpeter, the family physician, did them. Complete rest was ordered, little pieces of ice swallowed; morphine administered to check the cough, and other medicines to regulate the heart action. But recovery failed to set in; and while the child, Anton Klöterjahn, junior, a magnificent specimen of a baby, seized on his place in life and held it with prodigious energy and ruthlessness, a low, unobservable fever seemed to waste the young mother daily. It was, as we have heard, an affection of the trachea—a word that in Dr. Hinzpeter's mouth sounded so soothing, so consoling, so reassuring, that it raised their spirits to a surprising degree. But even though it was not the lungs, the doctor presently found that a milder climate and a stay in a sanatorium were imperative if the cure was to be hastened. The reputation enjoyed by Einfried and its director had done the rest.

Such was the state of affairs; Herr Klöterjahn himself related it to all and sundry. He talked with a slovenly pronunciation, in a loud, good-humoured voice, like a man whose digestion is in as capital order as his pocketbook; shovelling out the words pell-mell, in the broad accents of the northern coast-dweller; hurtling some of them forth so that each sound was a little explosion, at which he laughed as at a successful joke.

He was of medium height, broad, stout, and short-legged; his face full and red, with watery blue eyes shaded by very fair lashes; with wide nostrils and humid lips. He wore English sidewhiskers and English clothes, and it enchanted him to discover at Einfried an entire English family, father, mother, and three pretty children with their nurse, who were stopping here for the simple and sufficient reason that they knew not where else to go. With this family he partook of a good English breakfast every morning. He set great store by good eating and drinking and proved to be a connoisseur both of food and wines, entertaining the other guests with the most exciting accounts of dinners given in his circle of acquaintance back home, with full descriptions of the choicer and rarer dishes; in the telling his eyes would narrow benignly, and his pronunciation take on certain palatal and nasal sounds, accompanied by smacking noises at the back of his throat. That he was not fundamentally averse to earthly joys of another sort was evinced upon an evening when a guest of the cure, an author by calling, saw him in the corridor trifling in not quite permissible fashion with a chambermaid—a humorous little passage at which the author in question made a laughably disgusted face.

As for Herr Klöterjahn's wife, it was plain to see that she was devotedly attached to her husband. She followed his words and movements with a smile: not the rather arrogant toleration the ailing sometimes bestow upon the well and sound, but the sympathetic participation of a well-disposed invalid in the man-ifestations of people who rejoice in the blessing of abounding health.

Herr Klöterjahn did not stop long in Einfried. He had brought his wife hither, but when a week had gone by and he knew she was in good hands and well looked after, he did not linger. Duties equally weighty—his flourishing child, his no less flour-ishing business—took him away; they compelled him to go, leaving her rejoicing in the best of care.

Spinell was the name of that author who had been stopping some weeks in Einfried—Detlev Spinell was his name, and his looks were quite out of the common. Imagine a dark man at the beginning of the thirties, impressively tall, with hair already distinctly grey at the temples, and a round, white, slightly-bloated face, without a vestige of beard. Not that it was shaven —that you could have told; it was soft, smooth, boyish, with at most a downy hair here and there. And the effect was singular. His bright, doe-like brown eyes had a gentle expression, the nose was thick and rather too fleshy. Also, Herr Spinell had an upper lip like an ancient Roman's, swelling and full of pores; large, carious teeth, and feet of uncommon size. One of the gentlemen with the rebellious legs, a cynic and ribald wit, had christened him "the dissipated baby"; but the epithet was malicious, and not very apt. Herr Spinell dressed well, in a long black coat and a waistcoat with coloured spots.

He was unsocial and sought no man's company. Only once in a while he might be overtaken by an affable, blithe, expansive mood; and this always happened when he was carried away by an æsthetic fit at the sight of beauty, the harmony of two colours, a vase nobly formed, or the range of mountains lighted by the setting sun.

"How beautiful!" he would say, with his head on one side, his shoulders raised, his hands spread out, his lips and nostrils curled and distended. "My God! look, how beautiful!" And in such moments of ardour he was quite capable of flinging his arms blindly around the neck of anybody, high or low, male or female, that happened to be near.

On his table, for anybody to see who entered his room, there always lay the book he had written. It was a novel of medium length, with a perfectly bewildering drawing on the jacket, printed on a sort of filter-paper. Each letter of the type looked like a Gothic cathedral. Fräulein von Osterloh had read it once, in a spare quarter-hour, and found it "very cultured"—which was her circumlocution for inhumanly boresome. Its scenes were laid in fashionable salons, in luxurious boudoirs full of choice *objets d'art*, old furniture, Gobelins, rare porcelains, priceless stuffs, and art treasures of all sorts and kinds. On the description of these things was expended the most loving care; as you read you constantly saw Herr Spinell, with distended nostrils, saying: "How beautiful! My God! look, how beautiful!" After all, it was strange he had not written more than this one book; he so obviously adored writing. He spent the greater part of the day doing it, in his room, and sent an extraordinary number of letters to the post, two or three nearly every day— and that made it more striking, even almost funny, that he very seldom received one in return.

Herr Spinell sat opposite Herr Klöterjahn's wife. At the first meal of which the new guests partook, he came rather late into the dining room, on the ground floor of the side wing, bade good-day to the company generally in a soft voice, and betook himself to his own place, whereupon Dr. Leander perfunctorily presented him to the newcomers. He bowed, and self-consciously began to eat, using his knife and fork rather affectedly with the large, finely shaped white hands that came out from his very narrow coatsleeves. After a little he grew more at ease and looked tranquilly first at Herr Klöterjahn and then at his wife, by turns. And in the course of the meal Herr Klöterjahn addressed to him sundry queries touching the general situation and climate of Einfried; his wife, in her charming way, added a word or two, and Herr Spinell gave courteous answers. His voice was mild, and really agreeable; but he had a halting way of speaking that almost amounted to an impediment—as though his teeth got in the way of his tongue.

After luncheon, when they had gone into the salon, Dr. Leander came up to the new arrivals to wish them *Mahlzeit*,[5] and Herr Klöterjahn's wife took occasion to ask about their *vis-à-vis*.[6]

"What was the gentlemen's name?" she asked. "I did not quite catch it. Spinelli?"

"Spinell, not Spinelli, madame. No, he is not an Italian; he only comes from Lemberg, I believe."

"And what was it you said? He is an author, or something of the sort?" asked Herr Klöterjahn. He had his hands in the pockets of his very easy-fitting English trousers, cocked his head towards the doctor, and opened his mouth, as some people do, to listen the better.

"Yes . . . I really don't know," answered Dr. Leander. "He writes. . . . I believe he has written a book, some sort of novel. I really don't know what."

By which Dr. Leander conveyed that he had no great opinion of the author and declined all responsibility on the score of him.

"But I find that most interesting," said Herr Klöterjahn's wife. Never before had she met an author face to face.

"Oh, yes," said Dr. Leander obligingly. "I understand he has a certain amount of reputation," which closed the conversation.

But a little later, when the new guests had retired and Dr.

---

5. *Mahlzeit* (mäl′zīt), a good dinner, an expression used in some parts of Germany at the conclusion of a meal. 6. *vis-à-vis* (vē′zə vē′), opposite; here, a person sitting opposite one at a table.

Leander himself was about to go, Herr Spinell detained him in talk to put a few questions for his own part.

"What was their name?" he asked. "I did not understand a syllable, of course."

"Klöterjahn," answered Dr. Leander, turning away.

"What's that?" asked Herr Spinell.

"*Klöterjahn* is their name," said Dr. Leander, and went his way. He set no great store by the author.

· · · · ·

HAVE WE got as far on as where Herr Klöterjahn went home? Yes, he was back on the shore of the Baltic once more, with his business and his babe, that ruthless and vigorous little being who had cost his mother great suffering and a slight weakness of the trachea; while she herself, the young wife, remained in Einfried and became the intimate friend of Frau Spatz. Which did not prevent Herr Klöterjahn's wife from being on friendly terms with the rest of the guests—for instance with Herr Spinell, who, to the astonishment of everybody, for he had up to now held communion with not a single soul, displayed from the very first an extraordinary devotion and courtesy, and with whom she enjoyed talking, whenever she had any time left over from the stern service of the cure.

He approached her with immense circumspection and reverence, and never spoke save with his voice so carefully subdued that Frau Spatz, with her bad hearing, seldom or never caught anything he said. He tiptoed on his great feet up to the armchair in which Herr Klöterjahn's wife leaned, fragilely smiling; stopped two paces off, with his body bent forward and one leg poised behind him, and talked in his halting way, as though he had an impediment in his speech; with ardour, yet prepared to retire at any moment and vanish at the first sign of fatigue or satiety. But he did not tire her; she begged him to sit down with her and the Rätin [7]; she asked him questions and listened with curious smiles, for he had a way of talking sometimes that was so odd and amusing, different from anything she had ever heard before.

"Why are you in Einfried, really?" she asked. "What cure are you taking, Herr Spinell?"

"Cure? Oh, I'm having myself electrified a bit. Nothing worth

---

7. *Rätin,* the wife of an official; here, Frau Magistrate Spatz.

mentioning. I will tell you the real reason why I am here, madame. It is a feeling for style."

"Ah?" said Herr Klöterjahn's wife; supported her chin on her hand and turned to him with exaggerated eagerness, as one does to a child who wants to tell a story.

"Yes, madame. Einfried is a perfect Empire. It was once a castle, a summer residence, I am told. This side wing is a later addition, but the main building is old and genuine. There are times when I cannot endure Empire, and then times when I simply must have it in order to attain any sense of well-being. Obviously, people feel one way among furniture that is soft and comfortable and voluptuous, and quite another among the straight lines of these tables, chairs, and draperies. This brightness and hardness, this cold, austere simplicity and reserved strength, madame—it has upon me the ultimate effect of an inward purification and rebirth. Beyond a doubt, it is morally elevating."

"Yes, that is remarkable," she said. "And when I try I can understand what you mean."

Whereto he responded that it was not worth her taking any sort of trouble, and they laughed together. Frau Spatz laughed too and found it remarkable in her turn, though she did not say she understood it.

The reception room was spacious and beautiful. The high, white folding doors that led to the billiard room were wide open, and the gentlemen with the rebellious legs were disporting themselves within, others as well. On the opposite side of the room a glass door gave on the broad veranda and the garden. Near the door stood a piano. At a green-covered folding table the diabetic general was playing whist with some other gentlemen. Ladies sat reading or embroidering. The rooms were heated by an iron stove, but the chimney piece, in the purest style, had coals pasted over with red paper to simulate a fire, and chairs were drawn up invitingly.

"You are an early riser, Herr Spinell," said Herr Klöterjahn's wife. "Two or three times already I have chanced to see you leaving the house at half past seven in the morning."

"An early riser? Ah, with a difference, madame, with a vast difference. The truth is, I rise early because I am such a late sleeper."

"You really must explain yourself, Herr Spinell." Frau Spatz too said she demanded an explanation.

"Well, if one is an early riser, one does not need to get up so early. Or so it seems to me. The conscience, madame, is a bad business. I, and other people like me, work hard all our lives to swindle our consciences into feeling pleased and satisfied. We are feckless creatures, and aside from a few good hours we go around weighted down, sick and sore with the knowledge of our own futility. We hate the useful; we know it is vulgar and unlovely, and we defend this position, as a man defends something that is absolutely necessary to his existence. Yet all the while conscience is gnawing at us, to such an extent that we are simply one wound. Added to that, our whole inner life, our view of the world, our way of working, is of a kind—its effect is frightfully unhealthy, undermining, irritating, and this only aggravates the situation. Well, then, there are certain little counter-irritants, without which we would most certainly not hold out. A kind of decorum, a hygienic regimen, for instance, becomes a necessity for some of us. To get up early, to get up ghastly early, take a cold bath, and go out walking in a snow-storm—that may give us a sense of self-satisfaction that lasts as much as an hour. If I were to act out my true character, I should be lying in bed late into the afternoon. My getting up early is all hypocrisy, believe me."

"Why do you say that, Herr Spinell? On the contrary, I call it self-abnegation." Frau Spatz, too, called it self-abnegation.

"Hypocrisy or self-abnegation—call it what you like, madame. I have such a hideously downright nature—"

"Yes, that's it. Surely you torment yourself far too much."

"Yes, madame, I torment myself a great deal."

The fine weather continued. Rigid and spotless white the region lay, the mountains, house and garden, in a windless air that was blinding clear and cast bluish shadows; and above it arched the spotless pale-blue sky, where myriads of bright particles of glittering crystals seemed to dance. Herr Klöterjahn's wife felt tolerably well these days: free of fever, with scarce any cough, and able to eat without too great distaste. Many days she sat taking her cure for hours on end in the sunny cold on the terrace. She sat in the snow, bundled in wraps and furs, and hopefully breathed in the pure icy air to do her trachea good. Sometimes she saw Herr Spinell, dressed like herself, and in fur boots that made his feet a fantastic size, taking an airing in the garden. He walked with tentative tread through the snow, holding his arms in a certain careful pose that was stiff yet not without grace; coming up to the terrace he would bow very respectfully and mount the first step or so to exchange a few words with her.

"Today on my morning walk I saw a beautiful woman—good

Lord! how beautiful she was!" he said; laid his head on one side and spread out his hands.

"Really, Herr Spinell. Do describe her to me."

"That I cannot do. Or, rather, it would not be a fair picture. I only saw the lady as I glanced at her in passing, I did not actually see her at all. But that fleeting glimpse was enough to rouse my fancy and make me carry away a picture so beautiful that—good Lord! how beautiful it is!"

She laughed. "Is that the way you always look at beautiful women, Herr Spinell? Just a fleeting glance?"

"Yes, madame; it is a better way than if I were avid of actuality, stared them plump in the face, and carried away with me only a consciousness of the blemishes they in fact possess."

" 'Avid of actuality'—what a strange phrase, a regular literary phrase, Herr Spinell; no one but an author could have said that. It impresses me very much, I must say. There is a lot in it that I dimly understand; there is something free about it, and independent, that even seems to be looking down on reality though it is so very respectable—is respectability itself, as you might say. And it makes me comprehend, too, that there is something else besides the tangible, something more subtle—"

"I know only one face," he said suddenly, with a strange lift in his voice, carrying his closed hands to his shoulders as he spoke and showing his carious teeth in an almost hysterical smile, "I know only one face of such lofty nobility that the mere thought of enhancing it through my imagination would be blasphemous; at which I could wish to look, on which I could wish to dwell, not minutes and not hours, but my whole life long; losing myself utterly therein, forgotten to every earthly thought. . . ."

"Yes, indeed, Herr Spinell. And yet don't you find Fräulein von Osterloh has rather prominent ears?"

He replied only by a profound bow; then, standing erect, let his eyes rest with a look of embarrassment and pain on the strange little vein that branched pale blue and sickly across her pure translucent brow.

An odd sort, a very odd sort. Herr Klöterjahn's wife thought about him sometimes; for she had much leisure for thought. Whether it was that the change of air began to lose its effect or some positively detrimental influence was at work, she began to go backward, the condition of her trachea left much to be desired, she had fever not infrequently, felt tired and exhausted, and could not eat. Dr. Leander most emphatically recommended rest, quiet, caution, care. So she sat, when indeed she was not forced to lie, quite motionless, in the society of Frau Spatz, holding some sort of sewing which she did not sew, and following one or another train of thought.

Yes, he gave her food for thought, this very odd Herr Spinell; and the strange thing was she thought not so much about him as about herself, for he had managed to rouse in her a quite novel interest in her own personality. One day he had said, in the course of conversation:

"No, they are positively the most enigmatic facts in nature—women, I mean. That is a truism, and yet one never ceases to marvel at it afresh. Take some wonderful creature, a sylph, an airy wraith, a fairy dream of a thing, and what does she do? Goes and gives herself to a brawny Hercules at a country fair, or maybe to a butcher's apprentice. Walks about on his arm, even leans her head on his shoulder and looks round with an impish smile as if to say: 'Look on this, if you like, and break your heads over it.' And we break them."

With this speech Herr Klöterjahn's wife had occupied her leisure again and again.

Another day, to the wonderment of Frau Spatz, the following conversation took place:

"May I ask, madame—though you may very likely think me prying—what your name really is?"

"Why, Herr Spinell, you know my name is Klöterjahn!"

"H'm. Yes, I know that—or, rather, I deny it. I mean your own name, your maiden name, of course. You will in justice, madame, admit that anybody who calls you Klöterjahn ought to be thrashed."

She laughed so hard that the little blue vein stood out alarmingly on her brow and gave the pale sweet face a strained expression most disquieting to see.

"Oh, no! Not at all, Herr Spinell! Thrashed, indeed! Is the name Klöterjahn so horrible to you?"

"Yes, madame. I hate the name from the bottom of my heart. I hated it the first time I heard it. It is the abandonment of ugliness; it is grotesque to make you comply with the custom so far as to fasten your husband's name upon you; is barbarous and vile."

"Well, and how about Eckhof? Is that any better? Eckhof is my father's name."

"Ah, you see! Eckhof is quite another thing. There was a great actor named Eckhof. Eckhof will do nicely. You spoke of your father— Then is your mother—?"

"Yes, my mother died when I was little."

"Ah! Tell me a little more of yourself, pray. But not if it tires you. When it tires you, stop, and I will go on talking about Paris, as I did the other day. But you could speak very softly, or even whisper—that would be more beautiful still. You were born in Bremen?" He breathed, rather than uttered, the question with an expression so awed, so heavy with import, as to suggest that Bremen was a city like no other on earth, full of hidden beauties and nameless adventures, and ennobling in some mysterious way those born within its walls.

"Yes, imagine," said she involuntarily. "I was born in Bremen."

"I was there once," he thoughtfully remarked.

"Goodness me, you have been there, too? Why, Herr Spinell, it seems to me you must have been everywhere there is between Spitzbergen and Tunis!" [8]

"Yes, I was there once," he repeated. "A few hours, one evening. I recall a narrow old street, with a strange, warped-looking moon above the gabled roofs. Then I was in a cellar that smelled of wine and mould. It is a poignant memory."

"Really? Where could that have been, I wonder? Yes, in just such a grey old gabled house I was born, one of the old merchant houses, with echoing wooden floor and white-painted gallery."

"Then your father is a businessman?" he asked hesitatingly.

"Yes, but he is also, and in the first place, an artist."

"Ah! In what way?"

"He plays the violin. But just saying that does not mean much. It is *how* he plays, Herr Spinell—it is that that matters! Sometimes I cannot listen to some of the notes without the tears coming into my eyes and making them burn. Nothing else in the world makes me feel like that. You won't believe it—"

"But I do. Oh, very much I believe it! Tell me, madame, your family is old, is it not? Your family has been living for generations in the old gabled house—living and working and closing their eyes on time?"

"Yes. Tell me why you ask."

"Because it not infrequently happens that a race with sober, practical bourgeois traditions will towards the end of its days flare up in some form of art."

"Is that a fact?"

---

8. *between Spitzbergen and Tunis,* all of Europe. The Spitzbergen islands are in the Arctic Ocean north of Norway; Tunis is in North Africa.

"Yes."

"It is true, my father is surely more of an artist than some that call themselves so and get the glory of it. I only play the piano a little. They have forbidden me now, but at home, in the old days, I still played. Father and I played together. Yes, I have precious memories of all those years; and especially of the garden, our garden, back of the house. It was dreadfully wild and overgrown, and shut in by crumbling mossy walls. But it was just that gave it such charm. In the middle was a fountain with a wide border of sword lilies. In the summer I spent long hours there with my friends. We all sat round the fountain on little campstools—"

"How beautiful!" said Herr Spinell, and flung up his shoulders. "You sat there and sang?"

"No, we mostly crocheted."

"But still—"

"Yes, we crocheted and chattered, my six friends and I—"

"How beautiful! Good Lord! think of it, *how beautiful!*" cried Herr Spinell again, his face quite distorted with emotion.

"Now, what is it you find so particularly beautiful about that, Herr Spinell?"

"Oh, there being six of them besides you, and your being not one of the six, but a queen among them . . . set apart from your six friends. A little gold crown showed in your hair—quite a modest, unostentatious little crown, still it was there—"

"Nonsense, there was nothing of the sort."

"Yes, there was; it shone unseen. But if I had been there, standing among the shrubbery, one of those times, I should have seen it."

"God knows what you would have seen. But you were not there. Instead of that, it was my husband who came out of the shrubbery one day, with my father. I was afraid they had been listening to our prattle—"

"So it was there, then, madame, that you first met your husband?"

"Yes, there it was I saw him first," she said, in quite a glad, strong voice; she smiled, and as she did so the little blue vein came out and gave her face a constrained and anxious expression. "He was calling on my father on business, you see. Next day he came to dinner, and three days later he proposed for my hand."

"Really? It all happened as fast as that?"

"Yes. Or, rather, it went a little slower after that. For my father was not very much inclined to it, you see, and consented on condition that we wait a long time first. He would rather I had stopped with him, and he had doubts in other ways too. But—"

"But?"

"But I had set my heart on it," she said, smiling; and once more the little vein dominated her whole face with its look of constraint and anxiety.

"Ah, so you set your heart on it."

"Yes, and I displayed great strength of purpose, as you see—"

"As I see. Yes."

"So that my father had to give way in the end."

"And so you forsook him and his fiddle and the old house with the overgrown garden, and the fountain and your six friends, and clave unto Herr Klöterjahn—"

" 'And clave unto'—you have such a strange way of saying things, Herr Spinell. Positively biblical. Yes, I forsook all that; nature has arranged things that way."

"Yes, I suppose that is it."

"And it was a question of my happiness—"

"Of course. And happiness came to you?"

"It came Herr Spinell, in the moment when they brought little Anton to me, our little Anton, and he screamed so lustily with his strong little lungs—he is very, very strong and healthy, you know—"

"This is not the first time, madame, that I have heard you speak of your little Anton's good health and great strength. He must be quite uncommonly healthy?"

"That he is. And looks so absurdly like my husband!"

"Ah! . . . So that was the way of it. And now you are no longer called by the name of Eckhof, but a different one, and you have your healthy little Anton, and are troubled with your trachea."

"Yes. And you are a perfectly enigmatic man, Herr Spinell, I do assure you."

"Yes. God knows you certainly are," said Frau Spatz, who was present on this occasion.

And that conversation, too, gave Herr Klöterjahn's wife food for reflection. Idle as it was, it contained much to nourish those secret thoughts of hers about herself. Was this the baleful influence which was at work? Her weakness increased and fever often supervened, a quiet glow in which she rested with a feeling of mild elevation, to which she yielded in a pensive mood that was a little affected, self-satisfied, even rather self-righteous. When she had not to keep her bed, Herr Spinell would approach her with immense caution, tiptoeing on his great feet; he would pause two paces off, with his body inclined and one leg behind him, and speak in a voice that was hushed with awe, as though he would lift her higher and higher on the tide of his devotion until she rested on billowy cushions of cloud where no shrill sound nor any earthly touch might reach her. And when he did this she would think of the way Herr Klöter- jahn said: "Take care, my angel, keep your mouth closed, Gabriele," a way that made her feel as though he had struck her roughly though well-meaningly on the shoulder. Then as fast as she could she would put the memory away and rest in her weakness and elevation of spirit upon the clouds which Herr Spinell spread out for her.

One day she abruptly returned to the talk they had had about her early life. "Is it really true, Herr Spinell," she asked, "that you would have seen the little gold crown?"

Two weeks had passed since that conversation, yet he knew at once what she meant, and his voice shook as he assured her that he would have seen the little crown as she sat among her friends by the fountain—would have caught its fugitive gleam among her locks.

A few days later one of the guests chanced to make a polite inquiry after the health of little Anton. Herr Klöterjahn's wife gave a quick glance at Herr Spinell, who was standing near, and answered in a perfunctory voice:

"Thanks, how should he be? He and my husband are quite well, of course."

There came a day at the end of February, colder, purer, more brilliant than any that had come before it, and high spirits held sway at Einfried. The "heart cases" consulted in groups, flushed of cheek, the diabetic general carolled like a boy out of school, and the gentlemen of the rebellious legs cast aside all restraint. And the reason for all these things was that a sleighing party was in prospect, an excursion in sledges into the mountains, with cracking whips and sleigh bells jingling. Dr. Leander had arranged this diversion for his patients.

The serious cases, of course, had to stop at home. Poor things! The other guests arranged to keep it from them; it did them good to practise this much sympathy and consideration. But a few of those remained at home who might very well have gone. Fräulein von Osterloh was of course excused, she had too much on her mind to permit her even to think of going. She was needed at home, and at home she remained. But the disappointment was general when Herr Klöterjahn's wife announced her intention of stopping away. Dr. Leander exhorted her to come and get the benefit of the fresh air—but in vain. She said she was not up to it, she had a headache, she felt too weak—they had to resign themselves. The cynical gentleman took occasion to say:

"You will see, the dissipated baby will stop at home too."

And he proved to be right, for Herr Spinell gave out that he intended to "work" that afternoon—he was prone thus to characterize his dubious activities. Anyhow, not a soul regretted his absence; nor did they take more to heart the news that Frau Magistrate Spatz had decided to keep her young friend company at home—sleighing made her feel sea-sick.

Luncheon on the great day was eaten as early as twelve o'clock, and immediately thereafter the sledges drew up in front of Einfried. The guests came through the garden in little groups, warmly wrapped, excited, full of eager anticipation. Herr Klöterjahn's wife stood with Frau Spatz at the glass door which gave on the terrace, while Herr Spinell watched the setting-forth from above, at the window of his room. They saw the little struggles that took place for the best seats, amid joking and laughter; and Fräulein von Osterloh, with a fur boa round her neck, running from one sleigh to the other and shoving baskets of provisions under the seats; they saw Dr. Leander, with his fur cap pulled low on his brow, marshalling the whole scene with his spectacle-lenses glittering, to make sure everything was ready. At last he took his own seat and gave the signal to drive off. The horses started up, a few of the ladies shrieked and collapsed, the bells jingled, the short-shafted whips cracked and their long lashes trailed across the snow; Fräulein von Osterloh stood at the gate waving her handkerchief until the train rounded a curve and disappeared; slowly the merry tinkling died away. Then she turned and hastened back through the garden in pursuit of her duties; the two ladies left the glass door, and almost at the same time Herr Spinell abandoned his post of observation above.

Quiet reigned at Einfried. The party would not return before evening. The serious cases lay in their rooms and suffered. Herr Klöterjahn's wife took a short turn with her friend, then they went to their respective chambers. Herr Spinell kept to his, occupied in his own way. Towards four o'clock the ladies were served with half a litre of milk apiece, and Herr Spinell with a light tea. Soon after, Herr Klöterjahn's wife tapped on the wall between her room and Frau Spatz's and called:

"Shan't we go down to the salon, Frau Spatz? I have nothing to do up here."

"In just a minute, my dear," answered she. "I'll just put on my shoes—if you will wait a minute. I have been lying down."

The salon, naturally, was empty. The ladies took seats by the fireplace. The Frau Magistrate embroidered flowers on a strip of canvas; Herr Klöterjahn's wife took a few stitches too, but soon let her work fall in her lap and, leaning on the arm of her chair, fell to dreaming. At length she made some remark, hardly worth the trouble of opening her lips for; the Frau Magistrate asked what she said, and she had to make the effort of saying it all over again, which quite wore her out. But just then steps were heard outside, the door opened, and Herr Spinell came in.

"Shall I be disturbing you?" he asked mildly from the threshold, addressing Herr Klöterjahn's wife and her alone; bending over her, as it were, from a distance, in the tender, hovering way he had.

The young wife answered:

"Why should you? The room is free to everybody—and besides, why would it be disturbing us? On the contrary, I am convinced that I am boring Frau Spatz."

He had no ready answer, merely smiled and showed his carious teeth, then went hesitatingly up to the glass door, the ladies watching him, and stood with his back to them looking out. Presently he half turned round, still gazing into the garden, and said: "The sun has gone in. The sky clouded over without our seeing it. The dark is coming on already."

"Yes, it is all overcast," replied Herr Klöterjahn's wife. "It looks as though our sleighing party would have some snow after all. Yesterday at this hour it was still broad daylight, now it is already getting dark."

"Well," he said, "after all these brilliant weeks a little dullness is good for the eyes. The sun shines with the same penetrating clearness upon the lovely and the commonplace, and I for one am positively grateful to it for finally going under a cloud."

"Don't you like the sun, Herr Spinell?"

"Well, I am no painter . . . when there is no sun one becomes more profound. . . . It is a thick layer of greyish-white cloud. Perhaps it means thawing weather for tomorrow. But, madame, let me advise you not to sit there at the back of the room looking at your embroidery."

"Don't be alarmed; I am not looking at it. But what else is there to do?"

He had sat down on the piano stool, resting one arm on the lid of the instrument.

"Music," he said. "If we could only have a little music here."

"And yesterday afternoon Fräulein von Osterloh rendered 'Cloister Bells' at top speed," remarked Herr Klöterjahn's wife.

"But you play, madame!" said he, in an imploring tone. He stood up. "Once you used to play every day with your father."

"Yes, Herr Spinell, in those days I did. In the time of the fountain, you know."

"Play to us today," he begged. "Just a few notes—this once. If you knew how I long for some music—"

"But our family physician, as well as Dr. Leander, expressly forbade it, Herr Spinell."

"But they aren't here—either of them. We are free agents. Just a few bars—"

"No, Herr Spinell, it would be no use. Goodness knows what marvels you expect of me—and I have forgotten everything I knew. Truly. I know scarcely anything by heart."

"Well, then, play that scarcely anything. But there are notes here too. On top of the piano. No, that is nothing. But here is some Chopin."

"Chopin?"

"Yes, the Nocturnes. All we have to do is to light the candles—"

"Pray don't ask me to play, Herr Spinell. I must not. Suppose it were to be bad for me—"

He was silent; standing there in the light of the two candles, with his great feet, in his long black tail coat, with his beardless face and greying hair. His hands hung down at his sides.

"Then, madame, I will ask no more," he said at length, in a low voice. "If you are afraid it will do you harm, then we shall leave the beauty dead and dumb that might have come alive beneath your fingers. You were not always so sensible; at least not when it was the opposite question from what it is today, and you had to decide to take leave of beauty. Then you did not care about your bodily welfare; you showed a firm and unhesitating resolution when you left the fountain and laid aside the little gold crown."

"Listen," he said, after a pause, and his voice dropped still lower; "if you sit down and play as you used to play when your father stood behind you and brought tears to your eyes with the tones of his violin—who knows but the little gold crown might glimmer once more in your hair. . . ."

"Really," said she, with a smile. Her voice happened to break on the word, it sounded husky and barely audible. She cleared her throat and went on:

"Are those really Chopin's Nocturnes you have there?"

"Yes, here they are open at the place; everything is ready."

"Well, then, in God's name, I will play one," said she. "But only one—do you hear? In any case, one will do you, I am sure."

With which she got up, laid aside her work, and went to the piano. She seated herself on the music stool, on a few bound volumes, arranged the lights, and turned over the notes. Herr Spinell had drawn up a chair and sat beside her, like a music master.

She played the Nocturne in E-flat major, opus 9, number 2. If her playing had really lost very much then she must originally have been a consummate artist. The piano was mediocre, but after the first few notes she learned to control it. She displayed a nervous feeling for modulations of timbre and a joy in mobility of rhythm that amounted to the fantastic. Her attack was at once firm and soft. Under her hands the very last drop of sweetness was wrung from the melody; the embellishments seemed to cling with slow grace about her limbs.

She wore the same frock as on the day of her arrival, the dark, heavy bodice with the velvet arabesques in high relief, that gave her head and hands such an unearthly fragile look. Her face did not change as she played, but her lips seemed to become more clear-cut, the shadows deepened at the corners of her eyes. When she finished she laid her hands in her lap and went on looking at the notes. Herr Spinell sat motionless.

She played another Nocturne, and then a third. Then she stood up but only to look on the top of the piano for more music.

It occurred to Herr Spinell to look at the black-bound volumes on the piano stool. All at once he uttered an incoherent exclamation, his large white hands clutching at one of the books.

"Impossible! No, it cannot be," he said. "But yes, it is. Guess what this is—what was lying here! Guess what I have in my hands." [9]

"What?" she asked.

Mutely he showed her the title page. He was quite pale; he let the book sink and looked at her, his lips trembling.

"Really? How did that get here? Give it me," was all she said;

---

9. *what I have in my hands,* the music for the opera *Tristan und Isolde* (tris′tän ünd i zōl′də) by Richard Wagner (1813–1883).

set the notes on the piano and after a moment's silence began to play.

He sat beside her, bent forward, his hands between his knees, his head bowed. She played the beginning with exaggerated and tormenting slowness, with painfully long pauses between the single figures. The *Sehnsuchtsmotiv*,[10] roving lost and forlorn like a voice in the night, lifted its trembling question. Then silence, a waiting. And lo, an answer: the same timorous, lonely note, only clearer, only tenderer. Silence again. And then, with that marvellous muted *sforzando*,[11] like mounting passion, the love motif came in; reared and soared and yearned ecstatically upward to its consummation, sank back, was resolved; the cellos taking up the melody to carry it on with their deep, heavy notes of rapture and despair.

Not unsuccessfully did the player seek to suggest the orchestral effects upon the poor instrument at her command. The violin runs of the great climax rang out with brilliant precision. She played with a fastidious reverence, lingering on each figure, bringing out each detail, with the self-forgotten concentration of the priest who lifts the Host above his head. Here two forces, two beings, strove towards each other, in transports of joy and pain; here they embraced and became one in delirious yearning after eternity and the absolute. . . . The prelude flamed up and died away. She stopped at the point where the curtains part, and sat speechless, staring at the keys.

But the boredom of Frau Spatz had now reached that pitch where it distorts the countenance of man, makes the eyes protrude from the head, and lends the features a corpse-like and terrifying aspect. More than that, this music acted on the nerves that controlled her digestion, producing in her dyspeptic organism such *malaise* that she was really afraid she would have an attack. "I shall have to go up to my room," she said weakly. "Goodbye; I will come back soon."

She went out. Twilight was far advanced. Outside the snow fell thick and soundlessly upon the terrace. The two tapers cast a flickering, circumscribed light.

"The Second Act," [12] he whispered, and she turned the pages and began.

---

10. *Sehnsuchtsmotiv* (zān zŭkts′mō tēf′), "motif of longing," the theme with which the opera opens. 11. *sforzando* (sfôrt sän′dō), forcefully, a musical direction; here, a spirited passage which introduces the principal melody. 12. *The Second Act*, the scene in which the lovers Tristan and Isolde meet in the garden while Isolde's husband, King Mark, is away hunting.

What was it dying away in the distance—the ring of a horn? The rustle of leaves? The rippling of a brook? Silence and night crept up over grove and house; the power of longing had full sway, no prayers or warnings could avail against it. The holy mystery was consummated. The light was quenched; with a strange clouding of the timbre the death motif sank down: white-veiled desire, by passion driven, fluttered towards love as through the dark it groped to meet her.

Ah, boundless, unquenchable exultation of union in the eternal beyond! Freed from torturing error, escaped from fettering space and time, the Thou and the I, the Thine and the Mine at one forever in a sublimity of bliss! The day might part them with deluding show; but when night fell, then by the power of the potion they would see clear. To him who has looked upon the night of death and known its secret sweets, to him day never can be aught but vain, nor can he know a longing save for night, eternal, real, in which he is made one with love.

O night of love,[13] sink downwards and enfold them, grant them the oblivion they crave, release them from this world of partings and betrayals. Lo, the last light is quenched. Fancy and thought alike are lost, merged in the mystic shade that spread its wings of healing above their madness and despair. "Now, when deceitful daylight pales, when my raptured eye grows dim, then all that from which the light of day would shut my sight, seeking to blind me with false show, to the stanchless torments of my longing soul—then, ah, then, O wonder of fulfilment, even then I am the world!" Followed Brangäna's [14] dark notes of warning, and then those soaring violins so higher than all reason.

"I cannot understand it all, Herr Spinell. Much of it I only divine. What does it mean, this 'even then I am the world'?"

He explained, in a few low-toned words.

"Yes, yes. It means that. How is it you can understand it all so well yet cannot play it?"

Strangely enough, he was not proof against this simple question. He coloured, twisted his hands together, shrank into his chair.

"The two things seldom happen together," he wrung from his lips at last. "No, I cannot play. But go on."

And on they went, into the intoxicated music of the love-mys-

---

13. *O night of love,* the opening words of a duet sung by the lovers.
14. *Brangäna* (brän ga′nɔ), the servant of Isolde, who tries to warn the lovers of King Mark's return.

tery. Did love ever die? Tristan's love? The love of thy Isolde, and of mine? Ah, no, death cannot touch that which can never die—and what of him could die, save what distracts and tortures love and severs united lovers? Love joined the two in sweet conjunction, death was powerless to sever such a bond, save only when death was given to one with the very life of the other. Their voices rose in mystic unison, rapt in the wordless hope of that death-in-love, of endless oneness in the wonder-kingdom of the night. Sweet night! Eternal night of love! And all-encompassing land of rapture! Once envisaged or divined, what eye could bear to open again on desolate dawn? Forfend such fears, most gentle death! Release these lovers quite from need of waking. Oh, tumultuous storm of rhythms! Oh, glad chromatic upward surge of metaphysical perception! How find, how bind this bliss so far remote from parting's torturing pangs? Ah, gentle glow of longing, soothing and kind, ah, yielding sweet-sublime, ah, raptured sinking into the twilight of eternity! Thou Isolde, Tristan I, yet no more Tristan, no more Isolde. . . .

All at once something startling happened. The musician broke off and peered into the darkness with her hand above her eyes. Herr Spinell turned round quickly in his chair. The corridor door had opened, a sinister form appeared, leant on the arm of a second form. It was a guest of Einfried, one of those who, like themselves, had been in no state to undertake the sleigh-ride, but had passed this twilight hour in one of her pathetic, instinctive rounds of the house. It was that patient who had borne fourteen children and was no longer capable of a single thought; it was Frau Pastor Höhlenrauch, on the arm of her nurse. She did not look up; with groping step she paced the dim background of the room and vanished by the opposite door, rigid and still, like a lost and wandering soul. Stillness reigned once more.

"That was Frau Pastor Höhlenrauch," he said.

"Yes, that was poor Frau Höhlenrauch," she answered. Then she turned over some leaves and played the finale, played Isolde's song of love and death.

How colourless and clear were her lips, how deep the shadows lay beneath her eyes! The little pale-blue vein in her transparent brow showed fearfully plain and prominent. Beneath her flying fingers the music mounted to its unbelievable climax and was resolved in that ruthless, sudden *pianissimo* [15] which is like

---

15. *pianissimo* (pē′ə nēs′ə mō), a very soft passage.

having the ground glide from beneath one's feet, yet like a sinking too into the very depths of desire. Followed the immeasurable plenitude of that vast redemption and fulfilment; it was repeated, swelled into a deafening, unquenchable tumult of immense appeasement that wove and welled and seemed about to die away, only to swell again and weave the *Sehnsuchtsmotiv* into its harmony; at length to breathe an outward breath and die, faint on the air, and soar away. Profound stillness.

They both listened, their heads on one side.

"Those are bells," she said.

"It is the sleighs," he said. "I will go now."

He rose and walked across the room. At the door he halted, then turned and shifted uneasily from one foot to the other. And then, some fifteen or twenty paces from her, it came to pass that he fell upon his knees, both knees, without a sound. His long black coat spread out on the floor. He held his hands clasped over his mouth, and his shoulders heaved.

She sat there with hands in her lap, leaning forward, turned away from the piano, and looked at him. Her face wore a distressed, uncertain smile, while her eyes searched the dimness at the back of the room, searched so painfully, so dreamily, she seemed hardly able to focus her gaze.

The jingling of sleigh bells came nearer and nearer, there was the crack of whips, a babel of voices.

The sleighing party had taken place on the twenty-sixth of February, and was talked of for long afterwards. The next day, February twenty-seventh, a day of thaw, that set everything to melting and dripping, splashing and running, Herr Klöterjahn's wife was in capital health and spirits. On the twenty-eighth she brought up a little blood—not much, still it was blood, and accompanied by a far greater loss of strength than ever before. She went to bed.

Dr. Leander examined her, stony-faced. He prescribed according to the dictates of science—morphia, little pieces of ice, absolute quiet. Next day, on account of pressure of work, he turned her case over to Dr. Müller, who took it on in humility and meekness of spirit and according to the letter of his contract—a quiet, pallid, insignificant little man, whose unadvertised activities were consecrated to the care of the slight cases and the hopeless ones.

Dr. Müller presently expressed the view that the separation between Frau Klöterjahn and her spouse had lasted overlong. It would be well if Herr Klöterjahn, in case his flourishing business permitted, were to make another visit to Einfried. One might write him—or even wire. And surely it would benefit the young mother's health and spirits if he were to bring young Anton with him—quite aside from the pleasure it would give the physicians to behold with their own eyes this so healthy little Anton.

And Herr Klöterjahn came. He got Herr Müller's little wire and arrived from the Baltic coast. He got out of the carriage, ordered coffee and rolls, and looked considerably aggrieved.

"My dear sir," he asked, "what is the matter? Why have I been summoned?"

"Because it is desirable that you should be near your wife," Dr. Müller replied.

"Desirable! Desirable! But is it *necessary*? It is a question of expense with me—times are poor and railway journeys cost money. Was it imperative I should take this whole day's journey? If it were the lungs that are attacked, I should say nothing. But as it is only the trachea, thank God—"

"Herr Klöterjahn," said Dr. Müller mildly, "in the first place the trachea is an important organ. . . ." He ought not to have said "in the first place," because he did not go on to the second.

But there also arrived in Einfried, in Herr Klöterjahn's company, a full-figured personage arrayed all in red and gold and plaid, and she it was who carried on her arm Anton Klöterjahn, junior, that healthy little Anton. Yes, there he was, and nobody could deny that he was healthy even to excess. Pink and white and plump and fragrant, in fresh and immaculate attire, he rested heavily upon the bare red arm of his bebraided body-servant, consumed huge quantities of milk and chopped beef, shouted and screamed, and in every way surrendered himself to his instincts.

Our author from the window of his chamber had seen him arrive. With a peculiar gaze, both veiled and piercing, he fixed young Anton with his eye as he was carried from the carriage into the house. He stood there a long time with the same expression on his face.

Herr Spinell was sitting in his room "at work."

His room was like all the others at Einfried—old-fashioned, simple, and distinguished. The massive chest of drawers was mounted with brass lions' heads; the tall mirror on the wall was not a single surface, but made up of many little panes set in lead. There was no carpet on the polished blue paved floor, the stiff legs of the furniture prolonged themselves on it in clear-cut shadows. A spacious writing table stood at the window, across whose panes the author had drawn the folds of a yellow curtain, in all probability that he might feel more retired.

In the yellow twilight he bent over the table and wrote— wrote one of those numerous letters which he sent weekly to the post and to which, quaintly enough, he seldom or never received an answer. A large, thick quire of paper lay before him, in whose upper left-hand corner was a curious involved drawing of a landscape and the name Detlev Spinell in the very latest thing in lettering. He was covering the page with a small, painfully neat, and punctiliously traced script.

"Sir:" he wrote, "I address the following lines to you because I cannot help it; because what I have to say so fills and shakes and tortures me, the words come in such a rush, that I should choke if I did not take this means to relieve myself."

If the truth were told, this about the rush of words was quite simply wide of the fact. And God knows what sort of vanity it was made Herr Spinell put it down. For his words did not come in a rush; they came with such pathetic slowness, considering the man was a writer by trade, you would have drawn the conclusion, watching him, that a writer is one to whom writing comes harder than to anybody else.

He held between two fingertips one of those curious downy hairs he had on his cheek, and twirled it round and round, whole quarter-hours at a time, gazing into space and not coming forwards by a single line; then wrote a few words, daintily, and stuck again. Yet so much was true: that what had managed to get written sounded fluent and vigorous, though the matter was odd enough, even almost equivocal, and at times impossible to follow.

"I feel," the letter went on, "an imperative necessity to make you see what I see; to show you through my eyes, illuminated by the same power of language that clothes them for me, all the things which have stood before my inner eye for weeks, like an indelible vision. It is my habit to yield to the impulse which urges me to put my own experiences into flamingly right and unforgettable words and to give them to the world. And therefore hear me.

"I will do no more than relate what has been and what is: I will merely tell a story, a brief, unspeakably touching story, without comment, blame, or passing of judgment; simply in my own words. It is the story of Gabriele Eckhof, of the woman whom you, sir, call your wife—and mark you this: it is your story, it happened to you, yet it will be I who will for the first time lift it for you to the level of an experience.

"Do you remember the garden, the old, overgrown garden behind the grey patrician house? The moss was green in the crannies of its weather-beaten wall, and behind the wall dreams and neglect held sway. Do you remember the fountain in the centre? The pale mauve lilies leaned over its crumbling rim, the little stream prattled softly as it fell upon the riven paving. The summer day was drawing to its close.

"Seven maidens sat circlewise round the fountain; but the seventh, or rather the first and only one, was not like the others, for the sinking sun seemed to be weaving a queenly coronal among her locks. Her eyes were like troubled dreams, and yet her pure lips wore a smile.

"They were singing. They lifted their little faces to the leaping streamlet and watched its charming curve droop earthward —their music hovered round it as it leaped and danced. Perhaps their slim hands were folded in their laps the while they sang.

"Can you, sir, recall the scene? Or did you ever see it? No, you saw it not. Your eyes were not formed to see it nor your ears to catch the chaste music of their song. You saw it not, or else you would have forbade your lungs to breathe, your heart to beat. You must have turned aside and gone back to your own life, taking with you what you had seen to preserve it in the depth of your soul to the end of your earthly life, a sacred and inviolable relic. But what did you do?

"That scene, sir, was an end and culmination. Why did you come to spoil it, to give it a sequel, to turn it into the channels of ugly and commonplace life? It was a peaceful apotheosis and a moving, bathed in a sunset beauty of decadence, decay, and death. An ancient stock, too exhausted and refined for life and action, stood there at the end of its days; its latest manifestations were those of art: violin notes, full of that melancholy understanding which is ripeness for death. . . . Did you look into her eyes—those eyes where tears so often stood, lured by the dying sweetness of the violin? Her six friends may have had souls that belonged to life; but hers, the queen's and sister's, death and beauty had claimed for their own.

"You saw it, that deathly beauty; saw, and coveted. The sight of that touching purity moved you with no awe or trepidation. And it was not enough for you to see, you must possess, you must use, you must desecrate. . . . It was the refinement of a choice you made—you are a gourmand, sir, a plebeian gourmand, a peasant with taste.

"Once more let me say that I have no wish to offend you. What I have just said is not an affront; it is a statement, a simple, psychological statement of your simple personality—a personality which for literary purposes is entirely uninteresting. I make the statement solely because I feel an impulse to clarify for you your own thoughts and actions; because it is my inevitable task on this earth to call things by their right names, to make them speak, to illuminate the unconscious. The world is full of what I call the unconscious type, and I cannot endure it; I cannot endure all these unconscious types! I cannot bear all this dull, uncomprehending, unperceiving living and behaving, this world of maddening naïveté about me! It tortures me until I am driven irresistibly to set it all in relief, in the round, to explain, express, and make self-conscious everything in the world—so far as my powers will reach—quite unhampered by the result, whether it be for good or evil, whether it brings consolation and healing or piles grief on grief.

"You, sir, as I said, are a plebeian gourmand, a peasant with taste. You stand upon an extremely low evolutionary level; your own constitution is coarse-fibred. But wealth and a sedentary habit of life have brought about in you a corruption of the nervous system, as sudden as it is unhistoric; and this corruption has been accompanied by a lascivious refinement in your choice of gratifications. It is altogether possible that the muscles of your gullet began to contract, as at the sight of some particularly rare dish, when you conceived the idea of making Gabriele Eckhof your own.

"In short, you lead her idle will astray, you beguile her out of that moss-grown garden into the ugliness of life, you give her your own vulgar name and make of her a married woman, a housewife, a mother. You take that deathly beauty—spent, aloof, flowering in lofty unconcern of the uses of this world—and debase it to the service of common things, you sacrifice it to that stupid, contemptible, clumsy graven image we call 'nature' —and not the faintest suspicion of the vileness of your conduct visits your peasant soul.

"Again. What is the result? This being, whose eyes are like troubled dreams, she bears you a child; and so doing she endows the new life, a gross continuation of its author's own, with all the blood, all the physical energy she possesses—and she dies. She dies, sir! And if she does not go hence with your vulgarity upon her head; if at the very last she has lifted herself out of the depths of degradation, and passes in an ecstasy, with the deathly kiss of beauty on her brow—well, it is I, sir, who have seen to that! You, meanwhile, were probably spending your time with chambermaids in dark corners.

"But your son, Gabriele Eckhof's son, is alive; he is living and flourishing. Perhaps he will continue in the way of his father, become a well-fed, trading, tax-paying citizen; a capable, philistine pillar of society; in any case, a tone-deaf, normally functioning individual, responsible, sturdy, and stupid, troubled by not a doubt.

"Kindly permit me to tell you, sir, that I hate you. I hate you and your child, as I hate the life of which you are the representative: cheap, ridiculous, but yet triumphant life, the everlasting antipodes [16] and deadly enemy of beauty. I cannot say I despise you—for I am honest. You are stronger than I. I have no armour for the struggle between us, I have only the Word, avenging weapon of the weak. Today I have availed myself of this weapon. This letter is nothing but an act of revenge—you see how honourable I am—and if any word of mine is sharp and bright and beautiful enough to strike home, to make you feel the presence of a power you do not know, to shake even a minute your robust equilibrium, I shall rejoice indeed.— DETLEV SPINELL."

And Herr Spinell put this screed into an envelope, applied a stamp and a many-flourished address, and committed it to the post.

Herr Klöterjahn knocked on Herr Spinell's door. He carried a sheet of paper in his hand covered with neat script, and he looked like a man bent on energetic action. The post office had done its duty, the letter had taken its appointed way: it had travelled from Einfried to Einfried and reached the hand for which it was meant. It was now four o'clock in the afternoon.

Herr Klöterjahn's entry found Herr Spinell sitting on the sofa reading his own novel with the appalling cover design. He rose and gave his caller a surprised and inquiring look, though at the same time he distinctly flushed.

"Good afternoon," said Herr Klöterjahn. "Pardon the interruption. But may I ask if you wrote this?" He held up in his left hand the sheet inscribed with fine clear characters and struck it with the back of his right and made it crackle. Then he stuffed that hand into the pocket of his easy-fitting trousers, put his

---

16. *antipodes* (an tip′ə dēz), the complete opposite.

head on one side, and opened his mouth, in a way some people have, to listen.

Herr Spinell, curiously enough, smiled; he smiled engagingly, with a rather confused, apologetic air. He put his hand to his head as though trying to recollect himself, and said:

"Ah!—yes, quite right, I took the liberty—"

The fact was, he had given in to his natural man today and slept nearly up to midday, with the result that he was suffering from a bad conscience and a heavy head, was nervous and incapable of putting up a fight. And the spring air made him limp and good-for-nothing. So much we must say in extenuation of the utterly silly figure he cut in the interview which followed.

"Ah? Indeed! Very good!" said Herr Klöterjahn. He dug his chin into his chest, elevated his brows, stretched his arms, and indulged in various other antics by way of getting down to business after his introductory question. But unfortunately he so much enjoyed the figure he cut that he rather overshot the mark, and the rest of the scene hardly lived up to this preliminary pantomime. However, Herr Spinell went rather pale.

"Very good!" repeated Herr Klöterjahn. "Then permit me to give you an answer in person; it strikes me as idiotic to write pages of letter to a person when you can speak to him any hour of the day."

"Well, idiotic . . ." Herr Spinell said, with his apologetic smile. He sounded almost meek.

"Idiotic!" repeated Herr Klöterjahn, nodding violently in token of the soundness of his position. "And I should not demean myself to answer this scrawl; to tell the truth, I should have thrown it away at once if I had not found in it the explanation of certain changes—however, that is no affair of yours, and has nothing to do with the thing anyhow. I am a man of action, I have other things to do than to think about your unspeakable visions."

"I wrote 'indelible vision,'" said Herr Spinell, drawing himself up. This was the only moment at which he displayed a little self-respect.

"Indelible, unspeakable," responded Herr Klöterjahn, referring to the text. "You write a villainous hand, sir; you would not get a position in my office, let me tell you. It looks clear enough at first, but when you come to study it, it is full of shakes and quavers. But that is your affair, it's no business of mine. What I have come to say to you is that you are a tomfool —which you probably know already. Furthermore, you are a cowardly sneak; I don't suppose I have to give the evidence for that either. My wife wrote me once that when you meet a woman you don't look her square in the face, but just give her a side squint, so as to carry away a good impression, because you are afraid of the reality. I should probably have heard more of the same sort of stories about you, only unfortunately she stopped mentioning you. But this is the kind of thing you are: you talk so much about 'beauty'; you are all chicken-livered hypocrisy and cant—which is probably at the bottom of your impudent allusion to out-of-the-way corners too. That ought to crush me, of course, but it just makes me laugh—it doesn't do a thing but make me laugh! Understand? Have I clarified your thoughts and actions for you, you pitiable object, you? Though of course it is not my invariable calling—"

" 'Inevitable' was the word I used," Herr Spinell said; but he did not insist on the point. He stood there, crestfallen, like a big, unhappy, chidden, grey-haired schoolboy.

"Invariable or inevitable, whichever you like—anyhow you are a contemptible cur, and that I tell you. You see me every day at table, you bow and smirk and say good morning—and one fine day you send me a scrawl full of idiotic abuse. Yes, you've a lot of courage—on paper! And it's not only this ridiculous letter —you have been intriguing behind my back. I can see that now. Though you need not flatter yourself it did any good. If you imagine you put any ideas into my wife's head you never were more mistaken in your life. And if you think she behaved any different when we came from what she always does, then you just put the cap onto your own foolishness. She did not kiss the little chap, that's true, but it was only a precaution, because they have the idea now that the trouble is with her lungs, and in such cases you can't tell whether—though that still remains to be proved, no matter what you say with your 'She dies, sir,' you silly ass!"

Here Herr Klöterjahn paused for breath. He was in a furious passion; he kept stabbing the air with his right forefinger and crumpling the sheet of paper in his other hand. His face, between the blond English mutton chops, was frightfully red and his dark brow was rent with swollen veins like lightnings of scorn.

"You hate me," he went on, "and you would despise me if I were not stronger than you. Yes, you're right there! I've got my heart in the right place, by God, and you've got yours mostly in the seat of your trousers. I would most certainly hack you into bits if it weren't against the law, you and your gabble about the 'Word,' you skulking fool! But I have no intention of putting up with your insults; and when I show this part about the vulgar name to my lawyer at home, you will very likely get a little surprise. My name, sir, is a first-rate name, and I have made it so by my own efforts. You know better than I do whether anybody would ever lend you a penny piece on yours, you lazy lout! The law defends people against the kind you are! You are a common danger, you are enough to drive a body crazy! But you're left this time, my master! I don't let individuals like you get the best of me so fast! I've got my heart in the right place—"

Herr Klöterjahn's excitement had really reached a pitch. He shrieked, he bellowed, over and over again, that his heart was in the right place.

" 'They were singing.' Exactly. Well, they weren't. They were knitting. And if I heard what they said, it was about a recipe for potato pancakes; and when I show my father-in-law that about the old decayed family you'll probably have a libel suit on your hands. 'Did you see the picture?' Yes, of course I saw it; only I don't see why that should make me hold my breath and run away. I don't leer at women out of the corner of my eye; I look at them square, and if I like their looks I go for them. I have my heart in the right place—"

Somebody knocked. Knocked eight or ten times, quite fast, one after the other—a sudden, alarming little commotion that made Herr Klöterjahn pause; and an unsteady voice that kept tripping over itself in its haste and distress said:

"Herr Klöterjahn, Herr Klöterjahn—oh, is Herr Klöterjahn there?"

"Stop outside," said Herr Klöterjahn, in a growl. . . . "What's the matter? I'm busy talking."

"Oh, Herr Klöterjahn," said the quaking, breaking voice, "you must come! The doctors are there too—oh, it is all so dreadfully sad—"

He took one step to the door and tore it open. Frau Magistrate Spatz was standing there. She had her handkerchief before her mouth, and great egg-shaped tears rolled into it, two by two.

"Herr Klöterjahn," she got out. "It is so frightfully sad. . . . She has brought up so much blood, such a horrible lot of blood. . . . She was sitting up quite quietly in bed and humming a little snatch of music . . . and there it came . . . my God, such a quantity you never saw. . . ."

"Is she dead?" yelled Herr Klöterjahn. As he spoke he clutched the Rätin by the arm and pulled her to and fro on the sill. "Not quite? Not dead; she can see me, can't she? Brought up a little blood again, from the lung, eh? Yes, I give in, it may be from the lung. Gabriele!" he suddenly cried out, and his eyes filled with tears; you could see what a burst of good, warm, honest human feeling came over him. "Yes, I'm coming," he said, and dragged the Rätin after him as he went with long strides down the corridor. You could still hear his voice, from quite a distance, sounding fainter and fainter: "Not quite, eh? From the lung?"

Herr Spinell stood still on the spot where he had stood during the whole of Herr Klöterjahn's rudely interrupted call and looked out the open door. At length he took a couple of steps and listened down the corridor. But all was quiet, so he closed the door and came back into the room.

He looked at himself awhile in the glass, then he went up to the writing table, took a little flask and a glass out of a drawer, and drank a cognac—for which nobody can blame him. Then he stretched himself out on the sofa and closed his eyes.

The upper half of the window was down. Outside in the garden birds were twittering; those dainty, saucy little notes held all the spring, finely and penetratingly expressed. Herr Spinell spoke once: "Invariable calling," he said, and moved his head and drew in the air through his teeth as though his nerves pained him violently.

Impossible to recover any poise or tranquillity. Crude experiences like this were too much—he was not made for them. By a sequence of emotions, the analysis of which would lead us too far afield, Herr Spinell arrived at the decision that it would be well for him to have a little out-of-doors exercise. He took his hat and went downstairs.

As he left the house and issued into the mild, fragrant air, he turned his head and lifted his eyes, slowly, scanning the house until he reached one of the windows, a curtained window, on which his gaze rested awhile, fixed and sombre. Then he laid his hands on his back and moved away across the gravel path. He moved in deep thought.

The beds were still straw-covered, the trees and bushes bare; but the snow was gone, the path was only damp in spots. The large garden with its grottoes, bowers and little pavilions lay in the splendid colourful afternoon light, strong shadow and rich, golden sun, and the dark network of branches stood out sharp and articulate against the bright sky.

It was about that hour of the afternoon when the sun takes shape, and from being a formless volume of light turns to a visibly sinking disk, whose milder, more saturated glow the eye can tolerate. Herr Spinell did not see the sun, the direction the path took hid it from his view. He walked with bent head and hummed a strain of music, a short phrase, a figure that mounted wailingly and complainingly upward—the *Sehnsuchtsmotiv.* . . . But suddenly, with a start, a quick, jerky intake of breath, he stopped, as though rooted to the path, and gazed straight ahead of him, with brows fiercely gathered, staring eyes, and an expression of horrified repulsion.

The path had curved just here, he was facing the setting sun. It stood large and slantwise in the sky, crossed by two narrow strips of gold-rimmed cloud; it set the treetops aglow and poured its red-gold radiance across the garden. And there, erect in the path, in the midst of the glory, with the sun's mighty aureola above her head, there confronted him an exuberant figure, all arrayed in red and gold and plaid. She had one hand on her swelling hip, with the other she moved to and fro the graceful little perambulator. And in this perambulator sat the child—sat Anton Klöterjahn, junior, Gabriele Eckhof's fat son.

There he sat among his cushions, in a woolly white jacket and large white hat, plump-cheeked, well cared for, and magnificent; and his blithe unerring gaze encountered Herr Spinell's. The novelist pulled himself together. Was he not a man, had he not the power to pass this unexpected, sun-kindled apparition there in the path and continue on his walk? But Anton Klöterjahn began to laugh and shout—most horrible to see. He squealed, he crowed with inconceivable delight—it was positively uncanny to hear him.

God knows what had taken him; perhaps the sight of Herr Spinell's long, black figure set him off; perhaps an attack of sheer animal spirits gave rise to his wild outburst of merriment. He had a bone teething-ring in one hand and a tin rattle in the other; and these two objects he flung aloft with shoutings, shook them to and fro, and clashed them together in the air, as though purposely to frighten Herr Spinell. His eyes were almost shut, his mouth gaped open till all the rosy gums were displayed; and as he shouted he rolled his head about in excess of mirth.

Herr Spinell turned round and went thence. Pursued by the youthful Klöterjahn's joyous screams, he went away across the gravel, walking stiffly, yet not without grace; his gait was the hesitating gait of one who would disguise the fact that, inwardly, he is running away. ∎

Christian Morgenstern
(1871–1914)

PALMSTRÖM

Translated from the German by

W. D. Snodgrass and Lore Segal

Palmström, standing beside the brook,
Unfolds a handkerchief wide and red
On which a mighty oak is shown
And someone with an open book.

5 Blow his nose?—he would not dare!
For he belongs to that sort of men
Who are so often, nakedly,
Stricken by beauty, unaware.

What he has only just outspread,
10 Tenderly, now, he has to close;
No sensitive spirit will condemn
Him, marching on with unblown nose.

THE DAYNIGHTLAMP

Translated from the German by

W. D. Snodgrass and Lore Segal

Korf has a daynightlamp,
His own invention, which
At one flick of the switch,
Turns day, however bright,
5 To blackest night.

When, at the convention
He displays it on the ramp,
No man of comprehension
Who understands his field
10 Can fail to see, revealed—

(Brilliant day turns to night;
Applause storms through the house)
(Someone starts to shout
for the janitor, Mr. Camp:
15 "Lights! Lights!")—to see, outright,

The facts: aforesaid lamp,
Indeed has powers which
At one flick of the switch
Turns any day, how bright,
20 To blackest night.

THE MOUSETRAP

Translated from the German by

W. D. Snodgrass and Lore Segal

I

Palmström hasn't a crumb in the house;
Nevertheless, he has a mouse.

Von Korf, upset by his friend's distress,
Builds a room out of trellises

5 And places Palmström there, within,
Fiddling an exquisite violin.

It gets late; the stars shine bright;
Palmström makes music in the night,

Till, midway through the serenade,
10 In strolls the mouse, to promenade.

Behind it, by some secret trick
A trapdoor closes, quiet, quick.

Before it, Palmström, immediately,
Sinks into slumber, silently.

---

15 Von Korf arrives in the early dawn
And loads this useful invention on

The nearest medium-sized, as it were,
Moving van for furniture,

Which is hauled then, by a powerful horse,
20 Nimbly, into the distant forest.

There, profoundly isolated,
This strange couple are liberated:

First the mouse comes strolling out,
And then Palmström—after the mouse.

25 The animal, with no trace of fright,
Takes to its new home with delight.

Palmström, meanwhile, observing this,
Drives home with Korf, transformed by bliss.

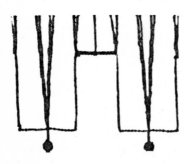

THE GLASSES

Translated from the German by

Walter Kaufman

Korf reads much, and he is quick;
hence it simply makes him sick
to find endless repetitions
and vast over-expositions.

5 Most points, he finds, can be made
in six words, at most in eight;
and in sentences that number
one can lead tapeworms to slumber.

He invents, sad and perplexed,
10 an ideal remedy:
spectacles whose energy
will condense a longish text.

Would one have to read this poem with glasses like this? No!
15 Thirty-three like this would—hark!—
yield a single question mark!!

THE IMPOSSIBLE FACT

Translated from the German by

Walter Kaufman

Palmström, strolling through the town,
tried to cross the bending road
when an automobile mowed
him down.

5 "How was (says he, still alive
and resolving to survive)
possible this mishap—or
could it really occur?

Is our statecraft here at fault
10 anent motorized assault?
Did the police regulation
give the driver a vacation?

Or was it against the norm
at this corner to transform
15 living men to dead condition:
did this driver lack permission?"

Rainer Maria Rilke (1875–1926)

GYM PERIOD

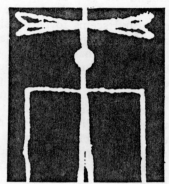

Translated from the German by
Carl Niemeyer

THE MILITARY SCHOOL OF ST. SEVERIN. The gymnasium. The class in their white cotton shirts stand in two rows under the big gas lights. The gym teacher, a young officer with a hard, swarthy face and contemptuous eyes, has given the order for exercises and is dividing the class into sections. "First section, horizontal bars; second section, parallel bars; third section, horses; fourth section, pole climbing. Fall out!" And the boys in their light, resined shoes scatter quickly. A few remain standing in the middle of the floor, hesitating and reluctant. They are the fourth section, the poor gymnasts, who do not enjoy playing on the equipment and are already tired after their twenty knee-bends, as well as somewhat bewildered and out of breath.

But one, Karl Gruber, ordinarily the very first on such occasions, already stands near the poles set up in a dimly-lit corner of the gymnasium just beside the lockers where the coats of the boys' uniforms now hang. He has seized the nearest pole and with unusual strength pulls it shaking out to the spot designated for practice. Gruber does not even let go. He jumps and grabs a hold rather high up. His legs, involuntarily wound around the pole in a position for climbing such as he never achieved before, cling to the shaft. He waits for the rest of the class and seems to be considering with peculiar pleasure the astonished anger of the little Polish sergeant, who calls to him to come down. But Gruber does not obey, and Jastersky, the blond sergeant, finally shouts, "Very well. Either you come down, Gruber, or you climb the rest of the way up. Otherwise I shall report you to the lieutenant in charge."

And then Gruber begins to climb, at first frenziedly, pulling up his legs a little, his eyes raised, estimating with some alarm the incalculable section of the pole still to come. Then his movements grow slower; and as though he were relishing every fresh hold as something new and delightful, he pulls himself higher than anyone usually goes. He pays no attention to the excitement of the exasperated sergeant, but climbs and climbs, his eyes staring upward, as though he had discovered an outlet in the gymnasium roof and were straining to reach it. The eyes of his whole section follow him. And in the other sections too some notice is taken of the climber who had hardly ever been able to climb even the first third of the way without getting a cough, a red face, and a bloodshot eye.

"Bravo, Gruber!" someone calls over from the first section. Many look up then, and for a while the gym is quiet.

But at this very moment when all eyes are upon him, Gruber, high up under the roof, gestures as though to shake them off; and when he obviously does not succeed, he rivets all their glances on the iron hook above him and swishes down the slippery pole, so that everyone is still looking up, whereas he, dizzy and hot, already stands below and gazes with strangely lusterless eyes at his burning palms.

Then one or another of the boys around him asks what got into him. "Do you want to make the first section?" Gruber laughs and seems about to reply, but he thinks better of it and lowers his eyes.

And then, when the noisy tumult has begun again, he retires quietly to his locker, sits down, looks about uneasily, and after two panting breaths laughs again and tries to say something. But already he is unobserved.

Only Jerome, also in the fourth section, notices that he is bent over like someone deciphering a letter in bad light again inspecting his hands. He walks over to him presently and asks, "Did you hurt yourself?"

Gruber starts. "What?" he asks in his habitual slobbering voice.

"Let's have a look." Jerome takes his hand and turns it toward the light. A little skin is scraped from the palm. "Say, I've got something to fix it," says Jerome, who always gets sticking-plaster sent from home. "Come to my room when we get out." But it is as though Gruber did not hear. He stares straight ahead into the gym as though he were seeing something indefinable, perhaps something not in the gym, perhaps outside against the window even though it is late on a dark autumn afternoon.

At this moment, the sergeant shouts in his haughty way, "Gruber!" Gruber remains as before. Only his outstretched feet slide gracelessly forward on the slippery floor. "Gruber!" roars the sergeant, and his voice breaks. Then he waits a while, and says in a quick gruff tone without looking at the boy, "Report after class. I shall see that you. . . ." And the class continues.

"Gruber," says Jerome and bends over his friend, who is leaning back farther and farther in his locker, "it was your turn to climb on the rope. Go ahead, try it. If you don't, Jastersky will fix up some kind of a story against you. You know how he is."

Gruber nods. But instead of getting up, he abruptly shuts his eyes and slips forward while Jerome is talking. As if borne by a wave, he slides slowly and silently, farther and farther—slides from his seat, and Jerome doesn't realize what is happening till Gruber's head bangs hard against the wooden seat and then droops forward. "Gruber!" he calls hoarsely. At first no one notices. Jerome stands helpless, his arms at his sides, and calls "Gruber! Gruber!" He doesn't even think to pull him up.

Then he is given a push. Someone says, "Dumbbell!" Someone else shoves him aside, and he watches them lift the motionless boy to carry him off somewhere, probably into the next room. The lieutenant in charge hurries in. In a harsh, loud voice he issues curt orders. The commands cut short the buzzing chatter. Silence. Only here and there is there any movement: swinging on the bars, gentle leaps, a belated laugh from someone who doesn't know what it's all about.

Then rapid questions. "What? What? Who? Gruber? Where?" And still more questions. Then aloud someone says, "Fainted."

And red-faced Jastersky, the sergeant, runs back of the lieutenant in charge and cries in his disagreeable voice, trembling with rage, "He's faking, lieutenant, he's faking." The lieutenant pays no attention. He looks straight ahead, gnaws his mustache so that his strong chin juts out sharper and firmer, and gives an occasional brief order. He and four pupils carrying Gruber disappear into the room.

At once, the four pupils return. A servant runs through the gym. The four get a good deal of attention and are plied with questions. "How does he look? What's the matter with him? Has he come to yet?" None of the four really knows anything. And then the lieutenant in charge calls to them that the class may continue and gives the command to Goldstein, the sergeant-major. So the exercises begin again, on the parallel and horizontal bars; and the little boys of the third section straddle the tall horse with their bowed legs.

Yet the activity is not as before. It is as though everyone were listening. Swinging on the parallel bars abruptly stops, and only small feats are performed on the horizontal bar. The voices are less confused, and the hum is fainter, as though all were uttering just one word, "Ssss. Ssss." In the meantime sly little Krix is listening at the door. The sergeant of the second section chases him away, lifting his hand to slap his bottom. Krix leaps back, catlike, his eyes bright and cunning. He has learned enough. And after a while, when no one is watching, he tells Pavlovich, "The regimental doctor's come."

Now Pavlovich's behavior is notorious. As boldly as though he were obeying an order, he goes about the gym from one section to another, saying loudly, "The regimental doctor's in there." And even the noncoms appear to be interested in the news. Glances toward the door become more and more frequent, the exercises slower and slower. A small boy with black eyes remains crouching on the horse and stares open-mouthed at the door. The strongest boys in the first class exert themselves a little, struggle against it, whirl their legs.

Pombert, the strong Tyrolean, bends his arm and contemplates his muscles, which stand out taut and strong under his shirt. His supple young limbs even make a few more turns on the bars, and suddenly the lively movement of his body is the only one in the whole gym. It is a great dazzling circle, somehow ominous in the midst of great stillness. Abruptly the little fellow brings himself to a stop, drops involuntarily to his knees, and makes a face as though he despised them all. But even his dull little eyes rest finally on the door.

Now the singing of the gasjets and the ticking of the wall clock are audible. And then the dismissal bell rattles. Today its tone is strange and peculiar. And it stops suddenly, incomplete, interrupting itself when its message is only half spoken. Sergeant-major Goldstein, however, knows his duty. He calls, "Fall in!" No one hears. No one can recall the meaning these words once had. Once? When? "Fall in!" croaks the sergeant-major angrily, and now the other noncoms cry in succession, "Fall in!" And also many of the pupils say, as if to themselves or in their sleep, "Fall in! Fall in!" But actually, all of them know there is still something to wait for.

And at this very moment the door is opening. For a second nothing happens; then Wehl, the lieutenant in charge, walks out, and his eyes are big and wrathful and his pace is decided. He marches as though he were on parade and says hoarsely, "Fall in!" With astonishing speed ranks are formed. Then no one moves. It is as though a field marshal were present. And now the command, "Attention!" A pause, and then dry and harsh, "Your friend Gruber has just died. Heart attack. Forward, march!" A pause.

And only after a little while, the voice of the pupil on duty, small and weak, "Company, column left! March!" Slow and unready, the group turns to the door. Jerome is the last. No one looks back. From the corridor chill, damp air blows against the boys. One of them suggests that it smells of carbolic acid. Pombert makes a vulgar joke about the smell. No one laughs. Suddenly Jerome feels somebody grab his arm, as though for assault. Krix is hanging on to him. "I saw him," he whispers breathlessly, and squeezes Jerome's arm while an inner laughter convulses him. He can hardly go on. "He's stark naked and caved in and all stretched out. And he's got a seal on the soles of his feet. . . ."

And then he giggles shrilly, as though someone had tickled him, giggles and bites down through Jerome's sleeve. ◼

THE CADET PICTURE OF MY FATHER

Adapted by

Robert Lowell

There's absence in the eyes. The brow's in touch
with something far. Now distant boyishness
and seduction shadow his enormous lips,
the slender aristocratic uniform
5 with its Franz Josef braid; both the hands bulge
like gloves upon the saber's basket hilt.
The hands are quiet, they reach out toward nothing—
I hardly see them now, as if they were
the first to grasp distance and disappear,
10 and all the rest lies curtained in itself,
and so withdrawn, I cannot understand
my father as he bleaches on this page—

Oh quickly disappearing photograph
in my more slowly disappearing hand!

Reprinted with the permission of Farrar, Straus & Giroux, Inc. and Faber
and Faber Ltd. from IMITATIONS by Robert Lowell. Copyright © 1958,
1959, 1960, 1961 by Robert Lowell.

JOSEPH'S SUSPICION

Translated from the German by
Paul Engle

The angel spoke and tried to hold
Back the man, and turn his fists away:
Do you not see in every fold
Of her, that she is cool as God's first day?

5 Darkly the other stared, and tried
To murmur only: what has changed her so?
Look, Carpenter, the angel cried,
Can you not see in this the Lord God go?

Because, with pride, you work in boards, will you
10 Blame Him, bitterly, Who well
And modestly out of that same wood grew
Green leaves, and let the live buds swell?

He understood. As he turned to the quick
Angel his actual, terror-given gaze
15 She was no longer there. He thrust his thick
Cap slowly off. And then sang praise.

"Joseph's Suspicion" by Rainer Maria Rilke from READING MODERN
POETRY, edited by Paul Engle and Warren Carrier. Copyright © 1955,
1968 by Scott, Foresman and Company.

THE KNIGHT

Translated from the German by

John Igo

The knight fares forth in sable mail
Into the stirring world.
And all is out there: the day and the vale
And friend and foe, the meal in the hall,
5 And May and the maid, and groves and the Grail,
And God himself is revealed several
Thousand times in the streets.

Yet in the armor of the knight
Behind the gloomy rings
10 Crouches Death, brooding, brooding:
When will the sword spring

Over the hedge of iron,
That strange releasing blade,
Taking me from my place
15 Where I spent so many a bending day,—
So that I can stretch myself at last
And play
And sing?

"The Knight" by Rainer Maria Rilke from POET LORE Vol. 60, No. 1.
Reprinted by permission of Literary Publications Foundation, Inc.

THE PANTHER

Translated from the German by
Paul Engle

From bending always over bars, his glance
Holds nothing more, grown tired, as if there curled
Against him but a thousand bars expanse,
Behind a thousand bars no other world.

5 The wary walking of that strong stride, dark
Around the littlest circle of his land
Is like a dance of power around an arc
Where, stupefied, a mighty Will may stand.

Only sometimes the live lid of the eye
10 Lifts, and an image enters quietly,
Travels the taut, still limbs without a cry—
And ceases in the heart to be.

7

TO THE POET

Translated from the German by

John Igo

(for Jude)

Everything is unfolding now, as we are,
For we are nothing but such happiness.
And, see, what in brutes was blood and darkness
Grows to soul in us, and in distress

5 Cries for further change. And cries for you.
But you regard it with the tranquil mood
Of some detached observer of a scene.
And therefore we think that we misunderstood

The thing it cried for. Yet, should we be lost,
10 Are you not he in whom we might be near it?
And where else, more intensely, could we be?

For us, the Infinite keeps passing by.
You must be there, you mouth, that we may hear it,
You interpreter of us,—for you we cry.

"To the Poet" by Rainer Maria Rilke from POET LORE Vol. 60, No. 1.
Reprinted by permission of Literary Publications Foundation, Inc.

A TALE OF DEATH AND A STRANGE POSTSCRIPT THERETO

from STORIES OF GOD

Translated from the German by
M. D. Herter Norton

I WAS still gazing up into the slowly fading evening sky, when someone said: "You seem to be very much interested in that country up there?"

My glance fell quickly, as if shot down, and I realized: I had come to the low wall of our little churchyard, and before me, on the other side of it, stood the man with the spade, sagely smiling. "*I'm* interested in *this* country here," he went on, pointing to the black, damp earth appearing here and there between the many dead leaves that rustled as they stirred, while I did not know a wind had sprung up. Suddenly I exclaimed, seized with a violent aversion: "Why do you do that?"

The gravedigger still smiled. "It is a way of earning one's bread—and besides, I ask you, aren't most people doing the same? They bury God *up there* as I bury men here." He pointed to the sky and explained to me: "Yes, that too is a great grave, in summer it is covered with wild forget-me-nots—"

I interrupted him: "There was a time when men buried God in the sky, that is true—"

"And is it any different now?" he asked, curiously sad.

I went on: "It used to be customary for everyone to throw a handful of sky over him, I know. But even then he really wasn't there any more, or at least—" I hesitated.

"You know," I began again, "in olden times people prayed like this—" and I spread my arms out wide, involuntarily feeling my breast expand at the gesture. "In those days God would cast

himself into all these human abysses, full of despair and darkness, and only reluctantly did he return into his heavens,
which, unnoticed, he drew down ever closer over the earth. But
a new faith began. As it could not make men understand
wherein its new God differed from their old one (for as soon as
they began to praise him, men promptly recognized the one
old God here too), the promulgator of the new commandment
changed the manner of praying. He taught the folding of hands
and declared: 'See, *thus* does our God wish to be implored, so he
must be another God from the one whom heretofore you have
thought to receive into your arms.' The people saw this, and the
gesture of open arms became a despicable and dreadful one,
and later it was fastened to the cross that all might see in it a
symbol of agony and death.

"Now when God next looked down upon the earth, he was
frightened. Besides the many folded hands, many Gothic cathe-
drals had been built, and so the hands and the roofs, alike steep
and sharp, stretched pointing towards him like the weapons of
an enemy. With God there is a different bravery. He turned
back into his heavens, and when he saw that the steeples and
the new prayers were growing in pursuit of him, he departed
out of his domain at the other side and thus eluded the chase.
He was himself astonished to find, out beyond his radiant
home, a beginning darkness that received him silently, and with
a curious feeling he went on and on in this dusk that reminded
him of the hearts of men.

Then for the first time it occurred to him that the heads of
men are lucid, but their hearts full of a similar darkness; and a
longing came over him to dwell in the hearts of men and no
longer to move through the clear, cold wakefulness of their
thinking. Well, God has continued on his way. Ever denser
grows the darkness around him, and the night through which
he presses on has something of the fragrant warmth of fecund
clods of earth. And in a little while the roots will reach out towards him with the old beautiful gesture of wide prayer. There
is nothing wiser than the circle. The God who has fled from us
out of the heavens, out of the earth will he come to us again.
And, who knows, perhaps you yourself will some day dig free
the door . . ."

The man with the spade said: "But that is a fairy-tale."

"In the words with which we speak," I answered gently,
"everything becomes a fairy-tale, for in them it can never have
happened."

The man stared for a while, reflecting. Then with impetuous

gestures he pulled on his coat, asking: "We can go together, can't we?"

I nodded: "I'm going home. I daresay we go the same way. But don't you live here?"

He stepped through the little latticed gate, swung it gently to on its plaintive hinges, and answered, "No."

After a few steps, he grew more confidential: "You were quite right just now," he said. "It is strange that anyone can be found who wants to do that job back there. I never used to think about it. But now, since I'm growing older, thoughts come to me sometimes, singular thoughts, like that about the sky, and others too. Death. What do we know of it? Apparently everything and perhaps nothing. Often children (I don't know whom they belong to) stand round me as I work. And then I get one of those ideas. I dig like a wild beast, so as to draw all my strength away from my brain and use it up in my arms. The grave gets much deeper than the regulations call for, and a mountain of earth rises beside it. But the children run away when they see my wild movements. They think I am angry for some reason." He pondered. "And it is a kind of anger. You grow callous, you think you've got the better of it, and then suddenly. . . . It's no good; death is something incomprehensible, terrible."

We were following a long road under fruit trees already quite leafless, and on our left the forest began, like a night that might at any moment engulf us.

"I would like to relate to you a little story," I said tentatively; "it's just long enough to last us till we get there."

The man nodded and lighted his old stub of a pipe. I began:

"There were two people, a man and a woman, and they loved each other. To love is to accept nothing, from anywhere, to forget everything and to want to receive everything from one person, both that which one already had and all else. That was the mutual wish of these two. But in the realm of time, by day, among the many, where so much comes and goes, often before one has got into real touch with it, it is not at all possible to carry through such loving; events rush in from all sides, and chance opens every door to them.

"For this reason the two decided to leave the daily world and go into solitude, far away from the striking of clocks and the noises of the city. And there, in a garden, they built themselves a house. And the house had two doors, one on its right side and one on its left. And the right-hand door was the man's door, and everything that was his was to pass through it into the house. The door on the left was the woman's door, and all that she cared about was to enter that way. And so it was. The one who woke first in the morning, went down and opened his door. And so until late at night a very great deal indeed came in, even though the house was not on the edge of the road. To those who know how to receive, the landscape comes into a house and the light and a breeze with a fragrance about its shoulders, and much more besides. But past things also, figures, destinies, came in by both these doors, and all were welcomed with the like simple hospitality, so that they felt as though they had always been at home in the house on the heath. This went on for a long time and the two were very happy because of it. The door at the left was opened rather more often, but by the right-hand door entered more motley guests. And before the first door one morning waited—Death. The man slammed his door quickly shut when he noticed him, and kept it tightly bolted all day long. After some time, Death appeared at the door on the left. Trembling, the woman flung it to and shot the broad bolt home. They did not speak to each other of this occurrence, but they opened both doors less often and tried to get along with what they had in the house. Of course they had to live much more meagerly than before. Their provisions grew scarce, and cares set in. They both began to sleep badly; and in one of those long, wakeful nights, they both at once suddenly heard a strange shuffling and knocking noise. It came from outside the house wall, equally far from the two doors, and sounded as though some one were beginning to break out the stones in order to make a new door midway in the wall. Even in their terror the two pretended they did not notice anything unusual. They began to talk, to laugh unnaturally loud, and when they were tired out, the rummaging in the wall had stopped. Since then both the doors have remained closed. The two live like prisoners. Their health is failing and they have strange fancies. The noise is repeated from time to time. Then they laugh with their lips, while their hearts almost die of fear. And they both know that the burrowing is getting always louder and clearer, and they must talk and laugh louder and louder with their always wearier voices." I ceased.

"Yes, yes—" said my companion, "so it is; that is a true story."

"I read this one in an old book," I went on to add, "and a very curious thing happened when I was doing so. At the end of the line which tells how Death came also to the woman's door, there had been drawn in old and faded ink a little star. It peeped out from between the words as between clouds, and for a moment I fancied that, were the lines to draw apart, they might reveal a lot of stars standing there behind them, as does sometimes happen when the spring sky clears late of an evening. Then I forgot all about the insignificant circumstance, until one day, on the smooth, glossy paper inside the back cover of the book, I found, as though mirrored in a lake, the same little star, and close beneath it delicate lines began which flowed away like waves over the pale, reflecting surface. The writing had become blurred in many places, but still I was able to decipher nearly all of it. It said something of this sort:

'I have read this story so often, on all possible kinds of days, that I sometimes believe I have written it down myself, out of my own memory. But for me it goes on as I set it down here:

'The woman had never seen Death; in all innocence she let him enter. But Death said, rather hurriedly and as one whose conscience is not clear: "Give this to your husband." And he added quickly, as she looked inquiringly at him: "It is seed, very good seed." Then he went away without looking back. The woman opened the little sack he had pressed into her hand; there really were seeds of some kind in it, hard, ugly grains. And the woman thought: "A seed is something incomplete, belonging to the future. One cannot tell what will come of it. I won't give my husband these unsightly grains; they don't look in the least like a gift. Rather will I tuck them in the flowerbed in our garden and wait to see what grows out of them. Then I will lead him to the plant and tell him how I came by it." And so the woman did. And they continued to live as before. The man, who could not forget that Death had stood before his portal, was at first somewhat uneasy, but when he saw the woman as hospitable and carefree as ever, he too soon opened the wide wings of his door again, so that much life and light came into the house.

'The following spring there stood in the middle of the bed among the slender tiger lilies, a small shrub. It had narrow, blackish leaves, rather pointed, like those of the laurel, and a peculiar gleam lay on their dark surface. Every day the man intended to ask whence the plant had sprung. But every day he failed to do so. In a similar reticence the woman from day to day withheld her explanation. But the suppressed question on the one side and the never-ventured answer on the other, drew the two together often before the little shrub, the green darkness of which contrasted so strangely with the garden. When the next spring came, they busied themselves with the shrub as much as with the other plants, and they were saddened when, surrounded by so much growing bloom, it came up unchanged and mute as in the first year, insensible to all sun. Then it was that they determined, without telling each other, to devote all their energy in the third spring to this plant, and as that spring appeared, they tenderly fulfilled, and hand in hand, what each had promised to himself. The garden all around grew wild, and the tiger lilies seemed paler than usual. But once, as after a night heavy and overcast, they stepped out into the garden, the quiet, shimmering morning garden, they saw that from the sharp black leaves of the strange shrub, a pale blue flower had sprung unscathed, bursting now the too-close sheath about its bud. And they stood before it united and silent, and now they knew less than ever what to say. For they were thinking: "Now is Death flowering," and together they bent down to savor the fragrance of the young bloom.—And since that morning everything has been different in the world.' This is what it said," I concluded, "inside the cover of the old book."

"And who would have written it?" urged the gravedigger.

"A woman, by the handwriting," I replied. "But what good would it have done to find out? The characters were very faded and rather old-fashioned. Probably she had long been dead."

My companion was lost in thought. "Only a story," he admitted at last, "and yet it touches one so."

"Ah, that is if one doesn't hear stories often," I said soothingly.

"You think so?" He gave me his hand and I held it fast. "But I would like so much to repeat it. May I?"

I nodded. Then he suddenly remembered:

"But I have no one. Whom should I tell it to?"

"Oh, that's easy. Tell it to the children who sometimes come to watch you. Whom else?"

And the children have really heard the last three stories.[1] That is, the one repeated by the evening clouds only in part, if I am correctly informed. The children are small, of course, and so they are much further from the evening clouds than we. But in the case of *that* story this is just as well. For in spite of Hans's long, well-worded speech, they would realize that the affair took place among children, and as experts would look upon my telling of it critically. But it is better that they should not learn with what effort and how awkwardly we experience the things that happen quite simply and so naturally to them. ∎

---

1. *stories*, a reference to tales appearing earlier in *Stories of God*, from which the selection is taken.

A STORY TOLD TO THE DARK

from STORIES OF GOD

Translated from the German by

M. D. Herter Norton

I WANTED to put on my coat and go to my friend Ewald. But I had lingered over a book, an *old* book at that, and evening had come, as in Russia spring comes. A moment ago the room had been distinct, even to its remotest corners, and now all the things in it acted as though they had never known anything but twilight; everywhere large dark blossoms opened, and as on dragonfly wings a luminous gleaming slipped about their velvet calyxes.

The lame man would surely no longer be at his window. So I stayed at home. What was it I had wanted to tell him? I no longer knew. But after a while I felt that someone was entreating me for this lost story—some lonely soul, perhaps, standing far away at the window of his dusky room, or perhaps this very darkness itself that surrounded me and him and all things. So it happened that I told my story to the dark. And it leaned ever closer to me so that I could speak more and more softly, quite as befits my story. It takes place in the present, by the way, and begins:

"After a long absence Doctor Georg Lassmann was returning to the simple home of his birth. He had never possessed much there, and now he had only two sisters still living in his native city, both married, apparently well married; to see them again after twelve years was the purpose of his visit. So he himself believed. But in the night, unable to sleep in the overcrowded train, it became clear to him that he was really going for the sake of his childhood, hoping to rediscover something in those old streets: a doorway, a tower, a fountain, anything to induce some joy or some sorrow by which he might recognize himself again. One loses oneself so in life. And then he remembered many things: the little apartment in the Heinrichsgasse with the shiny doorknobs and the dark-coated tiles, the well-cared-for furniture and his parents, those two threadbare beings, standing almost reverently beside it; the hurrying and harassed week-days and the Sundays that were like cleared-out rooms, the rare visitors whom one received laughing and embarrassed, the out-of-tune piano, the old canary, the heirloom armchair in which one might not sit, a name day, an uncle who came from Hamburg, a puppet show, a barrel organ, a children's party and someone calling: 'Klara.'

"The doctor has almost dropped off. They are in a station, lights run by and the listening hammer goes ringing along the wheels. And that is like Klara, Klara. Klara, the doctor muses, now wide awake, who was Klara anyway? And next instant he becomes aware of a face, a child's face with blond, straight hair. Not that he could describe it, but he has a sense of something quiet, helpless, resigned, of a pair of narrow childish shoulders squeezed still more together by a washed-out little dress, and he begins to imagine a face to go with them—but then he knows that he need not imagine it. It is there—or rather, it *was* there —then. So Doctor Lassmann recalls his single playmate Klara, not without effort. Until the day he went to boarding school, at the age of about ten, he shared with her everything that happened to him, little that it was (or was it much?). Klara had no sisters or brothers, and he had as good as none; for his older sisters did not concern themselves with him. But since then he had never asked anyone about her. How was that possible?—He leaned back. She had been a pious child, he still remembered, and then he asked himself: What can have become of her? For a time the thought frightened him that she might have died. An immeasurable dread overcame him in the closely-packed compartment; everything seemed to confirm this assumption: she had been a sickly child, she hadn't been very well off at home, she had often cried; undoubtedly: she is dead. The doctor could not stand it any longer; he disturbed certain of the sleepers, shoving his way between them into the corridor of the car. There he opened a window and gazed out into the blackness with the dancing sparks. That quieted him. And when he returned to the compartment later, despite his uncomfortable position he soon went to sleep.

"The reunion with his two married sisters passed off not without embarrassment. The three had forgotten how far apart, notwithstanding their close relationship, they had always remained, and endeavored for a while to act like brother and sisters. However they soon silently agreed to take refuge behind that polite mediate tone which social intercourse has invented for all occasions.

"It was at the house of his younger sister, whose husband was in particularly comfortable circumstances, a manufacturer with the title of Imperial Councilor; and it was after the fourth course at dinner that the doctor asked:

" 'Tell me, Sophie, what ever became of Klara?'

" 'Klara who?'

" 'I don't remember her name. The little one, you know, a neighbor's daughter, with whom I played as a child.'

" 'Oh, you mean Klara Söllner?'

" 'Söllner, that's it, Söllner. Now I remember: old Söllner was that awful old man—but what of Klara?'

"His sister hesitated. 'She married—and now she lives altogether in retirement.'

" 'Yes,' murmured the Imperial Councilor, and his knife slid rasping across his plate, 'quite retired.'

" 'You know her too?' The doctor turned to his brother-in-law.

" 'Y-ye-es—just slightly; she's pretty well known here, of course.'

"Husband and wife exchanged a look of understanding. The doctor noticed that for some reason they did not care to say more on the subject, and he let it drop.

"The more eagerness to pursue this theme did the Councilor show when the lady of the house had left them to their coffee.

" 'This Klara,' he asked with a sly smile, watching the ash that fell from his cigar into a silver bowl, 'wasn't she supposed to be a quiet child, and homely too?'

"The doctor said nothing. The Councilor moved confidentially closer.

" 'That was a story!—Did you never hear of it?'

" 'But I haven't seen anybody to talk to.'

" 'Talk to?' the Councilor laughed cunningly. 'You could have read it in the papers.'

" 'What?' asked the doctor nervously.

" 'Why, she ran off and left him—' From behind a cloud of smoke the manufacturer discharged this astonishing sentence and waited in unconfined well-being for the effect. But the effect did not seem to please him. He took on a businesslike manner, sat up straight and began to report in another, an injured tone, as it were: 'Well, they had married her to Lehr, of the building council. You wouldn't have known him. Not an old man—my age. Rich, thoroughly respectable, you know, thoroughly respectable. She hadn't a penny and in addition she had no looks, no bringing-up, etc. Still, Lehr didn't want a great lady, just a modest housekeeping wife. But Klara—she was taken into society all over, everybody was kindly disposed towards her —really, they acted—well, you know, she could easily have made a position for herself—but Klara, one day—hardly two years after the wedding, off she goes. Can you imagine: gone. Where? To Italy. A little pleasure trip, not alone, naturally. All that last year we hadn't invited them—as though we had suspected! Lehr, a good friend of mine, a man of honor, a man—'

" 'And Klara?' the doctor broke in, rising.

" 'Oh, yes—well, the chastisement of heaven fell upon her. You see, the man in question—an artist, they say, you know—a casual sort of bird, naturally, just—Well, when they got back from Italy, to Munich: good-bye, and she saw him no more. Now she's sitting there with her child!'

"Doctor Lassmann strode excitedly up and down: 'In Munich?'

" 'Yes, in Munich,' replied the Councilor and also rose. 'They say she's having a pretty miserable time—'

" 'How, miserable?'

" 'Well,' the Councilor gazed at his cigar, 'pecuniarily, and then anyhow—God, what an existence—'

"Suddenly he laid his well-groomed hand on his brother-in-law's shoulder and clucked with pleasure: 'You know they also used to say that she lived on—'

"The doctor turned short about and walked out the door. The Councilor, whose hand had fallen from the other's shoulder, needed ten minutes to recover from his astonishment. Then he went in to his wife and said angrily:

" 'I've always said so, your brother is decidedly queer.'

"And she, who had just dozed off, yawned lazily: 'Oh, Lord yes.'

"A fortnight later the doctor departed. He knew all at once that he must seek his childhood elsewhere. In the Munich directory he found: Klara Söllner, the name of the suburb, Schwabing,[1] the street and number. He announced his coming and drove out. A slender woman greeted him in a room full of light and kindliness.

" 'Georg, and you remember me?'

---

1. *Schwabing*, a suburb of pre-World War II Munich in which many professional people and artists lived.

"The doctor stood still in amazement. At last he said: 'So this is *you*, Klara.'

"She held her calm face with its clear brow quite still, as though she wanted to give him time to recognize her. It took long. Finally the doctor seemed to have found something that proved to him that his old playmate really stood before him. He sought her hand again and pressed it; then slowly let it go and looked about the room. It seemed to contain nothing superfluous. At the window a desk with papers and books, at which Klara must just have been sitting. The chair had been pushed back.

" 'You were writing?' . . . and the doctor felt how silly the question was.

"But Klara answered ingenuously: 'Yes, I'm translating.'

" 'For publication?'

" 'Yes,' Klara said simply, 'for a publishing house.'

"Georg noticed some Italian photographs on the walls. Among them Giorgione's *Concert*.

" 'Are you fond of this?' He stepped nearer to the picture.

" 'And you?'

" 'I have never seen the original; it's in Florence, isn't it?'

" 'In the Pitti.[2] You must go there.'

" 'For the purpose?'

" 'For the purpose.' There was a free and simple serenity about her. The doctor was looking thoughtful.

" 'What's the matter, Georg? Won't you sit down?'

" 'I've been sorry,' he faltered. 'I thought—but'—and the words escaped him suddenly—'but you aren't in the least miserable—!'

"Klara smiled. 'You have heard my story?'

" 'Yes, that is—'

" 'Oh,' she interrupted quickly, as she saw his brow darken, 'it's not people's fault if they speak *differently* of it. The things we experience often cannot be expressed, and any one who insists on telling them nevertheless, is bound to make mistakes—' A pause.

"And the doctor: 'What has made you so kind?'

" 'Everything,' she said softly and warmly. 'But why do you say: kind?'

" 'Because—because you really ought to have grown hard. You were such a weak, helpless child; children of that sort later either grow hard or—'

---

2. *the Pitti*, a palace in Florence which houses a great art collection.

" 'Or they die, you mean. Well, I died too. Oh, I died for many years. From the time I last saw you at home, until—' She reached for something from the table. 'See, this is his picture. It flatters him a little. His face is not so clear-cut, but—nicer, simpler. I'll show you our child in a moment, it's asleep in the next room. It's a boy. Called Angelo, like him. He is away now, traveling, far away.'

" 'And you are all alone?' asked the doctor absently, still absorbed in the photograph.

" 'Yes, I and the child. Isn't that enough? I will tell you how it is. Angelo is a painter. His name is little known; you would never have heard it. Until lately he had been struggling with the world, with his plans, with himself and with me. Yes, with me too; because for a year I've been begging him to travel. I felt how much he needed it. Once he asked jokingly: "Me or a child?" "A child," said I, and then he went.'

" 'And when will he be back?'

" 'When the child can say his name, that's how we arranged it.' The doctor was about to comment, but Klara laughed: 'And as it's a difficult name, it will take a while yet. Angelino won't be two till summer.'

" 'Extraordinary,' said the doctor.

" 'What, Georg?'

" 'How well you understand life. How big you have grown, how young! What have you done with your childhood? We were both such—such helpless children. But that can't be altered or made never to have happened.'

" 'You mean, we ought to have *suffered* from our childhood, by right?'

" 'Yes, I mean just that. From that heavy darkness behind us with which we preserve such feeble, vague relations. There comes a time when we have deposited in it all our firstlings, all beginning, all confidence, the seeds of all that which might perhaps some day come to be. And suddenly we realize: All that has sunk in a deep sea, and we don't even know just when. We never noticed it. As though some one were to collect all his money, and buy a feather with it and stick the feather in his hat: whish!—the first breeze will carry it away. Naturally he arrives home without his feather, and nothing remains for him but to look back and think when it could have flown off.'

" 'You are thinking of that, Georg?'

" 'Not any more. I've given it up. I begin somewhere behind my tenth year, at the point where I stopped praying. The rest doesn't belong to me.'

236   *Germany*

" 'And how is it, then, that you have remembered *me*?'

" 'That is just why I have come to you. You are the only witness to that time. I believed I could find again in you—what I can *not* find in myself. Some gesture, some word, some name that would carry a suggestion—some enlightenment—' The doctor's head sank into his cold, restless hands.

"Frau Klara pondered. 'I remember so little of my childhood, as though there were a thousand lives between. But now that you remind me of it so, something comes back to me. One evening. You came to us, unexpectedly; your parents had gone out, to the theater or something of the sort. Our house was all lit up. My father was expecting a guest, a relative, a distant wealthy relative, if I remember rightly. He was coming from, from—I don't know where, but in any case from some distance. We had already been awaiting him for two hours. The doors were open, the lamps were burning, my mother went over from time to time and smoothed an antimacassar on the sofa, my father stood at the window. Nobody dared sit down for fear of displacing a chair. As you happened to come, you waited with us. We children listened at the door. And the later it grew, the more marvelous a guest did we expect. Yes, we even trembled lest he come before he should have attained that last degree of gloriousness to which with every minute of his not-coming he drew nearer. We were not afraid that he might not appear at all; we knew for certain he would come, but we wanted to leave him time to grow great and mighty.'

"Suddenly the doctor raised his head and said sadly: 'So we both know that—that he *didn't* come. I had not forgotten it either.'

" 'No,' Klara corroborated, 'he didn't come—' And after a pause: 'But it was lovely all the same!'

" 'What?'

" 'Oh, well—the waiting, the many lamps—the stillness—the festive spirit.'

"Something stirred in the next room. Frau Klara excused herself for a moment; and as she came brightly and serenely back, she said: 'We can go in now. He's awake and smiling.— But what was it you wanted to say just now?'

" 'I was just wondering what could have helped you to—to yourself, to this calm possession of yourself. Life certainly hasn't made it easy for you. Evidently something helped you that I haven't got.'

" 'What should that be, Georg?' Klara sat down beside him.

" 'It is strange; when I first remembered you again, one night three weeks ago, on the train, I thought: She was a pious child. And now, since I have seen you, although you are so entirely different from what I had expected—in spite of that, and yet, I would almost say, only the more surely, I feel that what led you through all dangers was your—your piety.'

" 'What do you call piety?'

" 'Well, your relation to God; your love of God, your belief.'

"Frau Klara closed her eyes. 'Love of God? Let me think.' The doctor watched her intently. She seemed to speak her thoughts slowly, as they came to her: 'As a child—did I love God? I don't believe so. Why, I never even—it would have seemed to me insane presumption—that isn't the right word—like the worst sin, to think: He is. As though I had thereby compelled him to be *in me,* in that weak child with the absurdly long arms, in our poor apartment where everything was imitation and false, from the bronze wall-plaques of papier mâché to the wine in the bottles that bore such expensive labels. And later—' Klara made a parrying gesture with her hands, and her eyes closed tighter, as though she feared to see something dreadful through the lids —'why, I would have had to drive him out of me if he had been living in me then. But I knew nothing about him. I had quite forgotten him. I had forgotten *everything.*—Not until I came to Florence, when for the first time in my life I saw, heard, felt, realized and simultaneously learned to be thankful for all those things, did I think of him again. There were traces of him everywhere. In all the pictures I found bits of his smile, the bells were still alive with his voice, and on the statues I recognized the imprints of his hands.'

" 'And you found him there?'

"Klara looked at the doctor with large, happy eyes: 'I felt that he *was*—at some time once *was* . . . why should I have felt *more?* That was already more than enough.'

"The doctor got up and went to the window. From it one could see a stretch of field and the little old village church of Schwabing, and above it sky, no longer quite untouched by evening. Suddenly Doctor Lassmann asked, without turning round:

" 'And now?'

"Receiving no answer, he came quietly back.

" 'Now—' Klara faltered as he stood before her, and then raised her eyes full to his face, 'now I sometimes think: He will be.'

"The doctor took her hand and kept it a moment. His gaze seemed so abstracted, undefined.

" 'What are you thinking of, Georg?'

" 'I'm thinking that it's like that evening once more: *you* are again waiting for the wonderful guest, for God, and know that he will come— And I have joined you by chance—'

"Klara rose, calm and happy. She looked very young. 'Well, this time we'll really wait until it happens.' She said it so joyfully and so simply that the doctor had to smile. And so she led him into the adjoining room, to her child.—"

In this story there is nothing that children may not know. Still, the children have *not* heard it. I have told it only to the dark, to no one else. And the children are afraid of the dark, and run away from it, and if some time they have to stay in it, they press their eyes shut and put their fingers in their ears. But for them also the time will come when they love the dark. From it they will learn my story, and then they will understand it better, too.

Wieland Schmied (1929–   )

ANCIENT CHINESE MAP OF THE WORLD

Translated from the German by
Christopher Middleton

Overshadowed by the sprays
of a cleft tree, white and black,
ramified into a hundred delicate characters,
which we no longer can interpret,
5 the first map of the world lies before us.

We are startled
by the first attempt
to order and to survey
the world with its mountains,
10 rivers and vegetation.

It has always been our hope
to comprehend
what is, and what ceaselessly
presses upon us,
15 in a few simple signs.

But we are startled
when these our own signs
on which we relied,
have become alien to us
20 as the uninterpreted world.

Arthur Schnitzler (1862–1931)

THE BLIND GERONIMO AND HIS BROTHER

Translated from the German by
Harry Steinhauer

THE BLIND GERONIMO got up from the bench and took his guitar, which had been lying ready on the table near his wine glass, in his hand. He had heard the distant roll of the first carriages. Now he groped his way along the well-known path to the open door, and then he went down the narrow wooden steps which ran down in the open air to the covered courtyard. His brother followed him, and both at once took their position near the staircase, their backs turned to the wall, in order to be protected from the cold, wet wind which was blowing through the open gates over the moist, dirty ground.

All the carriages which took the road over the Stelvio Pass had to pass under the gloomy archway of the old inn. For the travelers who wanted to go from Italy to the Tirol, it was the last resting place before the heights. It did not invite one to stay long, for just at this spot the road was fairly level, without views, between bleak elevations. The blind Italian and his brother Carlo were practically at home here in the summer months.

The stagecoach drove in; soon after that other carriages came. Most of the travelers kept their seats, well wrapped in their plaids and coats; others got out and strolled impatiently back and forth between the gates. The weather became worse and worse; a cold rain splashed down. After a series of beautiful days autumn seemed to set in suddenly and all too early.

The blind man sang and accompanied himself on the guitar; he sang in an uneven voice, which sometimes suddenly turned into a shriek, as always when he had been drinking. At times he turned his head upward as though with an expression of futile pleading. But the features of his face, with its black beard-stubble and its bluish lips, remained completely immobile. His older brother stood beside him, almost motionless. When anyone dropped a coin into his hat he nodded thanks and looked into the face of the giver with a swift, almost wild look. But promptly, almost anxiously, he turned his eyes away again and, like his brother, stared into space. It was as if his eyes felt ashamed of the light that was granted them, and of which they could offer no ray to the blind brother.

"Bring me wine," said Geronimo, and Carlo went, obedient as always. While he went up the steps Geronimo began to sing again. He had long stopped listening to his own voice and so he was able to notice what was going on about him. Now he heard two whispering voices quite near him—those of a young man and a young woman. He thought how often these two might have walked back and forth the same way; for in his blindness and in his intoxication it sometimes seemed to him that the same people came over the pass day after day, now from north to south, again from south to north. And so he had known this young couple, too, for a long time.

Carlo came down and handed Geronimo a glass of wine. The blind man raised it to the young couple and said: "To your health, ladies and gentlemen!"

"Thanks," said the young man; but the young woman drew him away, for the blind man made her feel uncomfortable.

Now a carriage with a fairly noisy company drove in: a father, mother, three children, a maid.

"A German family," said Geronimo softly to Carlo.

The father gave each child a coin and each one was allowed to throw his coin into the beggar's hat. Each time Geronimo bowed his head in thanks. The oldest boy looked into the blind man's face with anxious curiosity. Carlo looked at the boy. As always when he saw such children, he had to think that Geronimo had been the same age when the accident through which he had lost his eyesight had happened. For even today, after almost twenty years, he remembered that day with perfect clarity. To this day he could hear in his ear the child's shrill scream with which little Geronimo had sunk on the grass; to this day he saw the sun playing and flickering on the white garden wall and again heard the Sunday bells which had sounded at that very moment. As he had often done, he had been shooting at the ash tree by the wall with his dart; and when he heard the scream he thought at once that he must have hurt his little brother who had just run past. He let the blowpipe slip from his hands, jumped through the window into the garden and rushed over to his little brother, who was lying in the grass, his hands clapped to his face, wailing. The blood was flowing down his right cheek and neck. At the same moment their father came home from the field, through the little garden door, and now both of them kneeled helplessly beside the wailing child. Neighbors hurried over; old woman Vanetti was the first person who succeeded in removing the little boy's hands from his face. Then came the smith, to whom Carlo was apprenticed at that time; he was somewhat adept at medicine, and he saw at once that the right eye was lost. The doctor who came from Poschiavo in the evening couldn't help any more either. In fact he even pointed out the danger for the other eye. And he proved to be right. A year later the world had sunk into night for Geronimo. At first they tried to persuade him that he could be cured later on, and he seemed to believe it. At that time Carlo, who knew the truth, wandered about for days and nights on the highway, between the vineyards, in the forests, and came close to committing suicide. But the ecclesiastic in whom he confided made it clear to him that it was his duty to live and to dedicate his life to his brother. Carlo realized this. He was seized by an immense sympathy. Only when he was with the blind boy, when he could stroke his hair, kiss his forehead, tell him stories, take him for walks in the fields behind the house and between the vineyards did his anguish decrease. Right from the beginning he had neglected his instruction at the smithy because he did not like to be separated from his brother, and later on he could no longer persuade himself to take up his trade again, in spite of the fact that his father urged him to do so and was concerned about him. One day Carlo noticed that Geronimo had completely stopped talking about his misfortune. He soon knew why: the blind boy had realized that he would never again see the sky, the hills, the streets, people, the light.

Now Carlo suffered even more than before, however much he sought to soothe himself with the thought that he had caused the accident quite unintentionally. And sometimes, when he contemplated his brother in the early morning, as he slept beside him, he was seized by such anxiety at the prospect of seeing him awake, that he ran out into the garden, just so that he would not have to be present when the dead eyes seemed, every day, to seek once more the light that was extinguished for them forever. It was at that time that Carlo hit upon the idea of having Geronimo, who had a pleasant voice, continue his musical education. The schoolmaster from Tola, who sometimes came over on Sundays, taught him to play the guitar. At that time, of course, the blind boy had no idea that the newly learned art would one day serve him as a livelihood.

With that sad summer day, misfortune seemed to have moved permanently into old Lagardi's house. The crops failed one year after another; a relative swindled the old man out of a small sum of money which he had saved; and when he fell down with a stroke and died in the open field on a sultry August day, he left nothing but debts. The little property was sold; the two brothers, without a roof and poor, left the village.

Carlo was twenty years old, Geronimo fifteen. At that time the life of begging and wandering began which they had led till today. At first Carlo had thought of finding some occupation which could support both him and his brother; but he did not succeed. Besides Geronimo could find peace nowhere; he always wanted to be on the road.

For twenty years now they had been moving around on the roads and passes, in northern Italy and southern Tirol, always in the place where the densest throng of tourists streamed past.

And even though, after so many years, Carlo no longer felt the burning torment with which the shining of the sun, the sight of a pleasant landscape had formerly always filled him, there was still a steady nagging sympathy in him, constant and unknown to him, like the beating of his heart and his breathing. And he was happy when Geronimo got drunk.

The carriage with the German family had driven away. Carlo sat down, as he liked to do, on the lowest steps of the stairway, but Geronimo remained standing, let his arms hang limply and held his head turned upward.

Maria, the maid, came out of the taproom.

"Did you make a lot today?" she called down.

Carlo did not even turn around. The blind man bent down for his glass, picked it up from the ground and drank it to Maria. She sometimes sat beside him in the taproom in the evening; he also knew that she was beautiful.

Carlo bent forward and looked out toward the highway. The wind was blowing and the rain pelted down so that the rumbling of the approaching carriage was lost in the loud noise. Carlo stood up and once more took his place at his brother's side.

Geronimo began to sing while the carriage, with only one passenger in it, was still driving up. The coachman hurriedly unhitched the horses, then hurried up to the taproom. For a while the tourist remained sitting in his corner, all wrapped up in a gray raincoat; he did not seem to be listening to the singing at all. But after a while he jumped out of the carriage and walked back and forth in great haste, without going far from the carriage. He kept rubbing his hands against each other to warm himself. Only now did he seem to notice the beggars. He took his position opposite them and looked at them for a long time as if he were testing them. Carlo bowed his head slightly as if in greeting. The tourist was a very young person with a pretty, beardless face and restless eyes. After he had stood before the beggars for quite a while, he hurried again to the gate through which he was to leave; and he shook his head in vexation at the sad prospect in the rain and mist.

"Well?" asked Geronimo.

"Nothing yet," replied Carlo. "He'll probably give when he leaves."

The tourist came back again and leaned against the shaft of the carriage. The blind man began to sing. Now the young man seemed suddenly to listen with great interest. The stable hand appeared and hitched the horses up again. And only now, as though he were just remembering, the young man put his hand in his pocket and gave Carlo a franc.

"O thanks, thanks," Carlo said.

The tourist sat down in the carriage and wrapped himself in his coat again. Carlo picked up the glass from the ground and went up the wooden steps. Geronimo went on singing. The tourist leaned out of the carriage and shook his head with an expression that indicated both superiority and sadness. Suddenly something seemed to occur to him and he smiled. Then he said to the blind man, who was standing scarcely two feet from him: "What is your name?"

"Geronimo."

"Well, Geronimo, just don't let anyone cheat you!" At this moment the coachman appeared on the top step of the staircase.

"How do you mean, sir, cheat me?"

"I gave your companion a twenty-franc piece."

"O thank you, thank you, sir."

"Yes; so look out."

"He is my brother, sir, he doesn't cheat me."

The young man hesitated for a while, but while he was still considering, the coachman had mounted his box and whipped up his horses. The young man leaned back with a movement of his head as if he wanted to say: Destiny, take thy course! and the carriage drove off.

The blind man waved lively gestures of gratitude after him with both hands. Now he heard Carlo who was just coming out of the taproom. He called down: "Come Geronimo, it's warm up here, Maria has made a fire."

Geronimo nodded, took his guitar under his arm and felt his way up the stairs by the railing. While he was still on the steps he called: "Let me feel it. It's a long time since I've felt a gold piece."

"What's up?" said Carlo. "What are you talking about?"

Geronimo had reached the top and took his brother's head in both hands, a sign with which he had always expressed joy or tenderness. "Carlo, my dear brother, there really are good people."

"Certainly," said Carlo. "So far we have two lire and thirty centesimi, and here is some Austrian money too, perhaps half-a-lire."

"And twenty francs—and twenty francs," cried Geronimo. "I know it's so!" He staggered into the taproom and sat down heavily on the bench.

"What do you know?" asked Carlo.

"Stop your jokes! Give it to me in my hand! What a long time since I've had a gold coin in my hand!"

"What is it you want? Where am I to get a gold coin? There are two or three lire."

The blind man thumped the table. "Now this is enough, enough! Do you mean to hide it from me?"

Carlo looked at his brother anxiously and in astonishment. He sat down beside him, moved quite close to him and took his arm as though to soothe him: "I'm hiding nothing from you.

How can you believe that? It didn't occur to anyone to give me a gold piece."

"But he told me so."

"Who?"

"Well, the young man who was pacing back and forth."

"What? I don't understand you."

"That's what he told me: 'What's your name?' and then: 'Look out, look out, don't let anyone cheat you.'"

"You must have been dreaming, Geronimo—why this is nonsense."

"Nonsense? But I heard it and my hearing is good. 'Don't let anyone cheat you; I gave him a gold piece . . .' no, this is what he said: 'I gave him a twenty-franc piece.'"

The landlord came in. "Well, what's up between you? Have you given up your business? A coach and four has just driven up."

"Come!" cried Carlo, "come!"

Geronimo sat there. "But why? Why should I come? What use is it to me? When you stand beside me and—"

Carlo touched his arm. "Quiet, come down now!"

Geronimo was silent and obeyed his brother. But on the steps he said: "We'll talk more about this; we'll talk about it."

Carlo did not understand what had happened. Had Geronimo suddenly gone mad? For though he became angry easily, he had never spoken this way before.

Two Englishmen sat in the carriage which had just arrived; Carlo raised his hat to them and the blind man sang. The one Englishman had got out and threw a few coins into Carlo's hat. Carlo said: "Thanks." And then, as though to himself "Twenty *centesimi.*" Geronimo's face remained impassive; he began a new song. The carriage with the two Englishmen drove off.

The brothers went up the stairs silently. Geronimo sat down on the bench; Carlo remained standing by the stove.

"Why don't you speak?" Geronimo asked.

"Well," Carlo replied, "it can only be as I told you." His voice was trembling slightly.

"What did you say?" Geronimo asked.

"Perhaps the man was insane."

"Insane? That would be splendid indeed. If a man says: 'I gave your brother twenty francs,' he's insane.—Eh, and why did he say: 'Don't let anyone cheat you'—eh?"

"Perhaps he wasn't insane either, but there are people who like to make jokes with us poor folk . . ."

"Eh!" Geronimo shrieked, "jokes?—yes, you had to say that

too—I've been waiting for it." He finished the glass of wine which stood before him.

"But Geronimo!" cried Carlo—and he found, in his astonishment, that he was hardly able to talk—"why should I . . . how can you believe . . . ?"

"Why does your voice tremble . . . eh . . . why . . . ?"

"Geronimo, I assure you, I . . ."

"Eh—and I don't believe you. Now you're laughing . . . I know for sure that you're laughing now."

The groom called from below: "Hey, blind man, there are people here."

Quite mechanically the brothers stood up and went down the steps. Two carriages had arrived at the same time, one with three gentlemen, another with an old couple. Geronimo sang; Carlo stood near him, distracted. What could he do? His brother did not believe him! How was this even possible?—And he gave Geronimo, who was singing his songs in a broken voice, an anxious, sidelong look. It seemed to him that he saw thoughts crossing his brow that he had never perceived there before.

The carriage had already left but Geronimo kept on singing. Carlo did not dare to interrupt him. He did not know what to say; he feared that his voice would tremble again. Then there was laughter from above and Maria cried: "Why do you keep on singing? You won't get anything from me."

Geronimo stopped in the middle of a tune; it sounded as if his voice and the strings had snapped at the same time. Then he went up the steps again and Carlo followed him. In the taproom he sat down beside him. What should he do? Nothing else was left for him: he must try once more to enlighten his brother.

"Geronimo," he said, "I swear to you . . . just consider, Geronimo, how can you believe that I . . ."

Geronimo was silent; his dead eyes seemed to look through the window out into the gray mist. Carlo went on: "Well, he needn't have been insane, of course, he may have made a mistake . . . yes, he made a mistake . . ." But he clearly felt that he himself did not believe what he was saying.

Geronimo moved away impatiently. But Carlo kept on talking with sudden animation: "Why should I—you know that I don't eat or drink more than you do, and when I buy a new jacket you know about it . . . what would I need so much money for? What am I to do with it?"

Then Geronimo hissed between his teeth: "Don't lie, I hear how you're lying!"

"I'm not lying, Geronimo, I'm not lying!" said Carlo in fright.

"Eh! have you given it to her already, yes? Or will she get it only later?" Geronimo shrieked.

"Maria?"

"Who else but Maria? Eh, you liar, you thief!" And, as though he didn't want to sit beside him at the table any longer, he thrust his elbow into his brother's side.

Carlo stood up. At first he stared at his brother, then he left the room and went into the courtyard by way of the staircase. With wide open eyes, he looked at the highway which faded before him in brownish mist. The rain had abated. Carlo put his hands into his trouser pockets and went out into the open. He felt as though his brother had driven him away. What had really happened? . . . He couldn't grasp it even now. What kind of a person could that have been? He offers a franc and says it was twenty. He must surely have had some reason for it . . . And Carlo searched his memory: had he somewhere made an enemy of someone, who had now sent another man here to take revenge . . . But as far back as he could think, he had never insulted anyone, had never had a serious quarrel with anyone. For he had done nothing in the last twenty years except to stand around in courtyards and at curbs with his hat in his hand . . . Could it be that someone was angry with him because of a woman? . . . But how long it was since he had had anything to do with one . . . the waitress in La Rosa had been the last one, the previous spring . . . but certainly no one envied him because of her . . . It was incomprehensible! . . . What sort of people could there be out there in that world which he did not know? . . . They came from everywhere . . . what did he know about them? . . . There must have been some reason why this stranger said to Geronimo: "I gave your brother twenty francs . . ." Well yes . . . But what was to be done now? . . . Suddenly it had become obvious that Geronimo distrusted him! . . . This he could not bear! He must do something against it . . . And he hurried back.

When he entered the taproom again Geronimo lay stretched out on the bench and seemed not to notice Carlo's entrance. Maria brought both of them food and drink. They did not say a word during the meal. When Maria cleared off the dishes, Geronimo suddenly gave a laugh and said to her: "What are you going to buy for it?"

"For what?"

"Well, what? A new skirt or earrings?"

"What does he want from me?" she said turning to Carlo.

Meanwhile the courtyard below echoed with heavily loaded vehicles, loud voices reached upstairs, and Maria hurried down. After a few minutes three drivers came and took their places at a table; the landlord went up to them and greeted them. They cursed the bad weather.

"Tonight you'll get snow," one of them said.

The second one told how, ten years ago in the middle of August, he had been snowed in on the pass and had almost been frozen. Maria sat down beside them. The groom came up, too, and inquired about his parents who lived down below, in Bormio.

Now another carriage with passengers came. Geronimo and Carlo went down, Geronimo sang, Carlo held out his hat and the tourists gave their alms. Geronimo now seemed quite calm. He sometimes asked: "How much?" and nodded lightly with his head to Carlo's answers. Meanwhile Carlo himself tried to gather his thoughts together. But he always had the obscure feeling that something terrible had happened and that he was quite helpless.

When the brothers went up the steps again, they heard the drivers upstairs talking at the same time and laughing. The youngest one called out to Geronimo: "Sing something for us too, we'll pay you!—Won't we?" said he turning to the others.

Maria, who was just coming with a bottle of red wine, said: "Don't start anything with him today, he's in a bad mood."

Instead of giving an answer Geronimo took his position in the middle of the room and began to sing. When he had finished the drivers applauded.

"Come here, Carlo!" one of them cried, "We'll throw our money into your hat too, like the people down below." And he took a small coin and held up his hand as though he would drop it into the hat which Carlo stretched out to him. At that point the blind man seized the driver's arm and said: "Better give it to me, better to me. It might fall outside."

"How do you mean outside?"

"Well, in Maria's lap."

They all laughed, the landlord and Maria too, only Carlo stood there motionless. Geronimo had never made such jokes before . . .

"Sit down with us," the drivers cried. "You're a merry fellow." And they moved closer together, to make room for Geronimo. The general talk grew louder and louder and more and more confused. Geronimo joined in, louder and merrier than usual, and did not stop drinking. When Maria came in again, he wanted to draw her to him; one of the drivers said laughing: "Can you possibly think she's beautiful? Why she's an old, ugly woman."

But the blind man drew Maria down on his lap. "You're all stupid," he said. "Do you think I need my eyes to see? I even know where Carlo is now—eh—he's standing there by the stove, has his hands in his pants pockets and is laughing."

They all looked at Carlo, who was leaning against the stove with his mouth open, and now really twisted his face into a grin, as if he mustn't make a liar out of his brother.

The groom came in; if the drivers wanted to reach Bormio before dark, they had to hurry. They stood up and took a noisy leave. The two brothers were alone again in the taproom. It was the hour when they sometimes took a nap. The whole inn fell into a calm, as always at this time during the first afternoon hours. Geronimo, with his head on the table, seemed to be sleeping. At first Carlo walked back and forth, then he sat down on the bench. He was very tired. It seemed to him that he was experiencing a heavy dream. He had to think of all sorts of things—of yesterday, the day before yesterday and all the days that came before, and especially of warm summer days and white highways over which he was accustomed to walk with his brother—and it was all so far away and unintelligible, as if it could never be the same again.

In the late afternoon the stagecoach from Tirol came and soon afterward, at brief intervals, carriages which were taking the same road to the south. The brothers had to go down into the courtyard four more times. When they went up for the last time twilight had fallen and the little oil lamp which hung down from the wooden ceiling was sputtering. In came some laborers who worked in a nearby stone quarry and had put up their wooden huts a few hundred feet below the inn. Geronimo sat down beside them; Carlo remained at his table alone. He felt as if his loneliness had already lasted a long time. He heard Geronimo over there telling about his childhood, talking loudly, almost shouting: that he still remembered everything quite well; persons and things that he had seen with his eyes: his father working in the field, the little garden with the ash tree beside the wall, the low little house that belonged to them, the shoemaker's two little daughters, the vineyard behind the church, in fact, even his own child's face looking back at him from the mirror. How often Carlo had heard all this. Today he could not bear it. It sounded different than usual: every word that Geronimo spoke acquired a new sense and seemed to turn against him. He stole out and returned to the highway, which was now quite dark. The rain had stopped, the air was very cold, and the idea of going on appeared almost enticing to Carlo —to go on and on, deep into the darkness, and in the end to lie down somewhere in a ditch, fall asleep, not to awake again. Suddenly he heard the rumbling of a carriage and caught sight of the gleam of light from two lamps which came nearer and nearer. In the carriage that rode by were two gentlemen. One of them, with a narrow, beardless face, started back in fright as Carlo's face emerged out of the darkness in the light of the lamps. Carlo, who had stopped, raised his hat. The carriage and lights vanished. Carlo stood in deep darkness again. Suddenly he started. For the first time in his life he was afraid of the dark. He felt as if he couldn't bear it one minute longer. In his dulled senses, the horror he felt with himself mingled strangely with a tormented sympathy for his blind brother and drove him home.

When he entered the taproom he saw the two tourists who had driven past him before, sitting at a table over a bottle of red wine and talking with each other very earnestly. They scarcely looked up when he entered.

At the other table Geronimo sat among the workers as before.

"Where have you been, Carlo?" the landlord said to him when he was still at the door. "Why do you leave your brother alone?"

"Why, what's wrong?" asked Carlo in fright.

"Geronimo is treating people. It makes no difference to me, of course, but you should consider that bad times will soon be coming again."

Carlo quickly stepped up to his brother and grasped his arm. "Come," he said.

"What do you want?" Geronimo shrieked.

"Come to bed," said Carlo.

"Leave me, leave me! I earn the money, I can do what I want with my money—eh—you certainly can't pocket it all. I suppose you think he gives it all to me. Oh no. I'm only a blind man. But there are people—there are people who tell me: 'I gave your brother twenty-francs.'"

The laborers laughed loudly.

"It's enough," said Carlo, "come." And he drew his brother to him, almost dragged him up the steps to the bleak attic room where they had their bed. All the way up Geronimo shrieked:

"Yes, now it's come to light, yes, now I know it! Oh, just wait. Where is she? Where's Maria? Or are you putting it in her bank account?—Eh, I sing for you, I play the guitar, you live on me —and you're a thief!" He fell down on his straw sack.

From the hall a weak light shone in; over there the door to the only guest room in the inn stood open, and Maria was preparing the beds for the night. Carlo stood before his brother and saw him lying there with his bloated face, his bluish lips, his damp hair clinging to his forehead, looking many years older than he was. And he slowly began to understand. The blind man's distrust could not date from today; it must have slumbered in him for a long time, and he had only lacked the occasion, perhaps the courage, to express it. And everything that Carlo had done for him had been in vain; in vain the remorse, in vain the sacrifice of his whole life. What was he to do now? Should he continue to lead him through the eternal night, on and on, day after day, who knows for how long, caring for him, begging for him, and having no other reward for it except distrust and abuse? If his brother took him for a thief, then any stranger could serve him as well or even better. Truly, to leave him alone, to separate from him forever—that would be the wisest thing. Then Geronimo would indeed have to realize his injustice, for he would learn only then what it means to be cheated and robbed, to be lonely and wretched. And he himself—what should he do? Well, he really wasn't old yet; if he was by himself, he could still do many sorts of things. As a hired hand, at least he would get his keep anywhere. But while these thoughts went through his head, his eyes were fixed steadily on his brother. And suddenly he saw him before him sitting alone on a stone at the side of a road bathed in sunlight, staring with his wide open, white eyes at the sky which could not blind him, stretching his hands out into the night that was always about him. And he felt that, just as the blind man had no one else in the world except him, so he too had no one else except this brother. He understood that the love for this brother was the whole content of his life, and knew for the first time with complete clarity: only the belief that the blind man returned this love and had forgiven him had permitted him to bear all the misery so patiently. He could not renounce this hope all at once. He felt that he needed his brother just as much as his brother him. He could not, he did not want to abandon him. He either had to endure his distrust or find a means of convincing the blind man of the baseless nature of his suspicion . . . Yes, if he could somewhere procure the gold coin! If he could tell the blind man tomorrow morning: "I only kept it so that you wouldn't spend it on drink with the laborers —so that people wouldn't steal it from you" . . . or anything else at all . . .

Steps were approaching on the wooden staircase; the tourists were going to bed. Suddenly the idea flashed through his mind: to knock at their door, tell the strangers the true story of today's occurrences and to ask them for the twenty francs. But he knew at once: that was completely hopeless! They wouldn't even believe the whole story. And he now remembered how the pale man had shrunk away in fright when he, Carlo, had suddenly appeared in the darkness in front of the carriage.

He stretched out on the straw sack. It was quite dark in the room. Now he heard the laborers going down the wooden steps with heavy tread, talking loudly. Soon after that both gates were locked. The servant went up and down the stairs once more, then all was quite still. Carlo now heard only Geronimo's snoring. Soon his thoughts became confused in incipient dreams. When he awoke, there was still deep darkness about him. He looked at the spot where the window was; when he strained his eyes, he perceived there, in the center of the impenetrable black, a deep gray rectangle. Geronimo was still sleeping the heavy sleep of the intoxicated. And Carlo thought of the day that was tomorrow; and he shuddered. He thought of the night after this day, of the day after this night, of the future which lay before him, and horror filled him at the loneliness that faced him. Why had he not been more courageous in the evening? Why had he not gone to the strangers and asked them for the twenty francs? Perhaps they might have had pity on him after all. And yet—perhaps it was good that he had not asked them. Yes, why was it good? . . . He sat up suddenly and he felt his heart beating. He knew why it was good: if they had refused him, he would have remained an object of suspicion to them all the same—but now . . . He stared at the gray spot, which began to shine faintly . . . What had gone through his head against his own will, was impossible of course, completely impossible! . . . The door over there was locked—and besides: they could wake up . . . Yes, there—the gray, shining spot in the middle of the darkness was the new day—

Carlo stood up, as if he were drawn to that place, and touched the cold window pane with his forehead. Why had he really got up? To think it over? . . . To try it? . . . Try what? . . . It was impossible, of course—and besides it was a crime. A crime? What do twenty francs mean to such people who travel a thousand miles for their pleasure? They wouldn't even notice that it was missing . . . He went to the door and opened it softly. Facing him was the other door, to be reached by taking two steps, locked. On a nail in the jamb, articles of clothing were hanging. Carlo moved his hand over them . . . Yes, if people left their wallets in their pockets, life would be very simple; then, soon, no one would have to go begging any more . . . But the pockets were empty. Well, what was there left to do? Back to his room again, on the straw sack. Perhaps there really was a better way of procuring twenty francs—less dangerous and more honest. If he really held back a few centesimi from the alms every time, until he had saved up twenty francs, and then bought the gold coin . . . But how long would that take—months, perhaps a year. Oh, if only he had courage! He was still standing in the hall. He looked over toward the door . . . What sort of line was that which fell vertically to the floor from above? Was it possible? The door was ajar, not locked? . . . but why was he astonished at that? The door had not been locked for months. And why should it? He remembered: this summer people had slept here only three times—artisans twice, and once a tourist who had hurt his foot. The door doesn't lock —now he only needs courage—yes, and luck. Courage? The worst that can happen to him is that the two men will wake up, and then he can always find an excuse. He peers through the crack into the room.

It is still so dark that he can just perceive the mere outlines of two figures lying on the beds. He listens: they are breathing calmly and evenly. Carlo opens the door lightly and, without a sound, walks into the room in his bare feet. The two beds stand lengthwise against the same wall opposite the window. In the center of the room is a table; Carlo steals up to it. He runs his hand over its surface and feels a bunch of keys, a pen knife, a little book—nothing more . . . Well, of course! . . . That he could even imagine they would lay their money on the table! Ah, now he can get out at once! . . . And yet, perhaps all that is needed is one good snatch and it's done . . . And he approaches the bed near the door; here on the easy chair something is lying—he feels for it—it's a revolver . . . Carlo starts . . . Wouldn't it be better to take possession of it right now? Why does this man have a revolver lying in readiness? If he wakes up and notices him . . . But no, he would just say: It's three o'clock, sir, time to get up . . . And he lets the revolver lie there.

And he steals deeper into the room. Here on the other easy chair, among the linen . . . Heavens! that's it . . . that is a wallet—he holds it in his hand . . . At this moment he hears a slight creaking. With a swift movement he stretches out full length at the foot of the bed . . . Again this creaking—heavy breathing—clearing of the throat—then silence again, deep silence. Carlo remains lying on the floor, the wallet in his hand, waiting. Nothing stirs any more. The dawn is already casting its pale light into the room. Carlo does not dare to stand up, but crawls forward on the floor to the door which is open far enough to let him through; he crawls on, out into the hall, and only here does he slowly get to his feet, taking a deep breath. He opens the wallet; it is divided into three compartments: at the left and right there are only small silver coins. Now Carlo opens the middle part, which is also closed by a clasp, and feels three twenty-franc pieces. For a moment he thinks of taking two of them, but he quickly rejects this temptation, takes out only one gold piece and closes the wallet. Then he kneels down, looks through the crack into the room in which there is complete silence again, and then he shoves the wallet forward so that it glides under the second bed. When the stranger awakes he will have to believe that it fell down from the chair. Carlo rises slowly. Then the floor creaks slightly and at the same moment he hears a voice from inside: "What is it? What's up?" Carlo takes two swift steps backwards, holding his breath, and slips into his own room.

He is safe and listens . . . Once more the bed over there creaks and then all is silent. Between his fingers he holds the gold piece. He has succeeded—succeeded. He has the twenty francs and he can say to his brother: "Do you see now that I'm not a thief?" And they will set out on the road this very day— towards the south, to Bormio, then through the Valtellina . . . then to Tirano . . . to Edolo . . . to Breno . . . to Lake Iseo like last year . . . This will be in no way suspicious, for the day before yesterday he himself had told the landlord: "In a few days we're going down."

It gets brighter all the time; the whole room lies before him in a gray twilight. Ah, if only Geronimo would wake up soon. It's so nice to hike in the early morning. They will set out even before sunrise. A "good morning" to the landlord, to the servant and Maria too, and then off, off . . . And only when they are two hours' distant, near the valley, will he tell Geronimo.

Geronimo stirs and stretches. Carlo calls to him: "Geronimo."

"Well, what's up?" And he supports himself with both his hands and sits up.

"Geronimo, we'll get up."

"Why?" And he fixes his dead eyes on his brother. Carlo knows that Geronimo now remembers the event of yesterday, but he also knows that he will not utter a syllable about it until he is drunk again.

"It's cold, Geronimo, let's leave. It won't improve this year any more; I think we'll go. By noon we can be in Boladore."

Geronimo got up. The sounds of the waking house became audible. Down in the courtyard the landlord was talking to the servant. Carlo got up and went down. He was always up early and often went out on the highway when it was still twilight. He went over to the landlord and said: "We want to take leave."

"Ah, are you leaving today?" asked the landlord.

"Yes. The cold is getting too bad now, when you stand in the yard and the wind blows through it."

"Well, my regards to Baldetti when you get down to Bormio, and tell him not to forget to send me the oil."

"Yes, I'll give him your regards. And—for last night's bed." He put his hand into his bag.

"Never mind, Carlo," said the landlord. "I'll present the twenty centesimi to your brother; after all, I've listened to him too. Good morning."

"Thanks," said Carlo. "For that matter, we're not in that much of a hurry. We'll see you again when you come back from the huts; Bormio will still be in the same place, won't it?" He laughed and went up the wooden steps.

Geronimo stood in the middle of the room and said: "Well, I'm ready to go."

"Right away," said Carlo.

Out of an old chest that stood in a corner of the room he took their few belongings and packed them into a bundle. Then he said: "A beautiful day, but very cold."

"I know," said Geronimo. They both left the bedroom.

"Go softly," said Carlo, "the two men who came last night are sleeping here." They went down cautiously. "The landlord sends you his regards," said Carlo; "he didn't charge us the twenty centesimi for tonight. Now he's out by the huts and won't be back for two hours. But we'll see him again next year."

Geronimo did not reply. They went out on the highway which lay in the twilight before them. Carlo took his brother's left arm and they both went down towards the valley silently. After a short stroll they were already at the spot where the road begins to run on in sweeping turns. Mists rose up towards them, and the heights above them seemed as though swallowed up by the clouds. And Carlo thought: now I'll tell him.

But Carlo did not say a word; he took the gold coin out of his pocket and handed it to his brother; the latter took it between the fingers of his right hand, then he touched it to his cheek and forehead, finally he nodded. "I knew it," he said.

"Is that so?" Carlo replied, and looked at Geronimo in surprise.

"Even if the stranger had told me nothing, I would have known it anyhow."

"Is that so?" said Carlo helplessly. "But you do understand why up there—before the others—I was afraid that you would spend all of it at once. And see, Geronimo, it is really time, I thought to myself, that you should buy yourself a new coat and a shirt and shoes too, I think; that's why I—"

The blind man shook his head vehemently. "What for?" And he ran his one hand over his coat. "Good enough, warm enough; now we'll get to the south."

Carlo did not understand why Geronimo did not seem to be glad at all, why he did not apologize. And he went on: "Geronimo, didn't I do right? Why aren't you glad? Now we have it, don't we? Now we have the whole of it. If I'd told you about it up there who knows . . . Oh, it's good that I didn't tell you—for sure!"

Then Geronimo shrieked: "Stop lying, Carlo, I have enough of that."

Carlo stopped and released his brother's arm. "I'm not lying."

"I know quite well that you're lying! . . . You're always lying! . . . You've lied a hundred times already! . . . You wanted to keep this one for yourself too, but you got scared, that's what it is."

Carlo lowered his head and did not reply. He took the blind man's arm again and went on with him. It hurt him that Geronimo talked this way; but he was really astonished at not being sadder.

The mists parted. After a long silence Geronimo spoke: "It's getting warm." He said it indifferently, casually, as he had said it a hundred times before, and Carlo felt at this moment: nothing had changed for Geronimo. For Geronimo, he had always been a thief.

"Are you hungry yet?" he asked.

Geronimo nodded; at the same time he took a piece of cheese and bread out of his jacket pocket and ate it. And they went on.

The stagecoach from Bormio met them; the coachman called to them: "Going down already?" Then other carriages came too, all going up.

"Air from the valley," said Geronimo, and at the same moment, after a sudden turn, the Valtellina lay at their feet.

Truly—nothing has changed, Carlo thought . . . Now I've even stolen for him—and this too has been for nothing.

The mists below them became thinner all the time; the light of the sun tore holes in them. And Carlo thought: "Perhaps it wasn't really wise to leave the inn so quickly . . . The wallet is lying under the bed . . . that is certainly suspicious." But how little all that mattered! What other evil could befall him? His brother, the light of whose eyes he had destroyed, thought himself robbed by him and had thought so for years and will always think so—what other evil could befall him?

There below them the great white hotel lay as though bathed in morning splendor, and deeper below them, where the valley begins to broaden, the village stretched out in a long line. The two went on silently and all the time Carlo's hand lay on the blind man's arm. They went past the park of the hotel, and Carlo saw guests in light summer clothes sitting on the terrace and eating breakfast. "Where do you want to rest?" Carlo asked.

"Well, in the *Eagle*, as always."

When they reached the little inn at the end of the village, they went in. They sat down in the taproom and ordered wine.

"What are you doing here so early?" asked the landlord.

Carlo was a little frightened at this question. "But is it so early? The tenth or eleventh of September, isn't it?"

"Last year it was certainly much later when you came down."

"It's so cold up there," said Carlo. "Last night we froze. Oh yes, I'm to tell you you mustn't forget to send the oil up."

The air in the taproom was heavy and sultry. A strange uneasiness befell Carlo; he very much wanted to be in the open air again, on the great highway which leads to Tirano, to Edolo, to Lake Iseo, everywhere, far away. Suddenly he stood up.

"Are we going already?" asked Geronimo.

"Don't we want to be in Boladore at noon today? The carriages stop at the *Stag* for their midday rest; it's a good place."

And they went. The barber Benozzi stood in front of his shop smoking. "Good morning," he cried. "Well, how does it look up there? I suppose it snowed last night?"

"Yes, yes," said Carlo, hastening his steps.

The village lay behind them, the road stretched white between meadows and vineyards, along the murmuring river. The sky was blue and still. "Why did I do it?" Carlo thought. He gave the blind man a sidelong glance. "Does his face look any different than usual? He always thought so—I've always been alone—and he has always hated me." And he felt as if he were walking on under a heavy burden which he would never be permitted to throw off his shoulders, and as if he could see the night through which Geronimo walked at his side, while the sun lay shining on all the roads.

And they went on, walked, walked for hours. From time to time Geronimo sat down on a milestone, or they both leaned against the railing of a bridge to rest. Again they walked through a village. In front of the inn stood carriages; tourists had gotten out and were walking back and forth; but the two beggars did not stay. Again, they went out onto the open highway. The sun rose higher and higher; midday must be near. It was a day like a thousand others.

"The tower of Boladore," said Geronimo. Carlo looked up. He was astonished how exactly Geronimo could calculate distances: the tower of Boladore had really appeared on the horizon. Someone was coming toward them from a fairly long distance away. It seemed to Carlo that the man had been sitting by the road and had suddenly stood up. The figure came closer. Now Carlo saw that it was a gendarme, the kind he met so often on the highway. Still, Carlo felt a slight tremor. But when the man came closer he recognized him and was calmed. It was Pietro Tenelli; only last May the two beggars had sat beside him in Ragazzi's inn in Morignone, and he had told them a gruesome story of how he had once almost been stabbed by a tramp.

"Someone has stopped," said Geronimo.

"Tenelli, the gendarme," said Carlo.

Now they had come up to him.

"Good morning, Mr. Tenelli," said Carlo and stopped before him.

"That's the way it is," said the gendarme. "For the present I must take you both to the station at Boladore."

"Eh!" cried the blind man.

Carlo turned pale. "But how is this possible?" he thought. "But it can't have anything to do with this. They can't know about it down here yet."

"It seems to be on your way, doesn't it?" the gendarme laughed. "It doesn't really matter to you if you come along with me."

"Why don't you say anything, Carlo?" Geronimo asked.

"Oh yes, I'm talking . . . Please, gendarme, how is it possible . . . what are we supposed to . . . or rather, what am I supposed to . . . really, I don't know . . ."

"That's the way it is. Perhaps you're really innocent. What do I know? Anyway we got a telegraphic report at the station to stop you because you are suspected, strongly suspected, of having stolen money from the people up there. Well, it's possible, of course, that you're innocent. So come on."

"Why don't you say anything, Carlo?" asked Geronimo.

"I'm talking—oh yes, I'm talking . . ."

"Well, come on! What sense is there of stopping on the road? The sun is burning. In an hour we'll be on the spot. On with you."

Carlo touched Geronimo's arm as always, and so they went on slowly, the gendarme behind them.

"Carlo, why don't you talk?" Geronimo asked again.

"But what do you want, Geronimo, what am I to say? Everything will come to light; I don't know myself . . ."

And it went through his head: shall I explain it to him before we stand before the Court? . . . It won't do, I fear. The gendarme is listening to us . . . Well, what does it matter? Before the Court I'll tell the truth, of course. "Your Honor," I'll say: "This is no theft like any other. It was this way, you must know . . ." And now he strove to find the words with which he could present the matter to the Court clearly and intelligibly. "Yesterday a gentleman was riding over the pass . . . he may have been a madman—or he was only mistaken after all . . . and this man . . ."

But what nonsense! Who will believe it? They won't even let him talk that long.—No one can believe this stupid story . . . not even Geronimo believes it . . .—And he gave him a sidelong glance. As usual, the blind man's head was moving rhythmically up and down as he walked, but his face was motionless and his empty eyes stared into the air. And Carlo suddenly knew what sort of thoughts were racing behind this brow . . . "That's the way things are," Geronimo must probably be thinking, "Carlo steals not only from me, he steals from other people, too . . . Well, he's lucky, he has eyes that see and he's making use of them . . ."—Yes, that's what Geronimo is thinking, I'm quite certain . . . And also the fact that they will find no money on me can't help me,—not before the Court, not before Geronimo. They'll lock me up and him, too . . . Yes, him just as much as me, for he has the coin, of course. And he could not think any more, he felt so very confused. It seemed to him that he understood nothing more of the whole matter, and he knew only one thing: that he would be glad to be put under arrest for a year . . . or for ten, if only Geronimo knew that he had become a thief for him alone.

And suddenly Geronimo stopped, so that Carlo, too, had to stop.

"Well, what's wrong?" the gendarme said peevishly. "Go on, go on." But then he saw in astonishment that the blind man dropped his guitar on the ground, raised his two arms and groped for his brother's cheeks with both hands. Then he brought his lips close to Carlo's mouth, who at first didn't know what was happening, and kissed him.

"Are you two crazy?" the gendarme asked. "Keep going, keep going. I have no wish to roast."

Geronimo picked up his guitar from the ground, without saying a word. Carlo drew a deep breath and again laid his hand on his blind brother's arm. Was it really possible? His brother was no longer angry with him? He finally realized—? And dubiously he gave him a sidelong glance.

"Go on!" the gendarme roared. "Will you . . . !" And he gave Carlo a punch between the ribs.

And Carlo, guiding the blind man's arm with firm pressure, went forward again. He took a much faster pace than before. For he saw Geronimo smile in that gentle, happy way, which he had not seen in him since his childhood. And Carlo smiled, too. He felt as if nothing bad could happen to him now—neither before the Court, nor anywhere else in the world.—He had found his brother again . . . No, he had him for the first time . . .   ■

Ernst Stadler (1883–1914)

SMALL TOWN

Translated from the German by

Christopher Middleton

The many narrow alleys that cut across
    the long through mainstreet
All run into the country.
    Everywhere the green begins.
5 Everywhere the sky pours in and fragrance of trees
    and the strong scent of ploughland.
Everywhere the town stops
    in a moist magnificence of pastures,

And through the grey slit between
10   low roofs hills lean
With vines that climb over them and shine
    with bright supporting poles in the sunlight.
Still higher the pinewood closes in: like a thick dark
    Wall to border on the red rejoicing
15 of the sandstone church.

At nightfall when the factories close
    the mainstreet is filled with people.
They walk slowly
    or in the middle of an alley they stop and stand.
20 They are blackened with work and engine soot.
    But their eyes uphold
Earth still, the tough power of the soil
    and the festive light of the fields.

"Small Town" by Ernst Stadler, translated by Christopher Middleton, from MODERN GERMAN POETRY 1910–1960, edited by Michael Hamburger and Christopher Middleton. Reprinted by permission of Grove Press, Inc., Verlag Heinrich Ellermann and MacGibbon & Kee. Copyright © 1962 by Michael Hamburger and Christopher Middleton.

Franz Baermann Steiner
(1909–1952)

KAFKA IN ENGLAND.

Translated from the German by

Michael Hamburger

Neither via Belsen,[1] nor as a maid of all work
The stranger came, by no means a refugee.
And yet the case was a sad one:
His nationality was in doubt,
5 His religion occasioned lisping embarrassment.

"Have you read Kafka?" [2] asks Mrs. Brittle at breakfast.
"He's rather inescapable and quite fundamental, I feel."
"Have you read Kafka?" asks Mr. Tooslick at tea,
"Then you'll understand the world much better—
10 Though nothing in him is real."
Miss Diggs says: "Is that so?
I thought that was reactionary. Don't you?"
Only little Geoffrey Piltzman
Dreams: "Who?

15 "I mean, who does well out of this,
They must be dead, after all,
I mean those people in Prague—well, no matter what
name . . ."
Yet the glory of him shines through the gateway all the same.

"Kafka in England" by Franz Baermann Steiner, translated by Michael Hamburger. Reprinted by permission of Grove Press, Inc., MacGibbon & Kee, and Dr. H. G. Adler. Copyright © 1962 by Michael Hamburger and Christopher Middleton.
1. *Belsen,* World War II German concentration camp located 25 miles northeast of Hanover, on the Aller River. Prisoners of Belsen were liberated by the British Second Army on April 15, 1945. Steiner probably chose this reference because Kafka was Jewish. 2. *Kafka.* See selection beginning on page 159.

Stefan Zweig (1881–1942)

THE
INVISIBLE
COLLECTION

Translated from the German by
Eden and Cedar Paul

AT THE FIRST JUNCTION beyond Dresden, an elderly gentleman entered our compartment, smiled genially to the company, and gave me a special nod, as if to an old acquaintance. Seeing that I was at a loss, he mentioned his name. Of course I knew him! He was one of the most famous connoisseurs and art dealers in Berlin. Before the war, I had often purchased autographs and rare books at his place. He took the vacant seat opposite me, and for a while we talked of matters not worth relating. Then, changing the conversation, he explained the object of the journey from which he was returning. It had, he said, been one of the strangest of his experiences in the thirty-seven years he had devoted to the occupation of art-pedlar. Enough introduction. I will let him tell the story in his own words, without using quote marks—to avoid the complication of wheels within wheels.

You know (he said) what has been going on in my trade since the value of money began to diffuse into the void like gas. War-profiteers have developed a taste for old masters (Madonnas and so on), for incunabula, for ancient tapestries. It is difficult to satisfy their craving; and a man like myself, who prefers to keep the best for his own use and enjoyment, is hard put to it not to have his house stripped bare. If I let them, they would buy the cuff links from my shirts and the lamp from my writing table. Harder and harder to find wares to sell. I'm afraid the term "wares" may grate upon you in this connexion, but you must excuse me. I have picked it up from customers of the new sort. Evil communications . . . Through use and wont I have come to look upon an invaluable book from one of the early Venetian presses much as the philistine looks upon an overcoat that cost so or so many hundred dollars, and upon a sketch by Guercino as animated by nothing more worthy of reverence than the transmigrated soul of a banknote for a few thousand francs.

Impossible to resist the greed of these fellows with money to burn. As I looked round my place the other night, it seemed to me that there was so little left of any real value that I might as well put up the shutters. Here was a fine business which had come down to me from my father and my grandfather; but the shop was stocked with rubbish which, before 1914, a street-trader would have been ashamed to hawk upon a handcart.

In this dilemma, it occurred to me to flutter the pages of our old ledgers. Perhaps I should be put on the track of former customers who might be willing to resell what they had bought in prosperous days. True, such a list of sometime purchasers has considerable resemblance to a battlefield laden with the corpses of the slain; and in fact I soon realized that most of those who had purchased from the firm when the sun was shining were dead or would be in such low water that it was probable they must have sold anything of value among their possessions. However, I came across a bundle of letters from a man who was presumably the oldest yet alive—if he was alive. But he was so old that I had forgotten him, since he had bought nothing after the great explosion in the summer of 1914. Yes, very, very old. The earliest letters were dated more than half a century back, when my grandfather was head of the business. Yet I could not recall having had any personal relationships with him during the thirty-seven years in which I had been an active worker in the establishment.

All indications showed that he must have been one of those antediluvian eccentrics, a few of whom survive in German provincial towns. His writing was copperplate, and every item in his orders was underlined in red ink. Each price was given in words as well as figures, so that there could be no mistake. These peculiarities, and his use of torn-out fly-leaves as writing paper, enclosed in a scratch assortment of envelopes, hinted at the penuriousness of a confirmed backwoodsman. His signature was always followed by his style and title in full: "Forest Ranger and Economic Councillor, Retired; Lieutenant, Retired; Holder of the Iron Cross First Class." Since he was obviously a veteran of the war of 1870–1871, he must by now be close on eighty.

For all his cheese-paring and for all his eccentricities, he had manifested exceptional shrewdness, knowledge, and taste as collector of prints and engravings. A careful study of his orders, which had at first totalled very small sums indeed, disclosed that in the days when a taler could still pay for a pile of lovely German woodcuts, this country bumpkin had got together a collection of etchings and the like outrivalling the widely trumpeted acquisitions of war profiteers. Merely those which, in the course of decades, he had bought from us for trifling sums would be worth a large amount of money today; and I had no reason to suppose that he had failed to pick up similar bargains elsewhere. Was his collection dispersed? I was too familiar with what had been going on in the art trade since the date of his last purchase not to feel confident that such a collection could scarcely have changed hands entire without my getting wind of the event. If he was dead, his treasures had probably remained intact in the hands of his heirs.

The affair seemed so interesting that I set forth next day (yesterday evening) on a journey to one of the most out-of-the-way towns in Saxony. When I left the tiny railway station and strolled along the main street, it seemed to me impossible that anyone inhabiting one of these gimcrack houses, furnished in a way with which you are doubtless familiar, could possibly own a full set of magnificent Rembrandt etchings together with an unprecedented number of Dürer woodcuts and a complete collection of Mantegnas. However, I went to the post office to inquire, and was astonished to learn that a sometime Forest Ranger and Economic Councillor of the name I mentioned was still living. They told me how to find his house, and I will admit that my heart beat faster than usual as I made my way thither. It was well before noon.

The connoisseur of whom I was in search lived on the second floor of one of those jerry-built houses which were run up in such numbers by speculators during the sixties of the last century. The first floor was occupied by a master tailor. On the second landing to the left was the name-plate of the manager of the local post office, while the porcelain shield on the right-hand door bore the name of my quarry. I had run him to earth! My ring was promptly answered by a very old, white-haired woman wearing a black lace cap. I handed her my card and asked whether the master was at home. With an air of suspicion she glanced at me, at the card, and then back at my face once more. In this God-forsaken little town a visit from an inhabitant of the metropolis was a disturbing event. However, in as friendly a tone as she could muster, she asked me to be good enough to wait a minute or two in the hall, and vanished through a doorway. I heard whispering, and then a loud, hearty, masculine voice: "Herr Rackner from Berlin, you say, the famous dealer in antiquities? Of course I shall be delighted to see him." Thereupon the old woman reappeared and invited me to enter.

I took off my overcoat, and followed her. In the middle of the cheaply-furnished room was a man standing up to receive me. Old but hale, he had a bushy moustache and was wearing a semi-military, frogged smoking jacket. In the most cordial way, he held out both hands towards me. But though this gesture was spontaneous and nowise forced, it was in strange contrast with the stiffness of his attitude.

He did not advance to meet me, so that I was compelled (I must confess I was a trifle piqued) to walk right up to him before I could shake. Then I noticed that his hand, too, did not seek mine, but was waiting for mine to clasp it. At length I guessed what was amiss. He was blind.

Ever since I was a child I have been uncomfortable in the presence of the blind. It embarrasses me, produces in me a sense of bewilderment and shame to encounter anyone, who is thoroughly alive, and yet has not the full use of his senses. I feel as if I were taking an unfair advantage, and I was keenly conscious of this sensation as I glanced into the fixed and sightless orbs beneath the bristling white eyebrows. The blind man, however, did not leave me time to dwell upon this discomfort. He exclaimed, laughing with boisterous delight:

"A red-letter day, indeed! Seems almost a miracle that one of the big men of Berlin should drop in as you have done. There's need for us provincials to be careful, you know, when a noted dealer such as yourself is on the warpath. We've a saying in this part of the world: 'Shut your doors and button up your pockets if there are gipsies about!' I can guess why you've taken the trouble to call. Business doesn't thrive, I've gathered. No buyers or very few, so people are looking up their old customers. I'm afraid you'll draw a blank. We pensioners are glad enough to find there's still some dry bread for dinner. I've been a collector in my time, but now I'm out of the game. My buying days are over."

I hastened to tell him he was under a misapprehension, that I had not called with any thought of effecting sales. Happening to be in the neighbourhood I felt loath to miss the chance of paying my respects to a long-standing customer who was at the same time one of the most famous among German collectors. Hardly had the phrase passed my lips when a remarkable change took place in the old man's expression. He stood stiffly in the middle of the room, but his face lighted up and his whole aspect was suffused with pride. He turned in the direction where he fancied his wife to be, and nodded as if to say, "D'you hear that?" Then, turning back to me, he resumed—having dropped the brusque, drill-sergeant tone he had previously used, and speaking in a gentle, nay, almost tender voice:

"How charming of you. . . . I should be sorry, however, if your visit were to result in nothing more than your making the personal acquaintanceship of an old buffer like myself. At any rate I've something worth while for you to see—more worth while than you could find in Berlin, in the Albertina at Vienna, or even in the Louvre (God's curse on Paris!). A man who has been a diligent collector for fifty years, with taste to guide him, gets hold of treasures that are not to be picked up at every street-corner. Lisbeth, give me the key of the cupboard, please."

Now a strange thing happened. His wife, who had been listening with a pleasant smile, was startled. She raised her hands towards me, clasped them imploringly, and shook her head. What these gestures signified was a puzzle to me. Next she went up to her husband and touched his shoulder, saying:

"Franz, dear, you have forgotten to ask our visitor whether he may not have another appointment; and, anyhow, it is almost dinnertime.—I am sorry," she went on, looking to me, "that we have not enough in the house for an unexpected guest. No doubt you will dine at the inn. If you will take a cup of coffee with us afterwards, my daughter Anna Maria will be here, and she is much better acquainted than I am with the contents of the portfolios."

Once more she glanced piteously at me. It was plain that she wanted me to refuse the proposal to examine the collection there and then. Taking my cue, I said that in fact I had a dinner engagement at the Golden Stag, but should be only too delighted to return at three, when there would be plenty of time to examine anything Herr Kronfeld wanted to show me. I was not leaving before six o'clock.

The veteran was as pettish as a child deprived of a favourite toy.

"Of course," he growled, "I know you mandarins from Berlin have extensive claims on your time. Still, I really think you will do well to spare me a few hours. It is not merely two or three prints I want to show you, but the contents of twenty-seven portfolios, one for each master, and all of them full to bursting. However, if you come at three sharp, I dare say we can get through by six."

The wife saw me out. In the entrance hall, before she opened the front door, she whispered:

"Do you mind if Anna Maria comes to see you at the hotel before you return? It will be better for various reasons which I cannot explain just now."

"Of course, of course, a great pleasure. Really, I am dining alone, and your daughter can come along directly you have finished your own meal."

An hour later, when I had removed from the dining room to the parlour of the Golden Stag, Anna Maria Kronfeld arrived. An old maid, wizened and diffident, plainly dressed, she contemplated me with embarrassment. I did my best to put her at her ease, and expressed my readiness to go back with her at once, if her father was impatient, though it was short of the appointed hour. At this she reddened, grew even more confused, and then stammered a request for a little talk before we set out.

"Please sit down," I answered. "I am entirely at your service."

She found it difficult to begin. Her hands and her lips trembled. At length:

"My mother sent me. We have to ask a favour of you. Directly you get back, Father will want to show you his collection; and the collection . . . the collection. Well, there's very little of it left."

She panted, almost sobbed, and went on breathlessly:

"I must be frank . . . You know what troublous times we are passing through, and I am sure you will understand. Soon after the war broke out, my father became completely blind. His sight had already been failing. Agitation, perhaps, contributed. Though he was over seventy, he wanted to go to the front, remembering the fight in which he had taken part so long ago. Naturally there was no use for his services. Then, when the advance of our armies was checked, he took the matter very much to heart, and the doctor thought that may have precipitated the oncoming of blindness. In other respects, as you will have noticed, he is vigorous. Down to 1914 he could take long walks, and go out shooting. Since the failure of his eyes, his only pleasure is in his collection. He looks at it every day. 'Looks at it,' I say, though he sees nothing. Each afternoon he has the portfolios on the table, and fingers the prints one by one, in the order which many years have rendered so familiar. Nothing else interests him. He makes me read reports of auctions; and the higher the prices, the more enthusiastic does he become.

"There's the dreadful feature of the situation. Father knows nothing about the inflation; that we are ruined; that his monthly pension would not provide us with a day's food. Then we have others to support. My sister's husband was killed at Verdun, and there are four children. These money troubles have been kept from him. We cut down expenses as much as we can, but it is impossible to make ends meet. We began to sell things, trinkets and so on, without interfering with his beloved collection. There was very little to sell, since Father had always spent whatever he could scrape together upon woodcuts, copper-plate engravings, and the like. The collector's mania! Well, at length it was a question whether we were to touch the collection or let him starve. We didn't ask permission. What would have been the use? He hasn't the ghost of a notion how hard food is to come by, at any price; has never heard that Germany was defeated and surrendered Alsace-Lorraine. We don't read him items of that sort from the newspapers!

"The first piece we sold was a very valuable one, a Rembrandt etching, and the dealer paid us a long price, a good many thousand marks. We thought it would last us for years. But you know how money was melting away in 1922 and 1923. After we had provided for our immediate needs, we put the rest in a bank. In two months it was gone! We had to sell another engraving, and then another. That was during the worst days of inflation, and each time the dealer delayed settlement until the price was not worth a tenth or a hundredth of what he had promised to pay. We tried auction-rooms, and were cheated there too, though the bids were raised by millions. The million- or milliard-mark notes were wastepaper by the time we got them. The collection was scattered to provide daily bread, and little of that.

"That was why Mother was so much alarmed when you turned up today. Directly the portfolios are opened, our pious fraud will be disclosed. He knows each item by touch. You see, every print we disposed of was immediately replaced by a sheet of blank cartridge-paper of the same size and thickness, so that he would notice no difference when he handled it. Feeling them one by one, and counting them, he derives almost as much pleasure as if he could actually see them. He never tries to show them to anyone here, where there is no connoisseur, no one worthy to look at them; but he loves each of them so ardently that I think his heart would break if he knew they had been dispersed. The last time he asked someone to look at them, it was the curator of the copper-plate engravings in Dresden, who died years ago.

"I beseech you"—her voice broke—"not to shatter his illusion, not to undermine his faith, that the treasures he will describe to you are there for the seeing. He would not survive the knowledge of their loss. Perhaps we have wronged him; yet what could we do? One must live. Orphaned children are more valuable than old prints. Besides, it has been life and happiness to him to spend three hours every afternoon going through his imaginary collection, and talking to each specimen as if it were a friend. Today may be the most enthralling experience since his sight failed. How he has longed for the chance of exhibiting his treasures to an expert! If you will lend yourself to the deception . . ."

In my cold recital, I cannot convey to you how poignant was this appeal. I have seen many a sordid transaction in my business career; have had to look on supinely while persons ruined by inflation have been diddled out of cherished heirlooms which they were compelled to sacrifice for a crust. But my heart has not been utterly calloused, and this tale touched me to the quick. I need hardly tell you that I promised to play up.

We went to her house together. On the way I was grieved (though not surprised) to learn for what preposterously small amounts these ignorant though kind-hearted women had parted with prints many of which were extremely valuable and some of them unique. This confirmed my resolve to give all the help in my power. As we mounted the stairs we heard a jovial shout: "Come in! Come in!" With the keen hearing of the blind, he had recognized the footsteps for which he had been eagerly waiting.

"Franz usually takes a siesta after dinner, but excitement kept him awake today," said the old woman with a smile as she let us in. A glance at her daughter showed her that all was well. The stack of portfolios was on the table. The blind collector seized me by the arm and thrust me into a chair which was placed ready for me.

"Let's begin at once. There's a lot to see, and time presses. The first portfolio contains Dürers. Nearly a full set, and you'll think each cut finer than the others. Magnificent specimens. Judge for yourself."

He opened the portfolio as he spoke, saying:

"We start with the Apocalypse series, of course."

Then, tenderly, delicately (as one handles fragile and precious objects), he picked up the first of the blank sheets of cartridge-paper and held it admiringly before my sighted eyes and his blind ones. So enthusiastic was his gaze that it was difficult to believe he could not see. Though I knew it to be fancy, I found it difficult to doubt that there was a glow of recognition in the wrinkled visage.

"Have you ever come across a finer print? How sharp the impression. Every detail crystal-clear. I compared mine with the one at Dresden; a good one, no doubt, but 'fuzzy' in contrast with the specimen you are looking at. Then I have the whole pedigree."

He turned the sheet over and pointed at the back so convincingly that involuntarily I leaned forward to read the non-existent inscriptions.

"The stamp of the Nagler collection, followed by those of Remy and Esdaille. My famous predecessors never thought that their treasure would come to roost in this little room."

I shuddered as the unsuspecting enthusiast extolled the blank sheet of paper; my flesh crept when he placed a fingernail on the exact spot where the alleged imprints had been made by long-dead collectors. It was as ghostly as if the disembodied spirits of the men he named had risen from the tomb. My tongue clave to the roof of my mouth—until once more I caught sight of the distraught countenance of Kronfeld's wife and daughter. Then I pulled myself together and resumed my role. With forced heartiness, I exclaimed:

"Certainly you are right. This specimen is peerless."

He swelled with triumph.

"But that's nothing," he went on. "Look at these two, the *Melancholia*, and the illuminated print of the *Passion*. The latter, beyond question, has no equal. The freshness of the tints! Your colleagues in Berlin and the custodians of the public galleries would turn green with envy at the sight."

I will not bore you with details. Thus it went on, a paean, for more than two hours, as he ransacked portfolio after portfolio. An eerie business to watch the handling of these two or three hundred blanks, to chime in at appropriate moments with praise of merits which for the blind collector were so eminently real that again and again (this was my salvation) his faith kindled my own.

Once only did disaster loom. He was "showing" me a first

proof of Rembrandt's *Antiope,* which must have been of inestimable value and which had doubtless been sold for a song. Again he dilated on the sharpness of the print, but as he passed his fingers lightly over it the sensitive tips missed some familiar indentation. His face clouded, his mouth trembled, and he said:

"Surely, surely it's the *Antiope?* No one touches the woodcuts and etchings but myself. How can it have got misplaced?"

"Of course it's the *Antiope,* Herr Kronfeld," I said, hastening to take the "print" from his hand and to expatiate upon various details which my own remembrance enabled me to conjure up upon the blank surface.

His bewilderment faded. The more I praised, the more gratified he became, until at last he said exultantly to the two women:

"Here's a man who knows what's what! You have been inclined to grumble at my 'squandering' money upon the collection. It's true that for half a century and more I denied myself beer, wine, tobacco, travelling, visits to the theatre, books, devoting all I could spare to these purchases you have despised. Well, Herr Rackner confirms my judgment. When I am dead and gone, you'll be richer than anyone in the town, as wealthy as the wealthiest folk in Dresden, and you'll have good reason for congratulating yourself on my 'craze.' But so long as I'm alive, the collection must be kept together. After I've been boxed and buried, this expert or another will help you to sell. You'll have to, since my pension dies with me."

As he spoke, his fingers caressed the despoiled portfolios. It was horrible and touching. Not for years, not since 1914, had I witnessed an expression of such unmitigated happiness on the face of a German. His wife and daughter watched him with tear-dimmed eyes, yet ecstatically, like those women of old who —affrighted and rapturous—found the stone rolled away and the sepulchre empty in the garden outside the wall of Jerusalem. But the man could not have enough of my appreciation. He went on from portfolio to portfolio, from "print" to "print," drinking in my words, until, outwearied, I was glad when the lying blanks were replaced in their cases and room was made to serve coffee on the table.

My host, far from being tired, looked rejuvenated. He had story after story to tell concerning the way he had chanced upon his multifarious treasures, wanting, in this connexion, to take out each relevant piece once more. He grew peevish when I insisted, when his wife and daughter insisted, that I should miss my train if he delayed me any longer. . . .

In the end he was reconciled to my going, and we said good-bye. His voice mellowed; he took both my hands in his and fondled them with the tactile appreciation of the blind.

"Your visit has given me immense pleasure," he said with a quaver in his voice. "What a joy to have been able at long last to show my collection to one competent to appreciate it. I can do something to prove my gratitude, to make your visit to a blind old man worth while. A codicil to my will shall stipulate that your firm, whose probity everyone knows, will be entrusted with the auctioning of my collection."

He laid a hand lovingly upon the pile of worthless portfolios.

"Promise me they shall have a handsome catalogue. I could ask no better monument."

I glanced at the two women, who were exercising the utmost control, fearful lest the sound of their trembling should reach his keen ears. I promised the impossible, and he pressed my hand in response.

Wife and daughter accompanied me to the door. They did not venture to speak, but tears were flowing down their cheeks. I myself was in little better case. An art dealer, I had come in search of bargains. Instead, as events turned out, I had been a sort of angel of good-luck, lying like a trooper in order to assist in a fraud which kept an old man happy. Ashamed of lying, I was glad that I had lied. At any rate I had aroused an ecstasy which seems foreign to this period of sorrow and gloom.

As I stepped forth into the street, I heard a window open, and my name called. Though the old fellow could not see me, he knew in which direction I should walk, and his sightless eyes were turned thither. He leaned out so far that his anxious relatives put their arms round him lest he should fall. Waving a handkerchief, he shouted:

"A pleasant journey to you, Herr Rackner."

His voice rang like a boy's. Never shall I forget that cheerful face, which contrasted so grimly with the careworn aspect of the passers-by in the street. The illusion I had helped to sustain made life good for him. Was it not Goethe who said:

"Collectors are happy creatures"? ∎

Louis Couperus[1] (1863–1923)

ABOUT MYSELF AND OTHERS

Translated from the Dutch by
James Penninck

THERE is nothing that amuses me as much as little, very little adventures. Sometimes life bores me terribly in the sense that often it does not afford me any amusement. I work much, read much, love my quarters, where I study and write. I often find life very dull, I mean lacking in interest, and am likely to exclaim: "My God, my God, how bored I feel!" I yawn, stretch out my arms in despair and go out. Sometimes I meet with a little, very little adventure, and that amuses me. Then I return home with a contented smile. I at once sit down to write, and surround myself with heavy books containing old history. I dote on little adventures. I am going to tell you about the little summer-adventure with my friend Louis.

"About Myself and Others" by Louis Couperus, translated by James Penninck from LEGEND OF THE BLUE COASTS. Reprinted by permission of L. J. Veen's Uitgeversmaatschappij N.V.
1. *Louis Couperus* (lü ē′ kü pā′rəs).

One evening I sat on a bench in the Promenades des Anglais. That is the hour and place for little bits of adventures. Apparently nothing happens there, except that people pass by, sit down and dream. In reality numerous little adventures spring up. Are humorous novelettes woven there? Is there a development into a romance, and, very occasionally, into a tragedy? Have no fear. The case in which my friend Louis was involved is nothing else than a miniature comedy, a tiny farce.

Well, I am sitting on a bench; a young man seats himself next to me. He is a good-looking fellow, a bit of a dandy in a white suit of clothes with white shoes, altogether dressed in an elegant and very simple manner. There is an absence of loud colours and he looks decidedly distinguished. He has fine eyes with long lashes. Doffing his straw hat he exposes deep-black hair. Perhaps he is little over twenty.

He regards me in an ingratiating manner.

He opens the conversation with a: "Fine evening."

"Splendid," I retort.

"The evenings in Nice during August are delightful."

I agree with him. "But the City is not very lively," I add.

"Quite true, the City is quiet. However, there will be an improvement as soon as the season starts. Are you living here?"

"Yes, sir."

"Summers included?"

"I have just returned from a trip."

"Is that so? I myself have just arrived."

"Do you intend staying during the winter?"

"Yes, I live with my aunt, who is here for her health."

"At this time of the year? Is your aunt in Nice now?"

"Yes, sir, by her doctor's advice."

It occurs to me that it is rather strange to have doctors advise his aunt to come to Nice for her health during August. But my imagination is very flexible. And I imagine that his aunt might reason thus: "They are going to send me to Nice, because I cannot stand a rigorous climate, so I might as well go now and at once take my choice of vacant residences . . . because I abhor moving."

However I do not share her point-of-view. Within a short time I intend to leave this place and don't expect to see aunt's nephew again. But aunt's nephew is inclined to be companionable. Evidently I interest him.

"Are you from the South?" he asks.

"I? no."

"Then you are from the North, a Parisian?"

"Neither of the two, my dear sir. I am not a Frenchman."

"Oh, so. You have no strange accent at all."

"I have lived a long time in France."

"Are you perhaps a Russian?"

"No, I am a Belgian from Brussels."

"I am from Montpellier. Tout ce qu'il y a de plus Midi.[2] Permit me to introduce myself. My name is de St. Gasc."

It occurs to me that it is a fine-sounding name. "Greatly pleased," I counter courteously. "My name is de Cèze. May I make a guess at your first name?"

That amuses him, and in a jovial tone he gives his consent.

"Amédée," I guess.

"Amédée de St. Gasc."

"Oh, no," he protests with a coquettish gesture, holding both hands up in the air.

"Gaston . . . Hector . . . Adhémar."

"No, no, no!" he ejaculates, "my name is Louis."

"Your name is Louis? Well, that is curious. My name is also Louis."

"Oh, yes?"

"Louis de Cèze. It is a standing joke on the part of my friends to omit my family name. They always call me 'Louis the Sixteenth.' "

He laughs as if pleased at the joke.

"Is your aunt also a de St. Gasc?"

"No," he says with a laugh, which seems very attractive.

And, after a slight pause, he adds:

"My aunt is Spanish, Madame Avelenada. My parents live in Montpellier. I have accompanied her to this place, because the doctors have advised Nice."

"In August," I supply inwardly.

"I am the favourite of my aunt, her pet child. A quiet existence, living with her. I don't know anybody here. During the afternoons I drive around with Aunt. In the evenings she makes no demands on me. She is not very bothersome. Enfin, I am her pet relative, you know." He smiles at me very understandingly, saying: "I am very glad to have made your acquaintance. I hope we will remain friends. You might show me Nice and Monte Carlo. I love to play occasionally and take a chance with a couple of hundred-franc bills."

---

2. *Tout . . . Midi.* The character is commenting on his regional pride. Montpellier is in southern France, and he says he is as southern as one can be.

He is trying to tell me that he can afford to throw a couple of hundred-franc bills around . . . that a couple of hundred-franc bills means nothing to Louis de St. Gasc. Of course if one is the pet child of Madame Avelenada . . .

"We might go together to Monte Carlo," I suggest. "I just love gambling. But I can't afford to lose much."

"Oh, I will lend you the money," says my friend Louis.

"That's mighty fine."

"Well, I enjoy your company very much. May I call you by your first name?"

"Why, certainly."

"I am not in the habit of being familiar. But you seem to invite an exception."

"Where do you and your aunt live?"

"In the Villa Aubert, Boulevard Dubouchage. A very well-furnished apartment. Aunt took her servants along. She is used to her cook. For dinner there will be partridges. Yes, yes, Aunt is fond of a good table."

Partridges in August, I think. I simply dote on fowl. Why does not our cook give us game once in awhile?

"And tell me about yourself, Louis," says my friend Louis in a sort of sentimental way.

"Well, my name is Louis, just like yours. Louis de Cèze. And what else?"

He is leaning against the back of the bench in a graceful attitude, smilingly awaiting further confidences, while watching the ocean.

"I have no aunt who spoils me. I am all alone," I supply.

"Alone . . . ?"

"Yes, do you know where the Hotel Majestic is situated at Cimiez?"

"I have seen it."

"I am employed there as a cashier."

He gazed at me in some surprise. "As a cashier?" he repeats.

"Yes," I said seriously. "That is quite a difficult position in such an immense hotel. It is not a bad place. My salary is one hundred and fifty francs a month."

"That is not much," he murmurs.

"I can live on it," I say modestly. "I have relations, I am of good family, but have run down a bit. What is there to tell . . . living expenses, women, debts, you understand. So I took the position. I have free living. A small room, near the servants' quarters in the attic. I receive my meals, not the menu of the dining-table, I assure you. No partridges, Mr. Louis."

He makes a wide gesture and murmurs something, as if trying to dismiss the subject, starting another lead:

"That is a splendid ring you wear."

"A souvenir," I explain. "I never would dispose of that."

"Do you like light-coloured cravats?"

"Yes, in the summer."

"I don't care for them. I always wear black neckties, they go well with a background of coloured shirts."

"You are very elegant," I remark.

"Oh, no," he parries the compliment, "you are elegant."

"Well," I come back, "the management demands that we are well dressed."

"An expensive hotel, is it not?"

"About twenty francs a day, room and meals. Running between twenty and thirty francs."

"Will you come with me to Monte Carlo some day?"

"If you will lend me some money . . . with pleasure. I cannot afford to play on my salary of one hundred and fifty francs."

"I will lend you some money. Will we go tomorrow?"

"Very well," I agree. "That suits me perfectly. Tomorrow by the eleven o'clock train."

So we shake hands on it and say: "Au revoir."

I have not the slightest inclination to go with my friend Louis to Monte Carlo. The next morning at the appointed hour of eleven I call our cook, who I saw had just returned from the market, into my room.

"Madeleine, it is now open season, why don't you ever serve partridges? Are they very expensive?"

"Partridges? Monsieur, in August? I haven't seen any in the market."

"A friend of mine already had partridges. . . ."

"But, Monsieur, that is impossible. There are no partridges. Perhaps the gentleman received some from a friend. They are not for sale in the market. Monsieur will have to be patient for a little while."

That affords me consolation. I now feel sure that Louis de St. Gasc has eaten no more partridges than Louis de Cèze.

That same afternoon I go by a roundabout way through the Boulevard Dubouchage and ring the bell of the Villa Aubert.

I ask the caretaker: "Concierge, is a Mr. de St. Gasc living here?"

"What name, sir?"

"De St. Gasc."

"No, sir."

"Sorry, it must be a villa farther on."

That evening, as usual, I proceed to the Promenade des Anglais.

Suddenly my friend Louis sits alongside of me.

"You broke your promise," he reproaches me in a gentle voice. "Why weren't you at the station for our trip to Monte Carlo?"

"It was impossible," I said seriously. "I was too busy with the hotel's finances. It is a very laborious occupation. Those ciphers make me dull."

"Poor fellow, what a job for 150 francs."

I make a gesture, which should indicate my resignation to the yoke with which Fate has burdened me.

Louis talks in order to soothen my rasped feelings. He talks very seriously . . . altogether a charming conversationalist. His discourse is of the sea, which supposedly foams with more effect over a real beach than it hurls itself against a stone ridge, which girdles the azure coastline. He tells me that he is passionately fond of horseback riding. On a horse, and then just roaming over long stretches of veldt. He is reminiscent about steeplechases, as he possesses many acquaintances of note, who own castles and hunting-preserves.

He talks vivaciously, and himself believes all he is telling. He gives me a description of his hunting-dress; how his new coat is lined, and of the cut of his new waistcoat. Quite different from the styles of last year. He mentions casually that he does not care for women, and then jumps suddenly to literature. He has read voluminously: Balzac, Flaubert, Zola, de Goncourt. . . . His literary taste is rather good.

"Do you like Zola?"

"Zola," I repeat. "Didn't he write 'Nana'?"

"Yes, didn't you read anything else from his pen?"

"No," I offer it as an excuse. "I don't read much. I am too busy with my ledgers."

"Have you read Goncourt?"

"Who is he?" I ask.

"A good author," he replies, regarding me with some slight pity.

Assured by this time that we have little in common in a literary sense, he makes a new start with the stage. But I haven't seen any of the latest plays, not even the *Rafale of Bernstein*. The pressing affairs of the hotel at Cimiez do not leave my evenings free, as happens in the case of the aunt's nephew, Louis de St. Gasc.

He does not find me very intelligent nor well-informed. But

he can cover other fields of conversation, and, notwithstanding my limited range of bookreading, we get along quite well.

The day after tomorrow is the twenty-fifth he informs me with a smile. The twenty-fifth of August.

"That is so," I exclaim. "I came near forgetting."

The twenty-fifth of August is the anniversary of St. Louis of France. As I have a Catholic aunt—although she is not Spanish —and as said aunt never forgets me on the twenty-fifth of August, I remember the date instantly, far better than literary data.

"Then," rejoins Louis de St. Gasc, "you have no leanings toward St. Louis de Gonzague?"

"Why no," I reply, "wasn't he a Portuguese? What have I to do with a Portuguese for a patron? I am very fond of St. Louis of France, because he was a king, who travelled. . . ."

"Historically you seem to be well instructed," engagingly smiles my friend Louis. "Now tomorrow is our nameday. Do you know," he moves up a little closer, "I would very much like to have a souvenir from you. A small affair to remember you by. I dote on small presents. You will let me have this small gold piece, won't you?"

"All right," I agree. "And what do I get from you?"

"Oh, whatever you like to have. I have it: a pin; do you care for pins? A jewelled stickpin for your scarf?"

"With pleasure," I state modestly, "but let it be of trifling value."

"Oh, yes," agrees Louis de St. Gasc, to whom bills of hundred francs are but slips of paper, not to overlook the wealthy aunt and the many acquaintances with castles and hunting-preserves. "Then I will give you the stickpin tomorrow. And when will you give me the little gold coin?"

"Tomorrow," I promise, elated at the thought of so much affection for the approach of our nameday.

"What is it?" he asks, with a greedy look at the gold piece, while with deft fingers he rubs over its surface.

"A Roman coin," I answer. "Quite ancient, that is, if it is genuine."

"Then it might not be genuine?"

"There are so many imitations."

"But I will get it the day after tomorrow?"

"Of course."

"In the evening after tomorrow I will bring the scarfpin."

"Excellent. But make no extra expense for me."

"Oh, let me have my own way about it. I say, Louis, if I

should . . . have to write you sometimes, should I address you at the Majestic?"

"Yes . . . but what would you write about?"

"Well" . . . nonchalantly . . . "I might have occasion. I would like to have your address." Then, "No General Delivery?"

"That is not necessary. Louis de Cèze, Majestic. Don't add 'cashier' to my name."

"No . . . certainly not. I am sorry, but tomorrow I won't be able to see you. Aunt is going to have friends for dinner. Till the day after tomorrow then, hè? I with the stickpin."

"And I with the gold coin," I add dramatically.

A handshake, very intimate, and a separation for one whole day.

On the next afternoon I proceed to the Majestic.

I ask the porter: "Any letters for Mr. Louis de Cèze?"

The porter runs over the mail: "No, sir."

"Should any letters arrive for Mr. Louis de Cèze please forward them to this address."

I hand him my card and conduct a search in my pocket for a five-franc piece.

"Here is a letter," suddenly discovers the porter. . . . "Mr. Louis de Cèze, Hotel Majestic." His discovery saves the five-francs piece, for which I bless the gods. Thereafter I read the letter.

"My dear Louis.

"I must see you without fail tomorrow morning, the morning of our nameday. Something terrible has happened to me. Imagine, after I left you yesterday, I was held up by apaches, near my home in the Avenue Dubouchage. It was very late, the street was deserted, and, of course, there was no policeman in sight. There were four of them; they have beaten me up and taken everything away from me, including some five hundred francs. I dragged myself home. I hardly dare to show my face to my aunt in the condition I am in. So I am going to stay in bed this morning and won't appear at dinner. But tomorrow morning I wish to see you. Not at my house though, as I must avoid to arouse any suspicion in my aunt. She is so shy and also ailing, and won't see anybody she does not know well. Therefore don't call at Villa Aubert, my dear fellow. But I must see you. Aunt is already angry with me, because I spend too much money. Should she hear of my experience she would be furious.

"Dear Louis, I am going to borrow some money on some jewellery of mine. I need two hundred francs. Couldn't you help me with two or three hundred francs? You would oblige me immensely. You will receive them back within a week, because I am going to write to Montpellier at once. I can count on your letting me have three hundred francs tomorrow morning, can't I? I am in great despair. Of course five hundred francs really mean nothing, but it just happens right after Aunt had reproached me with spending too much money.

"My very dear Louis, you are my only hope.
"Your loyal friend,
'LOUIS DE ST. GASC.'
"P.S.

"It also would give me pleasure to receive the little gold coin tomorrow morning for my nameday, my best friend. The scarfpin I shall buy as soon as I am out of my difficulties, as soon as I have received word from Montpellier."

To my own great chagrin I entirely forget to show myself in front of the Majestic with three hundred francs in my pocket and the little gold piece, detached from my watch chain in order to hand it to my friend Louis. It was all the fault of my Catholic (but not Spanish) aunt, who arrived to embrace me, bring me a bouquet of flowers and a little medal. A sweet woman indeed. Therefore it was evening before I met my friend de St. Gasc on the Promenade. He was already sitting there when I arrived.

He was decidedly angry.

But I also had many cares and seated myself next to him with a deep sigh. A few moments' silence, interrupted by my sighs deep down from the bottom of my stomach.

At last he condescended to open the conversation.

"Why didn't you come out of the hotel this morning for a few minutes? I have been waiting for you for fully one hour."

"Why?" I ask with eyes wide open and full of naïve surprise, "and where?"

"In front of the Majestic," he answers crossly. "In front of your hotel. Didn't you receive my letter?"

"A letter?" . . . still showing surprise and wide open eyes. . . . "No," I counter, "I haven't received any letter."

"You didn't receive any letter?"

"My dear chap, that's nothing to be wondered at. So many letters go astray. If I had known that you wished to see me . . . I myself am very much in need to talk to you, my good Louis. I am in a bad predicament. You must help me out, dear fellow, you must. Think of it: a shortage in the cash of the Majestic: nearly one thousand francs short. . . . How it happened . . . I don't know. I am honest . . . I am an honest man. Who stole it? I don't know. But I am responsible. That is the disgusting part of it. I might leave my little gold coin in pawn. If it is genuine I am certain to get a loan of one hundred francs on it. But what is one hundred francs? . . . My dear Louis, you must . . . do you hear, you *must* lend me nine hundred francs. Ask your aunt for them. Otherwise I am lost, dishonoured. I will lose my position and go to prison. Louis, my dearest Louis, help me, I implore you. What is nine hundred francs to you? I will write to my family. For the sake of the name, which I would stain, they undoubtedly will pay the money. Within a week, my dear Louis, you will have the money back again. My friend, my very best friend, my only friend, help me out!"

"I am sorry, my dear fellow" . . . this came in somewhat chilling tones . . . "but I just had written to you that I have been attacked by apaches."

"Attacked?"

"And robbed."

"Robbed?"

"Of five hundred francs."

"Louis, my dear friend Louis, what a terrible nameday for us. You know, I am going to denounce St. Louis of France. That settles him. Henceforth I take the Portuguese: St. Louis de Gonzague."

"Then you are not in a position to help me?" asks Louis de St. Gasc.

"I, help *you*?" I question him in a dull voice and overcome by despair. "I? who must have at least nine hundred francs, and, even at that, only when my gold coin is genuine. I? help *you*? You must help me. You must bleed your aunt."

"I am sorry" . . . by this time the voice has become icy . . . "but that is impossible. As far as I am concerned I am going to see an usurer. . . ."

"And I . . . I am going to commit suicide."

My friend Louis does not seem very much shocked by my decision.

He comes to his feet and stretches out his hand.

"I am going now, at once. I am going in search of an usurer. . . . No bad feelings, I hope, because I am not able to help you."

"Of course not," I assure him, pressing his hand.

The evenings on the Promenade des Anglais follow one after the other with the same beautiful environment, but they have lost their mutual resemblance.

Because my friend Louis is surely still engaged in the search for an usurer.

I have not seen him again. ■

Martin Andersen-Nexø [1] (1869–1954)

LIFE SENTENCE

Translated from the Danish

MATTIS LAU was the sole child of early-spent parents. His mother was in her forties when he was born, his father ten years older; he did not come as God's gift to a young, hot-blooded couple, but as a somewhat tardy hand-out to two people already in fear of age. Every child more or less carries the weight of the grown-ups' years; it is not exactly lessened if the child is born as late as in this case. When Mattis came, his parents had used up the rest of their surplus vitality. He had enough for all three of them, but it was hard to keep a fire blazing under the wails of his mother and his father's bleary eyes.

They never understood the urge in his play, but let it wither. He was allowed to do neither this nor that—neither to write with charcoal on the loam walls of the tumble-down fisherman's hut, nor under any circumstances to pound the rough spruce-wood table with one of the things that only had to fall into his busy little hands to turn into tools. Like most parents, they rated dead things above the living child; and little Mattis soon saw clearly that he was the most worthless thing on earth. It certainly was owing only to the parents' infinite goodness that a small boy got permission to stay alive after breaking a tooth off the rake, or tearing a few knots in the old fishing net. By rights he should have been beaten to pulp long ago.

Actually Mattis' parents weren't such bad child-beaters. They just let him know on sufficient occasions that justice was again being tempered with mercy. The stick hung over his childhood like a constant threat.

At an early age he had to do his share of work—which did not bother him at all. He merely wished to be alone with it; then, as it went on, his work turned quite of its own accord into the most fascinating play. But if his father and mother were present it soon became galling toil, as it long was for the parents.

Despite all, he grew up to be a real boy, who preferred the harbor and the beach to the schoolhouse and learned much that might come in handy once he got out into the world. And he would get out into the world! He was afraid of no boy in the fishing village, and the parents whimpered when they heard of his recklessness and his foolhardy pranks. They liked best to see him sit by the window in his free time, with a copybook in his hand; then they knew where he was, and he neither ruined nor ate so much. When somebody called, he had to show how good he was at reading and writing. Perhaps they were trying to make up somehow, through him, for their own failure to obtain an education; at any rate, he never made them so happy as on the day when he came home and reported that he was to stand first on the church platform.

After confirmation, most of the boys in his class were scattered to the four winds. Poor people's children take to the air early; down there by the beach, it was customary for the young to leave the nest as soon as they had the pastor's blessing to cease being children. The ones who had something in them went to sea; the others took jobs in the capital or on the far side of the island—but fly they must! Only stick-in-the-muds remained at home to care for the soil and the womenfolk. From long ago there were two kinds of men on the beach: those who had been to sea in their young days and now were plying the fisherman's trade, and then the stove-warmers who were working the land.

Throughout his childhood, Mattis had known that he wanted to go to sea when the time came—far out, where none knew its depth and where Father and Mother could not watch him from shore, clucking like troubled hens. And yet he resigned himself to staying at home and doing more and more of the two oldsters' work.

Between times, if he ever harbored plans to break out, they clung to him with trembling hands. His father led him round about the tiny patch of land, talked of it as though it were a patrimony and begged him not to desert all this. And his mother would confide with a chuckle that someone or other wasn't sleeping nights, on his account. One could always find him a nice girl with money way back in the closet, if only he continued to stay at home.

Mattis didn't give a damn for the promises and fine words. The shack wasn't a mite too good to put a match to it, and the girls he'd never seen were more alluring than the ones he knew. He was longing to get out—out where the rolling waves tossed the great tarred, oaken cradles from port to port.

And getting out was not even so very difficult. Often enough, when he came in with a catch of sea bass and lay alongside the windjammers to sell a fish, the captains offered him hire—all he had to do was climb aboard and let the dory drift ashore with the tide. But when the crucial moment came he stayed. Duty, toward the two old grumblers in the shack, held him fast—he could not escape.

"I have to wait till they're dead," he thought, pulling the heavy oars.

It always was easier for Mattis to row out to sea than back home; and he knew the reason quite well. The way home was the sour way of duty; that made it so arduous. He didn't feel a trace of filial love; it did not warm his heart to care for the two old people, who under cover of the parental name had always cramped his life. He would not mind if death were to deliver them. But it could never occur to him to desert them.

So he stayed at home and took the load off his gouty old father's back, looked after the nets and tilled the bit of soil—joylessly, yet so that there was enough to eat. He milked the two shaggy cows for his mother, cut nettles for the pigs and twice annually made a pilgrimage to town to pay the taxes. Inwardly he did not get richer, fooling around like this. He became close-mouthed and sluggish.

On one thing his mind was firmly made up: not to be caught by some wench. Once his parents died, he wanted to be his own master and free to go wherever in the world it drew him.

The Laus hailed from the interior of the island—from the Lauenhof, a farm situated a mile inland. It belonged to Hans Lau, an uncle of Mattis. Since he was the only one with a farm, he was regarded as the head of the family.

He was arrogant and ruthless by nature and took various liberties, while the Laus otherwise strictly observed the proprieties, as befits little people. He was reputed to be reckless at cards and a rake; the poor relations could not help admiring this, as big-farmer manners.

The farm was neither big nor good, by the way; most of its soil was rock. But it was still a farm, and all the Laus took pride in being farm-owner's children. It even flickered in the corners of the eyes of Mattis' used-up, shriveled father.

Hans Lau was well advanced in years, and as he had no children—at least in a manner of speaking—the question was to which of his nephews and nieces he would choose to leave his farm. Each family entertained a well-founded belief that it was the preferred one, and secretly acted on it. Thus the Laus came to draw apart from the rest of the poor in the district; there was something in their bearing as though they were merely disguised, and might take it into their heads one fine day to doff the poor man's garb. It was said of them that they were riding the high horse.

One day the Lauenhof owner turned up quite unexpectedly under his brother's low roof. Mattis was out behind the woodshed, tarring an old boat. He saw Hans Lau coming but he went on with his work; it angered him to see everything stood on its head if the uncle so much as showed himself.

Shortly after, his mother came round the corner of the house, on the run; he had not seen her so quick on her feet in a long time. "It's you he's come to see," she panted and pulled his sleeve; "now you'll probably be picked to own the farm. Be a little nice now!"

Mattis looked after his work and let his mother prattle; he did not seem to know that she was there. She had to watch out for his motions with the tar-brush. But she kept nagging and pestering, and followed him round about the boat, undaunted: "You should put your time to use and drop your grouchiness just this once," she persisted. "Uncle Hans wants to talk it over

with you personally. Can't you show a little manners for once!"
When he still didn't answer, she ran inside again, to catch as
much of what went on there as possible; her skirts flopped
about her heels. It was the greatest day in her life.

Mattis did not look up, but he heard his mother bustling and
he got mad. What did he care for Uncle Hans and his farm and
the whole business? He only saw his relatives when he needed
them, Uncle Hans did. When his mother promptly came back,
Mattis threw some tool on his shoulder and withdrew toward
the beach.

However, she had stated the case quite correctly. Hans Lau
wanted to make the farm over to Mattis. It was to be transferred
after his death, and until then he would pay Mattis and his
parents one hundred thalers a year—on the one condition that
Mattis marry at once. For his wife, Uncle Hans had chosen Bodil, the Lauenhof housekeeper, a good, faithful girl who had
sacrificed the best part of her youth to him and the farm. To reward her loyalty, Hans Lau wished to see her well married and
to know that she'd be on the farm, as its mistress, when he was
called away—in a little while.

Mattis had set his heart on being his own master, once he
were rid of his duty to support the parents. It was hard to budge
him. But the old people did not let him rest. They nagged him
from dawn to dusk, tempted him with the prospect of one day
being a big farmer and the head of the family. When this did
not help, they whined that he would not lift a finger to lighten
his old, toil-worn parents' old age. They sighed whenever he
approached, and at meal-times their talk inevitably turned to
parents who had worn themselves out for their children and
reaped the blackest ingratitude in return.

Soon all this became too much for Mattis; it was something
he couldn't get around. Duty had left deep tracks in him, in
which it was always easy to tread again. He was used to having
to make sacrifices, and one day he yielded. It was merely as if
the one porthole into the light and the world were being
slammed shut.

His uncle strangely revived after the wedding, to the great
indignation of the two oldsters. They had a long way to go yet,
before being farm-owners! As for Mattis, he didn't care. He kept
to himself, and it did not make him more sociable that Bodil
hastened to present him with a little boy. It just meant somebody else to stay clear of.

Mattis was not kind to the boy, nor did anyone expect him to
be. To see him was to get a splinter into his eye. It angered him

to witness the child's careless joy and it angered him when, cautioned by experience, it shunned him—it only had to come before his eyes for wrath to flare up in him. He did not exactly account to himself for the causes of his feeling toward the child. There had to be an explanation for everything—to oneself, too; and he explained his conduct to himself as being about that of a strict but just pedagogue. If the others winked at the youngster's first boyish pranks, he took firm, heavy-handed action. His youth had been hard; he was passing the legacy on now.

Bodil dared not oppose him; she had no very clear idea anyway of whether and how he might be handled. He never reproached her, but she was nonetheless afraid of him; there was something in his eyes that told her to watch her step.

It would have served no purpose either, to dispute with Mattis about his treatment of the child—he suffered enough under it. His inability to find a way out turned the very pangs of his conscience against little Hans. One day Mattis caught him. The boy was standing out in the shed, letting the grindstone whir, so that a bright waterspout stood between the stone and the floor; he was so absorbed in the game that he sensed nothing until his father had him by the neck. He cried out insanely with fear when he saw the father above him, and this cry paralyzed something in Mattis and stayed his heavy hand. Bewildered, he flung the boy into a pile of hay and staggered to work, dazed by the youngster's horrible dread of him.

The boy's desperate, plaintive wails rang over to him as he worked, drowned out the blows of his axe and incessantly trickled at him, like an indictment. He struck more forcefully, to deaden the sound, but he could not get rid of it. Finally he could not stand it any longer; he threw the axe away and rose, irately—what the hell, wasn't there a stick around so the damned brat could be shut up once and for all! He was blind with rage.

And suddenly it was as if the whole had burst—his rage and everything else—and collapsed within him. He led his hand over his eyes and fearfully stared over at the wall of the shed. The tortured small boy lying there, huddled and trembling and trying to swallow his tears so he wouldn't get a worse licking—that was he, Mattis! And the grindstone—why, he had just sneaked in and let it whir, because the spurting water was such fun when the stone really moved. Speed, speed! Nothing delighted his childish heart more, at the time, than to set something in rapid motion, that the sparks flew roundabout. But you weren't allowed to do that and so you did it in secret, as everything else that was worth while. It wetted the floor, and some day retribution fearfully caught up with you—as it now did with him. The floor was loam and couldn't be damaged; young as he was then, he had realized and understood that there was something called a curdled disposition. And now? His whole life had consisted of surrenders, piece by piece, until he too had become an embittered, shriveled sourpuss like his own father. Now he himself stalked the innocent joys of the child, catchpoll that he was.

The choked, broken sobs hurled accusation after accusation at him; they shattered him, until his heart ached and he could not breathe any more—he *had* to silence that sound! He looked round, helpless, bewildered, as if searching for the stick again, and then he suddenly rushed over to the boy and lifted him up. Mattis wasn't accustomed to embracing anyone; the little body surprised his palms and filled them with a tender warmth. How strangely dear it was to embrace someone! He took the boy on his knees and tried to get the small, dirty hands out of his face; he had never noticed them before; they were like a pair of little shovels, bearing every trace of their surroundings and hard inside, exactly like his own. He was a real boy who didn't spare his fists.

Silently the youngster let his hands be removed from his face —in fear, perhaps. But he would not look at Mattis' eyes; he turned his face away and kicked, to get down.

Mattis did not know what to do; it occurred to him to take the boy inside the shed, to the grindstone, and whirl it round till the water splashed over the floor. The boy was suspicious and kept close to the door, but his eyes could not resist; they stole out secretly, eager to catch something. And when a spray flew all the way across to his feet, it made him laugh.

"Well, how about splashing Father?" Mattis said and stood by the door—it was the first time that he gave this name to himself. The boy, still somewhat diffident, thrust himself over to the grindstone; soon the game was in full swing. It amused even Mattis, this play with the opaline water that stood in the air like a cock's tail and then suddenly burst into sprays. Here by the grindstone—a little late—he recaptured a piece of his childhood and vied with the boy in laughter.

At first Hans was still timid, and it was up to Mattis to come to him. The boy's distrust hurt and, at times, even angered him, but he had no choice. He humbled himself and went to look for the little chap and inveigle him. When nothing else worked, he could always win him over by tempting him with the grind-stone.

Soon, however, the tot came quite by himself and put his little hand into the big one, and Mattis marveled how quickly a child's soul can forgive and forget—and was ashamed of himself. There was not much to be done about it now; his own soul had long congealed and no longer could be transformed. But it seemed to him as though in being with the boy he lived the other side of his childhood, as it were—the one that might have been. And this was why he could not be without him.

Everything, both play and earnest, started with the grind-stone. When Hans got bigger, the stone was overshadowed by other and more fascinating things. Hans learned to fish and run a sailboat, and he helped his father till the soil. The boy was right behind Mattis all the time; they could not stand being apart, and in time grew strangely close to each other. Toward everyone else Mattis was and remained the surly grouch, and added to it was the fact now that he had the boy to defend.

"He's not going to live my life," Mattis told himself and saw to it that the boy was restrained as little as possible. When the others laid plans as to what he should become, Mattis cut off the debate with the curt statement that he was to have the right to make his own choice when the time came.

Mattis knew what the boy would choose—long before Hans knew it himself—and the knowledge made him anything but glad. But he sealed his feelings within himself, and after Hans' confirmation he himself took him to town and saw to it that he hired on with the right crew. When he got home he went out into the shed; there he sat almost the whole day, sunk in rumination, while his hard thumbnail chiseled and chiseled at the soft grindstone. He did not see the sense of everything.

It was not until the boy, too, came home after some weeks, explaining that he had been laid off because the sloop had sprung a leak and was to be laid up, that his existence began to have a meaning again. Mattis knew well that an explanation also was required for the fact that the boy came home instead of looking for another seagoing job—but he did not love him any less for it.

Working together, they frequently talked about having to listen round for a new hire for Hans, and on Mattis' part the talk was meant sincerely. He would have been the last to stand in the way of the boy's future.

However, the winter passed without anything turning up, and in the spring Hans declared that he would learn carpentry and then sail as a carpenter; this promised higher wages. Mattis had some objections but there was no real weight in them, and the boy's wish prevailed.

In the following summer the Lauenhof owner died at last. Mattis' parents were still living but they were very old and decrepit; the prospect of a Lauenhof residence had kept life in them far beyond a reasonable time. Mattis himself would have liked to sell the farm, but the old couple and Bodil objected. So he let them move up; he himself remained in the shack. He had nothing to do with the farm, and very little with the three of them, aside from their having imprisoned him. Now—at last— he was rid of all pressing bonds. He was not free and never became free; he felt that he had been imprisoned for too long a time to be able to become free again. But the bonds that held him now did not cut into his flesh. Here in the shack he had all that tied him to life: the sea which had sung its song in him since he was born, and the boy.

The boy remained living with him during his apprenticeship, and Mattis sunned himself in his young mind. He could not bear to think of it that he and Hans would have to part sooner or later; the boy was his link to the world, through which he lived and breathed. He no longer had any wish for his own future; quite imperceptibly, everything had turned into blind devotion and admiration for the lad. He no longer yearned for distant spaces, either. What he could still expect of life now had to be fulfilled through the boy.

Hans was to experience life for him. All that he himself had missed in his youth should be bestowed on the lad—gladly. But then, he could not even let him go.

Gradually this feeling grew into a gnawing hidden pain, into self-reproach for accepting the sacrifice of the boy and holding him back at home. One day the full, hard thought dawned on Mattis: he stood in Hans' way precisely as others had once stood in his. It cut him to the quick, but it terrified him to think of the only way out—for that led back into loneliness. He himself was to turn away the one being that had warmed his heart and gladdened him. Mattis, long accustomed to renunciation, fought a hard fight this time before he won.

One Sunday morning he took Hans out to sea. For several hours they dragged for bass, over the "grounds," where the "grass bass" keep themselves; then they rowed about and offered them for sale on various ships that lay at anchor, brought here by the land breeze. Mattis went aboard and bargained with the skippers while Hans remained in the boat to weigh the fish.

From one of the vessels, a large bark, Mattis climbed back into the boat with such strange movements that for a moment Hans thought, "They surely poured him some, there on board." But he suppressed the idea at once; his father never drank liquor. Mattis seated himself on the bench and stared in front of him; his expression was terribly serious, almost petrified.

"You'd better go aboard right away," he said in a hoarse voice. "They need a carpenter, and they offer good wages."

A sudden joy lit up the face of the son—until he caught the old man's lightless glance.

"But you—Father?" he asked slowly.

"I?—I'll row back and pack your stuff. I'll be back before nightfall—and the wind won't turn till then." Mattis stared up at the clouds.

"Yes, but I mean you, yourself. What'll you do then?"

"What I'll do? Well—I—" Mattis spoke tonelessly and fell abruptly silent.

"Come along, Father! You've got nothing to keep you here. We'll hire on together, here or on another ship. Let's go to sea together, you!"

Mattis sat there, withdrawn as if hearing nothing or listening to far-off music. Suddenly he straightened up. "Yes, we'll hire on together, you and I," he said and gripped Hans' hand. "Now go aboard."

"And you come with two bedrolls," Hans called down from the rail. Mattis nodded. Two bedrolls! Did the boy really mean it?

Could his youth not demand an end to having to drag a weight on his leg? He had been a good and loving son, he who had turned up in the nest as unexpectedly as a young cuckoo. Mattis had received his due from him and more; and now it had to be done with. There wasn't room for him on board.

He packed his son's sea chest and bedding, and let someone else row it out; he himself couldn't. He followed the boat with his eyes till it was alongside the ship; then he went into the tool-shed and set out to mend a net. He felt the wind beginning to turn, knew that the bark and the other sailboats out there were now weighing anchor. But he did not look up.

He had returned to his prison—what was the use of looking back! ▓

Bjornstjerne Bjornsen [1] (1832–1910)

THE FATHER

Translated from the Norwegian by
R. B. Anderson

THE MAN whose story is here to be told was the wealthiest and most influential person in his parish; his name was Thord Overaas. He appeared in the priest's study one day, tall and earnest.

"I have gotten a son," said he, "and I wish to present him for baptism."

"What shall his name be?"

"Finn—after my father."

"And the sponsors?"

They were mentioned, and proved to be the best men and women of Thord's relations in the parish.

"Is there anything else?" inquired the priest, and looked up.

The peasant hesitated a little.

"The Father," by Bjornstjerne Bjornsen. Translated by R. B. Anderson. Reprinted by permission of The American-Scandinavian Foundation.
1. *Bjornstjerne Bjornsen* (byœrn′styer nə byœrn′son).

"I should like very much to have him baptized by himself," he said, finally.

"That is to say on a week-day?"

"Next Saturday, at twelve o'clock noon."

"Is there anything else?" inquired the priest.

"There is nothing else," and the peasant twirled his cap, as though he were about to go.

Then the priest rose. "There is yet this, however," said he, and walking toward Thord, he took him by the hand and looked gravely into his eyes. "God grant that the child may become a blessing to you!"

One day sixteen years later, Thord stood once more in the priest's study.

"Really, you carry your age astonishingly well, Thord," said the priest; for he saw no change whatever in the man.

"That is because I have no troubles," replied Thord.

To this the priest said nothing, but after a while he asked: "What is your pleasure this evening?"

"I have come this evening about that son of mine who is to be confirmed tomorrow."

"He is a bright boy."

"I did not wish to pay the priest until I heard what number the boy would have when he takes his place in church tomorrow."

"He will stand number one."

"So I have heard; and here are ten dollars for the priest."

"Is there anything else I can do for you?" inquired the priest, fixing his eyes on Thord.

"There is nothing else." Thord went out.

Eight years more rolled by, and then one day a noise was heard outside of the priest's study, for many men were approaching, and at their head was Thord, who entered first.

The priest looked up and recognized him.

"You come well attended this evening, Thord," said he.

"I am here to request that the banns may be published for my son; he is about to marry Karen Storliden, daughter of Gudmund, who stands here beside me."

"Why, that is the richest girl in the parish."

"So they say," replied the peasant, stroking back his hair with one hand.

The priest sat a while as if in deep thought, then entered the names in his book, without making any comments, and the men wrote their signatures underneath. Thord laid three dollars on the table.

"One is all I am to have," said the priest.

"I know that very well; but he is my only child, and I want to do it handsomely."

The priest took the money.

"This is now the third time, Thord, that you have come here on your son's account."

"But now I am through with him," said Thord, and folding up his pocketbook he said farewell and walked away.

The men slowly followed him.

A fortnight later, the father and son were rowing across the lake, one calm still day, to Storliden's to make arrangements for the wedding.

"This thwart is not secure," said the son, and stood up to straighten the seat on which he was sitting.

At the same moment the board he was standing on slipped from under him; he threw up his arms, uttered a shriek, and fell overboard.

"Take hold of the oar!" shouted the father, springing to his feet and holding out the oar.

But when the son had made a couple of efforts, he grew stiff.

"Wait a moment!" cried the father, and began to row toward his son. Then the son rolled over on his back, gave his father one long look, and sank.

Thord could scarcely believe it; he held the boat still, and stared at the spot where his son had gone down, as though he must surely come to the surface again. There rose some bubbles, then some more, and finally one large one that burst; and the lake lay there as smooth and bright as a mirror again.

For three days and three nights people saw the father rowing round and round the spot, without taking either food or sleep; he was dragging the lake for the body of his son. And toward morning of the third day he found it, and carried it in his arms up over the hills to his gard.

It might have been about a year from that day, when the priest, late one autumn evening, heard someone in the passage outside of the door, carefully trying to find the latch. The priest opened the door, and in walked a tall, thin man, with bowed form and white hair. The priest looked long at him before he recognized him. It was Thord.

"Are you out walking so late?" said the priest, and stood still in front of him.

"Ah, yes? it is late," said Thord, and took a seat.

The priest sat down also, as though waiting. A long, long silence followed. At last Thord said:

"I have something with me that I should like to give to the poor; I want it to be invested as a legacy in my son's name."

He rose, laid some money on the table, and sat down again. The priest counted it.

"It is a great deal of money," said he.

"It is half the price of my gard. I sold it today."

The priest sat long in silence. At last he asked, but gently:

"What do you propose to do now, Thord?"

"Something better."

They sat there for a while, Thord with downcast eyes, the priest with his eyes fixed on Thord. Presently the priest said, slowly and softly:

"I think your son has at last brought you a true blessing."

"Yes, I think so myself," said Thord, looking up, while two big tears coursed slowly down his cheeks. ∎

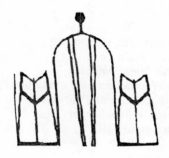

Henrik Ibsen (1828–1906)

THE MASTER BUILDER

Translated from the Norwegian by
Eva Le Gallienne

Characters

MASTER BUILDER HALVARD SOLNESS
MRS. ALINE SOLNESS, *his wife*
DOCTOR HERDAL, *the family doctor*
KNUT BROVIK, *former architect now employed by Solness*
RAGNAR BROVIK, *his son, a draughtsman*
KAJA FOSLI, *his niece, a bookkeeper*
MISS HILDE WANGEL *(vung′gəl)*
SOME LADIES
A CROWD IN THE GARDEN

The action takes place in the home of Master Builder Solness.

ACT ONE

SCENE: *A plainly furnished workroom in the house of* MASTER BUILDER SOLNESS. *In the left wall folding doors lead to the hall. To the right is the door to the inner rooms. In the back wall an open door leads to the draughtsmen's office. Downstage left a desk with books, papers, and writing materials. Above the door a stove. In the right-hand corner a sofa with a table and a couple of chairs. On the table a water pitcher and glass. Downstage right a smaller table with a rocking chair and an armchair. The work lights are lit in the draughtsmen's office and there are lighted lamps on the corner table and the desk.*

In the draughtsmen's office KNUT BROVIK *and his son* RAGNAR *are seated working over plans and calculations.* KAJA FOSLI *stands at the desk in the front room writing in a ledger.* KNUT BROVIK *is a thin old man with white hair and beard. He wears a somewhat threadbare but well-brushed black coat. He wears glasses and a white, rather discolored, neckcloth.* RAGNAR BROVIK *is a well-dressed, light-haired man in his thirties, with a slight stoop.* KAJA FOSLI *is a slight young girl just over twenty, carefully dressed and delicate-looking. She wears a green eyeshade. All three go on working for some time in silence.*

BROVIK *(rises suddenly from the drawing table, as though in distress; he breathes heavily and laboriously as he comes forward into the doorway).* It's no use! I can't bear it much longer!

KAJA *(goes toward him).* Dear Uncle—you feel very ill this evening, don't you?

BROVIK. I get worse every day.

RAGNAR *(has risen and comes forward).* Why don't you go home, Father—try and get some sleep?

BROVIK *(impatiently).* Go to bed, I suppose!

KAJA. Then, take a little walk—

RAGNAR. Yes, do. I'll go with you.

BROVIK *(insistently).* No, I won't go till he gets back. I must have it out with him *(With suppressed bitterness.)*—with the Boss. I must have it settled, once and for all.

KAJA *(anxiously).* Oh, no, Uncle—please wait—

RAGNAR. Better wait, Father.

BROVIK *(breathes painfully).* I haven't much time for waiting.

KAJA *(listening).* Sh! I hear him on the stairs! *(All three go back to work. A short pause.)*

(HALVARD SOLNESS *comes in from the hall. He is a middle-aged man but strong and vigorous, with close-cropped curly hair, a dark moustache, and thick dark eyebrows. His gray-green jacket is buttoned and has a turned-up collar and broad lapels. He wears a soft gray felt hat and carries a couple of portfolios under his arm.*)

SOLNESS *(by the door, points towards the draughtsmen's office and asks in a whisper).* Have they gone?

KAJA *(softly, shaking her head).* No. *(She takes off the eye-shade.)*

(SOLNESS *crosses the room, throws his hat on a chair, puts the portfolios on the table by the sofa and comes back toward the desk.* KAJA *continues to write in the ledger but seems nervous and uneasy.*)

SOLNESS *(out loud).* What are you entering there, Miss Fosli?

KAJA *(with a start).* It's just something that—

SOLNESS. Let me see, Miss Fosli—*(He bends over her, pretending to look in the ledger, and whispers.)* Kaja!

KAJA *(softly, still writing).* Yes?

SOLNESS. Why do you always take that shade off when I come in?

KAJA. Because I look so ugly with it on—

SOLNESS *(with a smile).* And you don't want to look ugly, Kaja?

KAJA *(half glancing at him).* No—not when you are here.

SOLNESS *(gently strokes her hair).* Poor, poor little Kaja!

KAJA *(bending her head).* Sh! They'll hear you!

(SOLNESS *strolls across to the right, turns and pauses at the draughtsmen's office.*)

SOLNESS. Did anyone call while I was out?

RAGNAR. Yes—those young people who want to build at Löv-strand—

SOLNESS *(in a growling tone).* Oh, those two! Well, they'll just have to wait—I'm not quite clear about the plans yet.

RAGNAR. They're very eager to see some drawings as soon as possible—

SOLNESS *(as before).* Yes, yes—I know! They're all the same!

BROVIK. They're so looking forward to having a home of their own.

SOLNESS. I know—the same old story! So they grab the first thing that comes along—a mere roof over their heads—nothing to call a home! No, thank you! If that's all they want, let them go to somebody else. Tell them that the next time they come!

BROVIK *(pushes his glasses up on his forehead and looks at him in amazement*). How do you mean—"somebody else"? Would you give up the commission?

SOLNESS (*impatiently*). Well, why not? I'm not interested in building that sort of trash! Anyhow—I know nothing about these people.

BROVIK. Oh, they're reliable enough. Ragnar knows them quite well—he sees quite a lot of them—they're thoroughly respectable young people.

SOLNESS. Respectable! Respectable! That's not the point! Why can you never understand me? You don't see what I mean! (*Angrily.*) I don't care to deal with a lot of strangers. Let them apply to whom they like as far as I'm concerned.

BROVIK (*rising*). You really mean that?

SOLNESS (*sulkily*). Why shouldn't I mean it? (*He walks about the room.*)

(BROVIK *exchanges a look with* RAGNAR, *who makes a gesture of warning; he then comes into the front room.*)

BROVIK. I'd like to have a talk with you, if I may.

SOLNESS. Of course.

BROVIK (*to* KAJA). Kaja—go in there for a few minutes.

KAJA (*uneasily*). But, Uncle—

BROVIK. Do as I say, child—and close the door after you.

(KAJA *goes reluctantly into the draughtsmen's office, and glancing anxiously and imploringly at* SOLNESS, *shuts the door.*)

BROVIK (*lowers his voice*). I don't want the poor children to know how ill I am.

SOLNESS. It's true—you haven't looked well lately.

BROVIK. I get weaker every day.

SOLNESS. Why don't you sit down?

BROVIK. Thanks—may I?

SOLNESS (*placing the armchair*). Here—sit here. Well?

BROVIK (*has seated himself with difficulty*). Well, you see— it's about Ragnar. I'm worried about Ragnar—what's to become of him?

SOLNESS. Why should you be worried about him? He can work here for me as long as he likes.

BROVIK. But that's just what he doesn't like; he feels he can't stay here any longer.

SOLNESS. Why not? He does pretty well here, it seems to me. But, of course, if he wants more money—

BROVIK. No, no! That has nothing to do with it. (*Impatiently.*) But he thinks it's time he did some work on his own account.

SOLNESS. Do you think Ragnar is capable enough for that?

BROVIK. That's just the point—I've begun to have doubts about the boy. After all, you've never given him a single word of encouragement. And yet—he must have talent—I can't help feeling that.

SOLNESS. But what does he know? He's had absolutely no experience—he's a good draughtsman—but is that enough?

BROVIK (*looks at him with concealed hatred and speaks in a hoarse voice*). Experience! You hadn't had much experience either when you came to work for me; but you managed to make a name for yourself! (*Breathes with difficulty.*) You pushed your way up—outstripping me and all the others!

SOLNESS. Well, you see, I was lucky.

BROVIK. Yes! You were lucky—that's true enough! All the more reason for you to be generous! I want to see Ragnar do some work on his own before I die. And then—I'd like to see them married, too.

SOLNESS (*sharply*). Married? Is Kaja so very keen on that?

BROVIK. Not Kaja so much; but Ragnar speaks of it every day. (*Imploringly.*) You must give him a chance! Help him to get some independent work! Let me see the boy do something on his own—

SOLNESS (*peevishly*). What the hell do you expect me to do? Drag commissions down from the moon for him?

BROVIK. He has the chance of a commission now—quite a big piece of work.

SOLNESS (*uneasily, startled*). Has he?

BROVIK. Yes, if you'd give your consent—

SOLNESS. What sort of work?

BROVIK (*with slight hesitation*). They might commission him to build that house at Lövstrand.

SOLNESS. That! I'm building that myself!

BROVIK. But it doesn't really interest you—

SOLNESS (*flaring up*). Not interest me! How dare you say that?

BROVIK. You said so yourself just now.

SOLNESS. Never mind what I said. So they'd let Ragnar build their house, would they?

BROVIK. Well, you see, he's a friend of theirs—and, just for fun, he's made some drawings—worked out some plans and estimates—

SOLNESS. And are they pleased with these drawings of his?

BROVIK. If you'd look them over—give them your approval—

SOLNESS. Then they'd give Ragnar the commission?

BROVIK. They seemed delighted with his ideas—they found them different—new and original, they said.

SOLNESS. New and original, eh? Not the old-fashioned stuff I go in for, I suppose! (*With suppressed irritation.*) So that's why they came while I was out; they wanted to see Ragnar!

BROVIK. No, no! They came to see you—they wanted to talk it over with you—find out if you would consider withdrawing from—

SOLNESS (*angrily*). I—withdraw!

BROVIK. If you approved of Ragnar's drawings—

SOLNESS. I retire in favor of your son!

BROVIK. Withdraw from the agreement, they meant—

SOLNESS. It comes to the same thing! (*Laughs angrily.*) So that's it, is it? Halvard Solness is to think about retiring now! He must make room for younger men—for the youngest of all, perhaps. He must make room—room—room!

BROVIK. God knows there's plenty of room for more than one single man—!

SOLNESS. I'm not so sure of that. But I tell you one thing—I shall never retire! I'll give way to no one! Never of my own free will. I'll never consent to that!

BROVIK (*rises with difficulty*). I see.—Don't you realize that I'm a dying man? Am I never to see any work of Ragnar's doing? Would you deny me the joy of seeing my faith in Ragnar justified?

SOLNESS (*turns away and mutters*). Don't say any more just now—

BROVIK. You must answer this one question! Am I to face death in such bitter poverty?

SOLNESS (*after a short struggle with himself he says in a low but firm voice*). You must face death as best you can.

BROVIK. Very well—so be it. (*Goes upstage.*)

SOLNESS (*following him, half in desperation*). Don't you understand—I can do nothing about it! I'm made that way—I can't change my nature!

BROVIK. No—I don't suppose you can. (*Reels and supports himself against the table.*) May I have a glass of water?

SOLNESS. Of course. (*Fills a glass and hands it to him.*) Here you are.

BROVIK. Thanks. (*Drinks and puts the glass down again.*)

SOLNESS (*goes and opens the door of the draughtsmen's office*). Ragnar—you'd better take your father home.

(RAGNAR *rises quickly. He and* KAJA *come into the front room.*)

RAGNAR. What's the matter, Father?

BROVIK. Give me your arm—Now, let us go.

RAGNAR. Very well. Put your things on too, Kaja.

SOLNESS. No. Miss Fosli must stay a moment—there's a letter I want written.

BROVIK (*looks at* SOLNESS). Good night. Sleep well—if you can.

SOLNESS. Good night.

(BROVIK *and* RAGNAR *go out by the hall door.* KAJA *goes to the desk.* SOLNESS *stands with bent head, to the right, by the armchair.*)

KAJA. Is there a letter?

SOLNESS (*curtly*). No, of course not. (*Looks at her sternly.*) Kaja!

KAJA (*anxiously, in a low voice*). Yes?

SOLNESS (*with an imperious gesture*). Come here! At once!

KAJA (*hesitantly*). Yes.

SOLNESS (*as before*). Nearer!

KAJA (*obeying*). What do you want of me?

SOLNESS (*looks at her for a moment*). Is all this your doing?

KAJA. No, no! You mustn't think that!

SOLNESS. But it's true that you want to get married—isn't it?

KAJA (*softly*). Ragnar and I have been engaged for four or five years—and so—

SOLNESS. And so you think it's about time you got married—is that it?

KAJA. Ragnar and Uncle are so insistent—I suppose I shall have to give in.

SOLNESS (*more gently*). But, Kaja—surely you must care for Ragnar a little bit, too?

KAJA. I cared a great deal for him once—before I came here to you.

SOLNESS. And now?

KAJA (*passionately, clasping her hands and holding them out toward him*). Now there's only one person in the world I care about—you know that! I shall never care for anyone else!

SOLNESS. Yes—that's what you say! And yet you'd go away—leave me here to struggle on alone.

KAJA. But couldn't I stay here with you—even if Ragnar—?

SOLNESS (*dismissing the idea*). No! That's out of the question! If Ragnar goes off and starts work on his own—he'll need you himself.

KAJA (*wringing her hands*). Oh, I don't see how I *can* leave you! It's utterly impossible!

SOLNESS. Then get these foolish ideas out of Ragnar's head! By all means marry him if you like—(*In a different tone.*) I mean . . . he has a good position here; for his own sake, try and persuade him not to give it up. For then—I'll be able to keep you here too, my dear little Kaja.

KAJA. Yes—yes—how wonderful that would be—if we could only manage it.

SOLNESS (*takes her head in his hands and whispers*). I can't do without you—I must have you near me, Kaja—do you understand? I must have you near me—

KAJA (*with nervous exultation*). Oh, God!

SOLNESS (*kisses her hair*). Kaja!—Kaja!

KAJA (*sinks down at his feet*). You're so good to me! So incredibly good to me!

SOLNESS (*vehemently*). Get up! For God's sake, get up! I hear someone coming! (*He helps her to her feet. She staggers over to the desk.*)

> (MRS. SOLNESS *enters by the door on the right. She is thin and seems wasted with grief, but shows traces of bygone beauty. Blond ringlets. Dressed in good taste, wholly in black. Speaks somewhat slowly, in a plaintive voice.*)

MRS. SOLNESS (*in the doorway*). Halvard!

SOLNESS (*turns*). Oh—Is that you, my dear?

MRS. SOLNESS (*with a glance at* KAJA). I hope I'm not disturbing you.

SOLNESS. Of course not—Miss Fosli has just a short letter to write—

MRS. SOLNESS. Yes—so I see.

SOLNESS. What did you want, Aline?

MRS. SOLNESS. I just wanted to tell you Dr. Herdal is in the drawing room—won't you come in and join us, Halvard?

SOLNESS (*gives her a suspicious glance*). Hm . . . Has the doctor anything special to say to me?

MRS. SOLNESS. Nothing special, Halvard. He really came to call on me, but he thought he'd like to say how-do-you-do to you at the same time.

SOLNESS (*laughs to himself*). Yes, I dare say—Well, just ask him to wait.

MRS. SOLNESS. Then you'll come in presently?

SOLNESS. Perhaps—Presently—presently, my dear—in a little while.

MRS. SOLNESS (*with another glance at* KAJA). You won't forget, Halvard? (*She withdraws, closing the door behind her.*)

KAJA (*softly*). Oh dear! I'm afraid Mrs. Solness was annoyed with me—

SOLNESS. Not at all. No more than usual, at any rate. Still, I think you'd better go now, Kaja.

KAJA. Yes—I suppose I *must* go now.

SOLNESS (*severely*). And mind you get this matter settled for me—do you hear?

KAJA. Oh, if it was only a question of *me*—

SOLNESS. I will have it settled, I say! By tomorrow at latest!

KAJA (*anxiously*). If the worst comes to the worst—I'd gladly break off my engagement—

SOLNESS (*angrily*). Break off your engagement! You must be mad!

KAJA (*distractedly*). I *must* stay here with you. It's impossible for me to leave you—utterly impossible!

SOLNESS (*in a sudden outburst*). But—damn it—what about Ragnar, then? It's Ragnar that I—

KAJA (*looks at him with eyes full of terror*). You mean . . . it's mostly because of Ragnar that you—?

SOLNESS (*controlling himself*). No—no! Of course not! You don't understand me—Don't you see—it's you that I want, Kaja —you above everything. And because of that, you must persuade Ragnar to stay on here. There—there—now, run along home.

KAJA. Yes. Well—good night.

SOLNESS. Good night. (*As she starts to go.*) Oh, by the way— did Ragnar leave those drawings of his here?

KAJA. I don't think he took them with him—

SOLNESS. Find them for me, will you? I might have a look at them, after all.

KAJA (*happily*). Oh! *Would* you?

SOLNESS. Just for your sake, little Kaja—Hurry up now! Find them for me. Quickly!—Do you hear?

(KAJA *hurries into the draughtsmen's office, searches anxiously in the table drawer, finds a portfolio and brings it in with her.*)

KAJA. Here they are—

SOLNESS. Good. Just put them on the table.

KAJA (*puts down the portfolio*). Good night—You *will* think kindly of me?

SOLNESS. You know I always do that—Good night, dear little Kaja. (*Glances to the door right.*) Go now—Go!

(MRS. SOLNESS *and* DR. HERDAL *enter by the door on the right. He is a stoutish elderly man, with a round, self-satisfied face.*)

MRS. SOLNESS (*still in the doorway*). Halvard, I really can't keep the doctor any longer.

SOLNESS. Bring him in here, then.

MRS. SOLNESS (to KAJA, *who is turning down the desk lamp*). Have you finished the letter, Miss Fosli?

KAJA (*confused*). The letter—?

SOLNESS. Yes.—It was just a short one.

MRS. SOLNESS. It must have been very short.

SOLNESS. You may go now, Miss Fosli. And be sure to be here in good time in the morning.

KAJA. I will, Mr. Solness. Good night, Mrs. Solness. (*Exits to hall.*)

MRS. SOLNESS. How very lucky you were to find that young girl, Halvard.

SOLNESS. Yes. She's useful in many ways.

MRS. SOLNESS. So it seems.

HERDAL. Is she good at bookkeeping, too?

SOLNESS. Well—she's had a good deal of experience these last two years—and she's so good-natured and willing—anxious to help in every way.

MRS. SOLNESS. That must be very gratifying.

SOLNESS. It is—especially when you're not accustomed to that sort of thing.

MRS. SOLNESS (*in a tone of gentle remonstrance*). How can you say that, Halvard?

SOLNESS. I'm sorry, my dear Aline. I beg your pardon.

MRS. SOLNESS. Don't mention it. So—Doctor, you'll come back later and join us for a cup of tea?

HERDAL. I have just one more patient to see—then I'll be back.

MRS. SOLNESS. Thank you, Doctor. (*She goes out by the door on the right.*)

SOLNESS. Are you in a hurry, Doctor?

HERDAL. No, not at all.

SOLNESS. May I talk to you for a little while?

HERDAL. With the greatest of pleasure.

SOLNESS. Good—then, let's sit down. (*He motions the doctor to take the rocking chair and sits down himself in the armchair. He gives the doctor a searching look.*) Tell me—did you notice anything about Aline?

HERDAL. Just now—while she was here?

SOLNESS. Yes. In her attitude toward me. Did you notice anything?

HERDAL (*smiling*). Well—one could hardly help noticing that your wife—

SOLNESS. Yes?

HERDAL. That your wife doesn't seem to care much for this Miss Fosli.

SOLNESS. Oh, is that all! Yes—I've noticed that myself.

HERDAL. And I suppose that's not really very surprising, is it?

SOLNESS. What?

HERDAL. That she should resent your seeing so much of another woman.

SOLNESS. Perhaps you're right—and Aline too. But I'm afraid that can't be helped.

HERDAL. Couldn't you get a man for the job?

SOLNESS. You mean an ordinary clerk? No, that wouldn't do at all.

HERDAL. But, what if your wife—you know how nervous and delicate she is—what if this situation is too much of a strain for her?

SOLNESS. Even so—that can make no difference. I've strong reasons for keeping Kaja Fosli; no one else can take her place.

HERDAL. No one else?

SOLNESS (curtly). No, no one!

HERDAL. Might I ask you a rather personal question, Mr. Solness?

SOLNESS. By all means.

HERDAL. One must admit that in some things women have an uncomfortably keen intuition—

SOLNESS. That's true, but—?

HERDAL. And, if your wife so thoroughly resents this Kaja Fosli—

SOLNESS. Well?

HERDAL. Is there really not the faintest reason for this instinctive dislike?

SOLNESS (looks at him and rises). Aha!

HERDAL. Now don't be angry—be frank with me; isn't there?

SOLNESS (with curt decision). No.

HERDAL. None whatever, eh?

SOLNESS. Only her own suspicious nature.

HERDAL. I gather there have been quite a number of women in your life, Mr. Solness.

SOLNESS. That may be true—

HERDAL. And you were quite attached to some of them, no doubt?

SOLNESS. I don't deny it.

HERDAL. But in this case—there's nothing of that sort?

SOLNESS. Nothing at all—on my side.

HERDAL. But—on hers?

SOLNESS. I don't think you have the right to ask that question, Doctor.

HERDAL. Well—we were discussing your wife's intuition, you know—

SOLNESS. Yes—so we were. For that matter—Aline's intuition, as you call it, has been proved right more than once.

HERDAL. There! You see!

SOLNESS (sits down). Dr. Herdal—I'd like to tell you a strange story—that is, if you'd care to hear it—

HERDAL. I like listening to strange stories.

SOLNESS. Very well. Perhaps you remember that I took Knut Brovik and his son into my employ—when the old man's business failed—

HERDAL. Yes—I remember vaguely—

SOLNESS. They're useful fellows, you see—both highly gifted, each in his own way. But then, of course, young Ragnar got himself engaged—and decided he wanted to get married and start to build on his own account. They're all the same, these young people—

HERDAL (laughing). They do have a bad habit of wanting to get married!

SOLNESS. But that didn't happen to suit me—I needed Ragnar myself—and the old man too; he's a first-class engineer; good at calculating bearing-strains, cubic contents—all that technical stuff, you know—

HERDAL. No doubt that's indispensable.

SOLNESS. Yes, it is; but Ragnar was determined to work on his own; nothing would dissuade him.

HERDAL. Then what made him stay on with you?

SOLNESS. I'll tell you how that happened. One day Kaja Fosli came here to the office. She came to see them on some errand or other—she had never been here before. When I saw how infatuated Ragnar was with her, it occurred to me that if I were to give her a job here, I might get him to stay on too—

HERDAL. That was logical enough—

SOLNESS. Yes, but wait a minute! I never said a word about it at the time. I just stood looking at her, and wished with all my might that I could persuade her to work here. I simply said a few friendly words to her, and then she went away.

HERDAL. Well?

SOLNESS. Well, the next day, toward evening—after old Brovik and Ragnar had gone home—she came here again, and behaved as if we'd come to some agreement.

HERDAL. Agreement? What about?

SOLNESS. About the very thing I'd had in mind the day before —though I had actually never said a word about it.

HERDAL. That was strange—

SOLNESS. Yes, wasn't it? It was as though she'd read my thoughts. She asked what her duties were to be—when I wanted her to start work—and so on—

HERDAL. I suppose she thought she'd like a job here, so she could be near Ragnar.

SOLNESS. That's what I thought at first; but that wasn't it. No sooner had she started to work here, than she began to drift away from him.

HERDAL. Over to you, you mean?

SOLNESS. Exactly. She seemed to be constantly aware of me. Whenever I look at her—even when her back's turned—I can tell that she feels it; she trembles nervously whenever I come near her—

HERDAL. That's easily explained—

SOLNESS. Perhaps. But how did she know what I was thinking that first evening? Why did she behave as if I had asked her to come here, when actually I had only thought about it? I had wished it—had willed it, if you like, but silently; inwardly. How did she know? Can you explain that, Dr. Herdal?

HERDAL. No, I must confess I can't.

SOLNESS. No—you can't, can you? That's why I've never mentioned it— But it's become a damn nuisance to me in the long run; every day I have to keep up this pretense—and it's not fair to her, poor girl. (*Vehemently.*) But there's nothing I can do about it. If she leaves me—then Ragnar will leave too.

HERDAL. Haven't you explained this to your wife?

SOLNESS. No.

HERDAL. Well—why on earth don't you?

SOLNESS (*looks at him intently and says in a low voice*). Because—well—because I find a sort of salutary self-torture in allowing Aline to do me this injustice.

HERDAL (*shakes his head*). I'm afraid I don't understand you, Mr. Solness.

SOLNESS. Yes—don't you see? It's like paying off part of a huge, immeasurable debt.

HERDAL. To your wife?

SOLNESS. Yes. It seems to relieve my mind. I feel I can breathe more freely for a while.

HERDAL. I don't understand you in the least.

SOLNESS. Very well—then let's not talk about it. (*He saunters across the room, comes back and stops beside the table. He looks at the doctor with a sly smile.*) Well, Doctor? I suppose you think you've drawn me out very cleverly?

HERDAL (*with some irritation*). "Drawn you out?" Again I haven't the faintest idea what you mean, Mr. Solness.

SOLNESS. Oh, come! Why deny it? Do you suppose I haven't noticed it?

HERDAL. Noticed what?

SOLNESS (*slowly, in a low voice*). The way you've been observing me of late.

HERDAL. Observing you? *I*? Why should I do that?

SOLNESS. Because you think that I'm—Damn it! Because you think the same of me that Aline does!

HERDAL. And what does *she* think of you?

SOLNESS (*recovering his self-control*). Aline has begun to think that I'm—well—let's call it ill.

HERDAL. You? Ill? She's never mentioned such a thing to me. What does she think is the matter with you?

SOLNESS (*leans over the back of the chair and says in a whisper*). Aline is convinced that I am mad. That's what she thinks.

HERDAL (*rising*). But, my dear Mr. Solness—!

SOLNESS. I tell you it *is* so! And she's convinced you of it too! Don't think I haven't noticed it. I'm not fooled so easily, Dr. Herdal!

HERDAL (*looks at him in amazement*). I give you my word, Mr. Solness, such a thought has never crossed my mind.

SOLNESS (*with an incredulous smile*). It hasn't—eh?

HERDAL. Never! Nor your wife's mind either—I could swear to that.

SOLNESS. I wouldn't do that if I were you. Who knows? Perhaps, in a way, she may be right.

HERDAL. Well, really—I must say!

SOLNESS (*interrupting with a sweep of his hand*). Well, well —my dear Doctor—we won't discuss it any further. We must simply agree to differ. (*Changes to a tone of quiet amusement.*) But I suppose, Doctor—

HERDAL. What?

SOLNESS. Since you don't believe that I'm ill—or crazy—or mad—or whatever you want to call it—

HERDAL. Well?

SOLNESS. I suppose you consider me a very happy man?

HERDAL. Would I be mistaken in that?

SOLNESS (*laughs*). No, no! Of course not! God forbid! To be Halvard Solness—Solness the great Master Builder! What could be more delightful!

HERDAL. You've been an amazingly lucky man—I should think you'd admit that!

SOLNESS. I have indeed—I can't complain on that score.

HERDAL. Ever since the old house burned down—that was your first bit of luck.

SOLNESS (*seriously*). It was Aline's old home—don't forget that.

HERDAL. Yes. It must have been a great grief to her.

SOLNESS. She never got over it—though that was twelve or thirteen years ago.

HERDAL. No—the consequences were too tragic.

SOLNESS. It was all too much for her.

HERDAL. Still—that fire is what started your career; you built your success on those ruins; you were just a poor boy from a country village, and now you're at the head of your profession. You must admit, luck was on your side, Mr. Solness.

SOLNESS (*looks at him in embarrassment*). Yes—That's just why I'm so horribly afraid.

HERDAL. You afraid? Why? Because you've had the luck on your side?

SOLNESS. Yes—it fills me with terror. Some day that luck will turn, you see.

HERDAL. Nonsense! What should make the luck turn?

SOLNESS (*firmly. With assurance*). The younger generation.

HERDAL. The younger generation? Oh, come now! You're not an old man yet! Your position here is more assured than ever.

SOLNESS. The luck will turn. I know it. I feel the day approaching. Some young man will suddenly shout: "Get out of my way!"; then all the others will crowd after him, clamoring, threatening: "Make room! Make room! Make room!" You'll see, Doctor—one of these days the younger generation will come knocking at my door—

HERDAL (*laughing*). Well, what if they do?

SOLNESS. What if they do? That will be the end of Master Builder Solness.

(*There is a knock at the door on the left.*)

SOLNESS (*with a start*). What is that? Didn't you hear?

HERDAL. Someone knocked at the door.

SOLNESS (*loudly*). Come in!

(HILDE WANGEL *enters from the hall. She is of medium height, supple, and delicate of build. Somewhat sunburnt. She wears hiking clothes, carries a knapsack on her back, a plaid in a strap and an alpenstock.*)

HILDE (*goes straight up to Solness, her eyes sparkling with happiness*). Good evening!

SOLNESS (*looks at her doubtfully*). Good evening—

HILDE (*laughs*). Don't tell me you don't recognize me!

SOLNESS. I'm sorry—but, just for the moment—

HERDAL (*approaching*). But I recognize you, my dear young lady—

HILDE (*pleased*). Oh! I remember you! You're the one who—

HERDAL. Of course! (*To* SOLNESS.) We met up in the mountains last summer. (*To* HILDE.) What became of the other ladies?

HILDE. They went on to the West Coast—

HERDAL. Didn't they approve of all the fun we had?

HILDE. Probably not!

HERDAL (*shaking his finger at her*). You must admit—you did flirt with us a bit!

HILDE. What did you expect? I couldn't compete with all that knitting.

HERDAL (*laughs*). No! Knitting's not much in your line!

SOLNESS. Have you just arrived in town?

HILDE. Just this moment.

HERDAL. All alone, Miss Wangel?

HILDE. All alone!

SOLNESS. Wangel? Is your name Wangel?

HILDE (*looks at him with amused surprise*). Of course it is!

SOLNESS. Are you by any chance Dr. Wangel's daughter—from Lysanger?

HILDE (*as before*). Of course! Whose daughter did you think I was?

SOLNESS. Oh, then I suppose we met up there; that summer I built the tower on the old church.

HILDE (*more seriously*). Of course that's when we met!

SOLNESS. Well—that's a long time ago.

HILDE (*looks at him intently*). It's exactly the ten years.

SOLNESS. You must have been a mere child then.

HILDE (*carelessly*). I was about twelve or thirteen—

HERDAL. Is this your first trip to town, Miss Wangel?

HILDE. Yes, it is.

SOLNESS. And have you no friends here?

HILDE. Just you—and your wife, of course.

SOLNESS. Oh, so you know her too?

HILDE. Very slightly—we met quite briefly, at the sanatorium.

SOLNESS. Oh, up there?

HILDE. Yes. She asked me to come and see her if ever I came to town. (*Smiles.*) Not that that was necessary, of course.

SOLNESS. Funny she should never have mentioned it.

(HILDE *puts her stick down by the stove, takes off her knap-sack and lays it and the plaid on the sofa.* DR. HERDAL *offers to help her.* SOLNESS *stands and gazes at her.*)

HILDE. Well—is it all right for me to stay the night here?

SOLNESS. I expect that can be managed—

HILDE. You see—I didn't bring any clothes with me—just what I have on. I have a change of underwear in my knapsack—but that'll have to go to the wash—it's very dirty.

SOLNESS. We'll take care of that—I'll just call my wife.

HERDAL. Meanwhile, I'll visit my patient.

SOLNESS. Yes, do. And you'll come back later?

HERDAL (*with a playful glance at* HILDE). Don't worry—I'll be back! (*Laughs.*) You were right after all, Mr. Solness—

SOLNESS. How do you mean?

HERDAL. The younger generation did come knocking at your door!

SOLNESS (*cheerfully*). In quite a different way though!

HERDAL. Oh, in a very different way! That's undeniable!

(DR. HERDAL *goes out by the hall door.* SOLNESS *opens the door on the right and calls through to the other room.*)

SOLNESS. Aline! Would you be kind enough to come in here a minute? There's a Miss Wangel here—a friend of yours.

MRS. SOLNESS (*appears in the doorway*). Who did you say it was? (*Sees* HILDE.) Oh, it's you, Miss Wangel. (*Goes to her and shakes hands.*) So you did come to town, after all.

SOLNESS. Miss Wangel just arrived. She wants to know if she may stay the night here.

MRS. SOLNESS. Here with us? Of course—with pleasure.

SOLNESS. Just till she can get her clothes in order, you know.

MRS. SOLNESS. I'll help you as best I can—it's no more than my duty. Your trunk will be here presently, I suppose?

HILDE. Oh, I have no trunk!

MRS. SOLNESS. Well—everything will work out for the best, I dare say. If you'll just stay and talk to my husband for a while, I'll see about getting a room comfortable for you.

SOLNESS. Why not put her in one of the nurseries? They're all ready as it is—

MRS. SOLNESS. Yes—we have plenty of room there—(*To* HILDE.) Sit down now and rest a little. (*She goes out right.*)

(HILDE *with her hands behind her back strolls about the room looking at various things.* SOLNESS *stands down front beside the table and follows her with his eyes.*)

HILDE (*stops and looks at him*). Are there so many nurseries here?

SOLNESS. There are three nurseries in the house.

HILDE. You must have a great many children!

SOLNESS. No, we have no children. So you'll have to be the child here for the time being.

HILDE. Yes—for tonight. I shan't cry! I intend to sleep like a log!

SOLNESS. You must be very tired.

HILDE. Not a bit! No, it's not that; but it's such fun just to lie in bed and dream—

SOLNESS. Do you usually dream at night?

HILDE. Almost always.

SOLNESS. What do you dream about most?

HILDE. I won't tell you! Some other time, perhaps. *(She again strolls about the room, stops at the desk and examines some of the books and papers.)*

SOLNESS. Are you looking for something?

HILDE. No—I was just interested in all these things. *(Turns toward him.)* Perhaps I shouldn't touch them?

SOLNESS. Go right ahead!

HILDE. Do you write in this great ledger?

SOLNESS. No. That's for the accountant.

HILDE. A woman?

SOLNESS *(smiles)*. Yes, of course.

HILDE. Does she work here every day?

SOLNESS. Yes.

HILDE. Is she married?

SOLNESS. No; she's single.

HILDE. Indeed!

SOLNESS. But she expects to marry soon.

HILDE. Well—that'll be nice for her.

SOLNESS. Yes—but not so nice for me—for then I'll have no one to help me.

HILDE. You're sure to find someone else just as good.

SOLNESS. How would you like to stay here—and write in the ledger?

HILDE. Not I, thank you! Nothing like that for me! *(She again strolls across the room and sits down in the rocking chair. SOLNESS joins her at the table.)* There are better things than that to be done around here!—*(Looks at him with a smile.)*—Don't you think so too?

SOLNESS. Unquestionably! I suppose you'll start by visiting all the shops and decking yourself out in the height of fashion.

HILDE *(amused)*. No—I think I'll leave the shops alone!

SOLNESS. Why?

HILDE. Well—you see—I'm all out of money!

SOLNESS. No trunk and no money—eh?

HILDE. Neither the one nor the other! But what does that matter now!

SOLNESS. You know—I really like you for that!

HILDE. Only for that?

SOLNESS. For that among other things—(*Sits in the armchair.*) Is your father still alive?

HILDE. Yes—Father's alive.

SOLNESS. Do you plan to study here?

HILDE. No, that hadn't occurred to me.

SOLNESS. But I suppose you'll be here for some time?

HILDE. It depends how things turn out. (*She sits awhile looking at him, half seriously, half smiling. Then she takes off her hat and puts it on the table in front of her.*) Master Builder?

SOLNESS. Yes?

HILDE. Have you a very bad memory?

SOLNESS. Bad memory? No—not that I know of—

HILDE. Well—aren't you going to talk to me about what happened up there?

SOLNESS (*startled for a moment*). At Lysanger? (*Indifferently.*) I don't see much to talk about in that.

HILDE (*looks at him reproachfully*). How can you sit there and say such things!

SOLNESS. Well—suppose you talk to *me* about it.

HILDE. When the tower was finished—don't you remember all the excitement in the town?

SOLNESS. Yes—I shall never forget that day.

HILDE (*smiles*). Oh, you won't, won't you? That's kind of you!

SOLNESS. Kind?

HILDE. There was a band in the churchyard and hundreds and hundreds of people—we schoolgirls were dressed all in white—and we all carried flags—

SOLNESS. Oh, yes! Those flags! I certainly remember them—

HILDE. And then you climbed up the scaffolding—right to the very top. You had a great wreath in your hand, and you hung it high up on the weather vane—

SOLNESS (*curtly interrupting*). I used to do that in those days—it's an old custom, you know.

HILDE. It was wonderfully thrilling to stand below and look up at you. What if he were to fall over—he, the Master Builder himself!

SOLNESS (*as though trying to divert her from the subject*).

That might easily have happened too; one of those little devils dressed in white, carried on so and kept screaming up at me—

HILDE (*sparkling with pleasure*).—"Hurrah for Master Builder Solness!"

SOLNESS.—and then she kept brandishing her flag and waving it so wildly—the sight of it made me feel quite dizzy.

HILDE (*seriously. In a low voice*). That particular little devil— that was I.

SOLNESS (*staring at her intently*). Of course—I see that now. It must have been you.

HILDE. It was so wonderfully thrilling! It didn't seem possible to me that any Master Builder in the whole world could build such a tremendously high tower. And then to see you up there yourself—right at the very top—as large as life! And to know that you weren't in the least bit dizzy—that was what made one so—dizzy to think of it!

SOLNESS. How could you be so sure that I was not—?

HILDE. You dizzy? Of course not! I knew that with my whole being! Besides—if you had been—you could never have stood up there and sung.

SOLNESS (*looks at her in amazement*). Sung? Did I sing?

HILDE. Of course you did!

SOLNESS (*shakes his head*). I've never sung a note in my life.

HILDE. Well—you sang then! It sounded like harps in the air.

SOLNESS (*thoughtfully*). There's something very strange about all this.

HILDE (*is silent awhile, looking at him; then says in a low voice*). But of course the *real* thing—happened afterwards.

SOLNESS. What "real" thing?

HILDE (*sparkling with vivacity*). I surely needn't remind you of *that*?

SOLNESS. Please—*do* remind me a little of *that* too!

HILDE. Don't you remember, a great dinner was given for you at the Club—

SOLNESS. Yes. That must have been the same afternoon—for I left the next morning.

HILDE. And from the Club, you came on to our house—

SOLNESS. I believe you're right, Miss Wangel! It's amazing! You seem to remember every little detail—

HILDE. "Little details"—is that what you call them? I suppose it was a "little detail" too that I happened to be alone in the room when you came in?

SOLNESS. Oh? Were you alone?

HILDE (*ignoring this*). You didn't call me a "little devil" then.

SOLNESS. No. I suppose not—

HILDE. You told me I looked lovely in my white dress. You said I looked like a little princess.

SOLNESS. I expect you did, Miss Wangel. And I remember feeling so free and buoyant that day—

HILDE. And then you said that when I grew up I was to be *your* princess—

SOLNESS *(laughing a little)*. Well—well! I said that too, did I?

HILDE. Yes, you did. And when I asked how long I'd have to wait, you said you'd come back again in ten years—and carry me off like a troll—to Spain, or some such place. And you promised to buy me a kingdom there.

SOLNESS *(as before)*. There's nothing like a good dinner to make you feel generous! But—did I really say all that?

HILDE *(laughing to herself)*. Yes, you did. You even told me what the kingdom was to be called.

SOLNESS. Well—what?

HILDE. It was to be called the Kingdom of Orangia, you said.

SOLNESS. A very appetizing name!

HILDE. I didn't like it a bit! It sounded almost as if you were making fun of me.

SOLNESS. Of course I *couldn't* have been doing that.

HILDE. Well, I should hope not—considering what you did next.

SOLNESS. What in God's name did I do next?

HILDE. Don't tell me you've forgotten that too! I know better; you couldn't *help* remembering it.

SOLNESS. Won't you give me just a little hint? Well?

HILDE *(looks at him intently)*. You came and kissed me, Master Builder.

SOLNESS *(rising, open-mouthed)*. I did!

HILDE. Yes, you did. You took me in your arms and bent my head back and kissed me—many times.

SOLNESS. Now really—my dear Miss Wangel—!

HILDE. You surely don't intend to deny it?

SOLNESS. I most certainly *do* deny it!

HILDE *(looks at him scornfully)*. Oh, indeed! *(She goes slowly up to the stove and remains standing motionless, her face averted from him, her hands behind her back. Short pause.)*

SOLNESS *(moves up behind her cautiously)*. Miss Wangel—! *(HILDE is silent and doesn't move.)* Now don't stand there like a statue. You must have dreamt these things—*(Lays his hand on her arm.)* Now look here! *(HILDE moves her arm impatiently. A thought strikes him.)* Or perhaps—wait a minute! There's some mystery behind all this—I must have thought about it. I must have willed it, wished it, longed to do it, and then—Perhaps that would explain it. (HILDE *is still silent.*) Oh, very well then—damn it!—then I *did* do it, I suppose!

HILDE (*turns her head a little but without looking at him*). Then you admit it now?

SOLNESS. Anything you like.

HILDE. You took me in your arms?

SOLNESS. Yes—

HILDE. Bent my head back?

SOLNESS. Very far back—

HILDE. And kissed me?

SOLNESS. Yes, I did.

HILDE. Many times?

SOLNESS. As many times as you like.

HILDE (*turns toward him quickly. Once more her eyes are sparkling with happiness*). There, you see! I got it out of you at last!

SOLNESS (*with a slight smile*). Yes—how could I possibly have forgotten a thing like that.

HILDE (*again a little sulkily, retreats from him*). Oh, you've probably kissed so many girls in your day!

SOLNESS. No—you mustn't think that of me!

(HILDE *sits down in the armchair.* SOLNESS *stands leaning against the rocking chair and watches her intently.*)

SOLNESS. Miss Wangel!

HILDE. Well?

SOLNESS. And then what happened? I mean—what came of all this between us two?

HILDE. Nothing came of it—you know that perfectly well—just then all the others came in, and then—isch!

SOLNESS. Of course—all the others came in. To think of my forgetting that too.

HILDE. I don't believe you've really forgotten anything. You're just a bit ashamed, that's all. You couldn't possibly forget a thing of that sort.

SOLNESS. No—one wouldn't think so.

HILDE (*again sparkling with life*). I suppose, now, you'll tell me you've forgotten what date it was?

SOLNESS. What date?

HILDE. Yes—on what day of what month did you hang the wreath on the tower? Well? Tell me at once!

SOLNESS. I'm afraid I've forgotten the actual date—I remember it was ten years ago, some time in the autumn.

HILDE (*nods her head slowly several times*). Yes, it *was* ten years ago—on the nineteenth of September.

SOLNESS. Yes, it must have been around that time. Fancy your remembering that too! But, wait a minute—isn't it—? Yes! It's the nineteenth of September today.

HILDE. Yes it is. And the ten years are up. And you didn't come as you had promised me.

SOLNESS. Promised? Threatened, I suppose you mean.

HILDE. Why? It didn't seem like a threat to me.

SOLNESS. Well, then—making a little fun of you, perhaps.

HILDE. Was that all you wanted? To make fun of me?

SOLNESS. I was just teasing you, I suppose—I don't remember anything about it—but it couldn't have been anything else; after all, at that time you were only a child.

HILDE. Don't be so sure! Perhaps I wasn't quite such a child either. Not quite such a callow little brat as you imagine.

SOLNESS (*with a searching look*). Did you really, in all seriousness, expect me to come back again?

HILDE (*conceals a half-teasing smile*). Of course I did!

SOLNESS. You really expected me to come back to your home and carry you off with me?

HILDE. Just like a troll—yes!

SOLNESS. And make a princess of you?

HILDE. That's what you promised.

SOLNESS. And give you a kingdom as well?

HILDE (*gazing at the ceiling*). Why not? Oh, perhaps not an ordinary, *everyday* sort of kingdom—

SOLNESS. But something else just as good?

HILDE. Oh, at *least* as good! (*Looks at him a moment.*) I thought to myself—if he can build the highest church tower in the world, he must surely be able to raise some sort of a kingdom as well—

SOLNESS (*shakes his head*). I can't quite make you out, Miss Wangel.

HILDE. Can't you? It all seems so simple to me.

SOLNESS. No, I can't make out whether you mean all you say —or whether you're just joking.

HILDE (*smiles*). Making fun of you, perhaps—I too?

SOLNESS. Precisely—making fun of us both. (*Looks at her.*) How long have you known that I was married?

HILDE. I've always known that. Why? What makes you ask?

SOLNESS (*lightly*). Oh, nothing—it just occurred to me. (*Looks at her seriously and says in a low voice.*) Why have you come here?

HILDE. I want my kingdom—the time is up!

SOLNESS (laughs involuntarily). What an amazing girl you are!

HILDE (gaily). Out with my kingdom, Master Builder. (Raps the table with her fingers.) My kingdom on the table!

SOLNESS (pushing the rocking chair nearer and sitting down). No, but seriously—why have you come? What do you really want to do here?

HILDE. Well, to begin with—I want to go round and look at all the things you've built.

SOLNESS. That'll give you plenty of exercise!

HILDE. Yes—I know you've built a tremendous lot!

SOLNESS. I have. Especially these last few years—

HILDE. Many church towers too? Immensely high ones?

SOLNESS. No, I don't build church towers any more. Nor churches either.

HILDE. Then what do you build now?

SOLNESS. Homes for human beings.

HILDE (thoughtfully). Couldn't you build some sort of a—some sort of a church tower over those homes as well?

SOLNESS (with a start). What do you mean by that?

HILDE. I mean—something that soars—that points straight up into the free air—with the vane at a dizzy height!

SOLNESS (pondering). How extraordinary that you should say that. That's what I've always longed to do.

HILDE (impatiently). Well—why don't you do it then?

SOLNESS (shakes his head). I don't think people would approve of it.

HILDE. Wouldn't they? How can they be so stupid!

SOLNESS (in a lighter tone). I'm building a home for myself, however—just over there—

HILDE. For yourself?

SOLNESS. Yes—it's almost finished—and there's a tower on that.

HILDE. A high tower?

SOLNESS. Yes.

HILDE. Very high?

SOLNESS. Much too high for a home—people are sure to say!

HILDE. I'll go out and see that tower first thing in the morning, Master Builder.

SOLNESS (sits resting his cheek on his hand and gazes at her). What's your name, Miss Wangel—Your first name, I mean?

HILDE. My name's Hilde, of course.

SOLNESS (as before). Hilde, eh?

HILDE. You must have known that! You called me Hilde yourself, that day when you—misbehaved.

SOLNESS. Did I really?

HILDE. Yes. Only then you said "little Hilde"—I didn't like that.

SOLNESS. So you didn't like that, Miss Hilde.

HILDE. Not at a time like that! *Princess* Hilde, however, would sound very well, I think.

SOLNESS. Princess Hilde of—what was to be the name of the kingdom?

HILDE. I'll have nothing more to do with that stupid kingdom! I'm determined to have quite a different one.

SOLNESS *(leaning back in the chair, still gazing at her)*. Isn't it strange! The more I think of it, the more it seems to me that all these years I've been tormented by—

HILDE. By what?

SOLNESS. By some half-forgotten experience that I kept trying to recapture. But I never could remember clearly what it was.

HILDE. You should have tied a knot in your handkerchief, Master Builder.

SOLNESS. Then I should have only tormented myself wondering what the knot was about.

HILDE. Yes! There are trolls of that sort in the world too!

SOLNESS *(rises slowly)*. What a good thing it is that you've come to me now.

HILDE *(looks deep into his eyes)*. Is it a good thing?

SOLNESS. Yes—don't you see? I've been so lonely here—gazing at everything so helplessly. *(In a lower voice.)* I must tell you, Hilde—I've begun to be so afraid—so terribly afraid of the younger generation.

HILDE *(with a little snort of contempt)*. The younger generation! Surely that's nothing to be afraid of!

SOLNESS. Oh, yes it is! That's why I've locked and barred myself in. *(Mysteriously.)* I tell you one of these days the younger generation will thunder at my door—they'll break through and overwhelm me!

HILDE. In that case, I think that you yourself should go out and open the door to the younger generation.

SOLNESS. Open the door?

HILDE. Of course! Let them come in to you—in friendship.

SOLNESS. No, no! Don't you see? The younger generation comes bringing retribution. It heralds the turn of fortune; it marches triumphantly, under a new banner.

HILDE *(rises, looks at him, and says with quivering lips)*. Can I be of use to you, Master Builder?

SOLNESS. You can indeed! For you too march under a new banner, it seems to me. Yes! Youth matched against youth!

(DR. HERDAL *comes in by the hall door.*)

HERDAL. Well! So you and Miss Wangel are still here.

SOLNESS. Yes—we found so much to talk about—

HILDE. Old things as well as new.

HERDAL. Did you really?

HILDE. It's been the greatest fun! Mr. Solness has the most remarkable memory. He remembers things so vividly—down to the tiniest detail!

(MRS. SOLNESS *enters by the door right.*)

MRS. SOLNESS. Your room is ready now, Miss Wangel.

HILDE. How very kind you are.

SOLNESS (*to* MRS. SOLNESS). The nursery?

MRS. SOLNESS. Yes, the middle one. Well—shall we go in to supper?

SOLNESS (*nodding to* HILDE). Hilde shall sleep in the nursery, she shall!

MRS. SOLNESS (*looks at him*). Hilde?

SOLNESS. Yes, Miss Wangel's name is Hilde. I knew her when she was a little girl.

MRS. SOLNESS. Did you really, Halvard? Come, let us go in. Supper is on the table.

(*She takes* DR. HERDAL'S *arm and goes out with him to the right.* HILDE *has meanwhile been collecting her belongings.*)

HILDE (*softly and rapidly to* SOLNESS). Was that true what you said just now? Can I be of use to you?

SOLNESS (*takes her things from her*). You are the one being I have needed most.

HILDE (*looks at him with happy eyes full of wonder and clasps her hands*). But then—oh, how wonderful the world is!

SOLNESS (*eagerly*). How do you mean?

HILDE. Why then— I *have* my kingdom!

SOLNESS (*involuntarily*). Hilde!

HILDE (*again with quivering lips*). Almost—I was going to say. (*She goes out to the right,* SOLNESS *following her.*)

CURTAIN

ACT TWO

SCENE: *A small, prettily furnished drawing room in* SOLNESS' *house. In the back, a glass door leading out to the veranda and garden. The right-hand corner is cut off transversely by a large bay window, in which are flower stands. The left-hand corner is similarly cut off by a transverse wall, in which is a small door papered like the wall. On each side, an ordinary door. In front, on the right, a console table with a large mirror over it. Well-filled stands of plants and flowers. In front, on the left, a sofa with a table and chairs. Further back, a bookcase. Well forward in the room, in front of the bay window, a small table and some chairs. It is early in the day.*

SOLNESS *sits by the little table with* RAGNAR BROVIK'S *portfolio open in front of him. He is turning the drawings over and closely examining some of them.* MRS. SOLNESS *moves about noiselessly with a small watering pot, attending to her flowers. She is dressed in black as before. Her hat, cloak, and gloves lie on a chair near the mirror. Unobserved by her,* SOLNESS *now and then follows her with his eyes. Neither of them speaks.*

KAJA FOSLI *enters quietly by the door on the left.*

SOLNESS (*turns his head and says with casual indifference*). Oh—it's you.

KAJA. I just wanted to let you know that I was here—

SOLNESS. Very well. Did Ragnar come too?

KAJA. No, not yet. He had to wait for the doctor. But he's coming presently to find out—

SOLNESS. How is the old man feeling?

KAJA. Not at all well. He begs you to excuse him—he'll have to stay in bed today.

SOLNESS. Of course. Let him rest. But you'd better get to your work now—

KAJA. Yes. (*Pauses at the door.*) Would you like to speak to Ragnar when he comes?

SOLNESS. No—I've nothing special to say to him.

(KAJA *goes out again to the left.* SOLNESS *remains seated, turning over the drawings.*)

MRS. SOLNESS (*over beside the plants*). I expect he'll die now, as well.

SOLNESS (*looks up at her*). As well as who?

MRS. SOLNESS (*not answering him*). Yes—old Brovik is going to die too. You'll see, Halvard.

SOLNESS. My dear Aline, don't you think you should go out for a little walk?

MRS. SOLNESS. Yes, I suppose I should. (*She continues to attend to the flowers.*)

SOLNESS (*bending over the drawings*). Is she still asleep?

MRS. SOLNESS (*looking at him*). Miss Wangel? So it's Miss Wangel you're thinking about.

SOLNESS (*indifferently*). I just happened to remember her.

MRS. SOLNESS. Miss Wangel was up long ago.

SOLNESS. Really. Was she?

MRS. SOLNESS. When I went to see her, she was putting her things in order. (*She goes to the mirror and slowly begins to put on her hat.*)

SOLNESS (*after a short pause*). Well—we've found a use for one of our nurseries after all, Aline.

MRS. SOLNESS. So we have.

SOLNESS. It seems to me that's better than having them all empty.

MRS. SOLNESS. Yes, you're right—that emptiness is dreadful.

SOLNESS (*closes the portfolio, rises and goes to her*). You'll see, Aline—from now on things are going to be much better— more cheerful. Life will be easier—especially for you.

MRS. SOLNESS (*looks at him*). From now on?

SOLNESS. Yes, you'll see, Aline—

MRS. SOLNESS. Because *she* has come here? Is that what you mean?

SOLNESS (*checking himself*). I mean—after we've moved into the new house.

MRS. SOLNESS (*takes her coat*). Really, Halvard? Do you think things will be better then?

SOLNESS. Of course they will, Aline. I'm sure you must think so too.

MRS. SOLNESS. I think nothing at all about the new house.

SOLNESS (*downcast*). It's hard for me to hear you talk like that, considering it's mostly for your sake that I built it.

(*He offers to help her on with her coat.*)

MRS. SOLNESS (*evading him*). I'm afraid you do far too much for my sake.

SOLNESS (*with a certain vehemence*). You mustn't say such things, Aline; I can't bear it!

MRS. SOLNESS. Then I won't say them, Halvard.

SOLNESS. But I stick to what I said—you'll see—things'll be much easier for you over there.

MRS. SOLNESS. Heavens! Easier for me!

SOLNESS (*eagerly*). Yes, I tell you; you *must* see that! There'll be so many things to remind you of your old home.

MRS. SOLNESS. Father's and Mother's home—that was burned to the ground.

SOLNESS (*in a low voice*). Yes, poor Aline! I know what a great grief that was to you.

MRS. SOLNESS (*breaking out in lamentation*). You can build as much as you like, Halvard—you'll never be able to build another real home for me.

SOLNESS (*crosses the room*). Then for God's sake don't let's talk about it any more!

MRS. SOLNESS. We don't as a rule talk about it—you always carefully avoid the subject.

SOLNESS (*stops suddenly and looks at her*). Avoid? Why should I avoid it?

MRS. SOLNESS. Don't think I don't understand you, Halvard. I know you want to spare me—you try to find excuses for me—as much as you possibly can.

SOLNESS (*looks at her in astonishment*). For *you,* Aline? *I* find excuses for *you!*

MRS. SOLNESS. Yes, Halvard—for me; I know that only too well.

SOLNESS (*involuntarily; to himself*). That too!

MRS. SOLNESS. As for the old house—it was meant to be, I suppose. But it's what came after the fire—the dreadful thing that followed! That's what I can never—!

SOLNESS (*vehemently*). You must stop thinking about *that,* Aline!

MRS. SOLNESS. How can I help thinking about it! And for once I must speak about it too! I can't bear it any longer—I'll never be able to forgive myself!

SOLNESS (*exclaiming*). Yourself—!

MRS. SOLNESS. Yes. I should have been strong, Halvard. I had my duties both to you and to the little ones. I shouldn't have let the horror overwhelm me—nor the grief at the loss of my old home. (*Wrings her hands.*) Oh, Halvard, if I'd only had the strength!

SOLNESS (*softly, much moved, comes toward her*). Aline—promise me that you will never think these thoughts again—promise me that!

MRS. SOLNESS. Promise! One can promise anything!

SOLNESS (*clenches his hands and crosses the room*). Oh, this is all hopeless—hopeless! Can we never have any brightness in our home? Never a ray of sunlight?

MRS. SOLNESS. This is not a *home*, Halvard.

SOLNESS. No. You're right. (*Gloomily.*) And I don't suppose it'll be any better in the new house either.

MRS. SOLNESS. No. It won't be any better. It'll be just as empty and desolate there, as it is here.

SOLNESS (*vehemently*). Then why in God's name did we build it?—Can you tell me that?

MRS. SOLNESS. That's a question only you can answer, Halvard.

SOLNESS (*with a suspicious glance at her*). What do you mean by *that*, Aline?

MRS. SOLNESS. What do I mean?

SOLNESS. Yes—damn it! You said it so strangely. What are you trying to imply, Aline?

MRS. SOLNESS. Halvard—I assure you—

SOLNESS (*comes closer*). I know what I know, Aline. I'm neither blind nor deaf—just remember that!

MRS. SOLNESS. What are you talking about, Halvard? What is it?

SOLNESS (*stands in front of her*). You know perfectly well you manage to find a furtive hidden meaning in the most innocent word I happen to say!

MRS. SOLNESS. *I* do, Halvard! How can you say that!

SOLNESS (*laughs*). It's natural enough, I suppose—when you're dealing with a sick man—

MRS. SOLNESS (*anxiously*). Sick! Are you ill, Halvard?

SOLNESS (*violently*). A half-mad man, then—a lunatic, if you prefer to call it that!

MRS. SOLNESS (*feels blindly for a chair and sits down*). Halvard—for God's sake!

SOLNESS. But you're both wrong, do you hear? Both you and the doctor! I'm in no such state! (*He walks up and down the room.* MRS. SOLNESS *follows him anxiously with her eyes. Finally he goes up to her and says calmly.*) As a matter of fact there's absolutely nothing wrong with me.

MRS. SOLNESS. No. There isn't, is there? But then, what is it that troubles you so?

SOLNESS. It's this terrible burden of debt—I sometimes feel I can't bear it any longer!

MRS. SOLNESS. Debt? But you owe no one anything, Halvard.

SOLNESS (*softly. With emotion*). I owe a boundless debt to you—to you—to *you*, Aline.

MRS. SOLNESS (*rises slowly*). What are you hiding from me, Halvard? Tell me the truth.

SOLNESS. I'm not hiding anything from you. I've never harmed you—never deliberately, never intentionally, that is—and yet I feel crushed by a terrible sense of guilt.

MRS. SOLNESS. Toward me?

SOLNESS. Yes—mostly toward you.

MRS. SOLNESS. Then you must be—ill—after all, Halvard.

SOLNESS (*gloomily*). Yes. I suppose I must be—or not far from it. (*He looks toward the door on the right, which is opened at this moment.*) Ah! Now it gets lighter!

(HILDE *comes in. She has made some alteration in her dress.*)

HILDE. Good morning, Master Builder!

SOLNESS (*nods*). Did you sleep well?

HILDE. Splendidly! Like a child in a cradle! I lay there and stretched myself like—like a princess!

SOLNESS (*smiles a little*). You were quite comfortable then?

HILDE. I was indeed!

SOLNESS. Did you have any dreams?

HILDE. Yes—but horrid ones!

SOLNESS. Really?

HILDE. Yes. I dreamt I was falling over a high steep precipice. Do you ever dream that sort of thing?

SOLNESS. Yes, now and then.

HILDE. It's wonderfully thrilling, though; you feel yourself falling further and further—down and down—

SOLNESS. I know! It makes your blood run cold.

HILDE. Do you draw your legs up under you when you're falling?

SOLNESS. As high as I possibly can.

HILDE. So do I!

MRS. SOLNESS (*takes her gloves*). I'd better go into town now, Halvard. (*To* HILDE.) I'll try and get some of the things you need, Miss Wangel.

HILDE (*starts to throw her arms round her neck*). Dear, darling Mrs. Solness! You're really much too kind to me—incredibly kind!

MRS. SOLNESS (*deprecatingly, freeing herself*). Not at all—it's no more than my duty. I'm only too glad to do it.

HILDE (*offended, pouts*). There's really no reason why I shouldn't go myself—now that I look so respectable. What do you think?

MRS. SOLNESS. To tell you the truth, I'm afraid people might stare at you a little.

HILDE (*contemptuously*). Is *that* all? That'd be fun!

SOLNESS (*with suppressed ill-humor*). Yes, but then people might think *you* were mad too.

HILDE. Mad? Why? Is the place so full of mad people?

SOLNESS (*points to his own forehead*). Here is *one*, at any rate—

HILDE. You—Master Builder!

MRS. SOLNESS. Now really, my dear Halvard!

SOLNESS. You surely must have noticed it.

HILDE. No, I can't say I have—(*Thinks a moment and laughs a little.*) Though there was *one* thing—

SOLNESS. Do you hear that, Aline?

MRS. SOLNESS. What thing, Miss Wangel?

HILDE. I won't tell you.

SOLNESS. Oh, yes—do!

HILDE. No, thanks—I'm not quite as mad as *that!*

MRS. SOLNESS. When you are alone, Miss Wangel's sure to tell you, Halvard.

SOLNESS. Oh—you think so?

MRS. SOLNESS. Of course. After all, she's such an old friend of yours—you've known her ever since she was a child, you tell me. (*She goes out by the door on the left.*)

HILDE (*after a short pause*). Your wife doesn't seem to like me very much.

SOLNESS. Why do you say that?

HILDE. Wasn't it pretty obvious?

SOLNESS (*evasively*). It's just her manner—Aline's become very shy these past few years—

HILDE. Oh—has she really?

SOLNESS. But underneath she's an immensely kind, gentle, good-hearted creature—you'll see, when you know her better—

HILDE. Perhaps. But I wish she wouldn't talk so much about her duty.

SOLNESS. Her duty?

HILDE. Yes. Why did she have to say she'd get those things for me because it was her *duty*? I hate that ugly, horrid word!

SOLNESS. Why?

HILDE. I don't know—it sounds so cold and harsh and prickly: Duty, duty, duty! It *is* prickly! Don't you think so too?

SOLNESS. I've never thought about it.

HILDE. Well it *is!* And if she's as kind as you say she is— why does she use a word like that?

SOLNESS. Well—what on earth should she have said?

HILDE. She could have said she'd *love* to do it, because she'd taken such a tremendous fancy to me. She could have said something like that—something warm and friendly—don't you see?

SOLNESS (*looks at her*). That's what you'd have liked, is it?

HILDE. Yes, of course. (*She wanders about the room, stops at the bookcases and examines the books.*) What a lot of books you have!

SOLNESS. Yes—I seem to have collected a good many—

HILDE. Do you read them all too?

SOLNESS. When I was young I used to try to. Do you read much?

HILDE. No, never! I've given it up—it all seems so irrelevant.

SOLNESS. That's just how I feel.

(HILDE *wanders about a little, stops at the small table, opens the portfolio and turns over the contents.*)

HILDE. Are these your drawings?

SOLNESS. No, they were done by a young man who's my assistant here.

HILDE. Then he's been studying with you, I suppose.

SOLNESS. He's learned something from me, I dare say.

HILDE. Then he must be very clever. (*Looks at a drawing.*) Isn't he?

SOLNESS. He could be worse. He serves my purpose—

HILDE. I expect he's frightfully clever!

SOLNESS. Why? Do you see that in the drawings?

HILDE. What? These things! No! But if he's a pupil of yours—

SOLNESS. I've had lots of pupils in my time—but they haven't amounted to much.

HILDE. I can't think how you can be so stupid, Master Builder!

SOLNESS. Stupid? Why do you think me stupid?

HILDE. You must be—or you wouldn't waste your time teaching all these people—

SOLNESS. Why not?

HILDE. What for? You're the only one who should be allowed to build. You should build everything yourself, Master Builder—you alone!

SOLNESS (*involuntarily*). Hilde!

HILDE. Well?

SOLNESS. Whatever put that idea into your head?

HILDE. Why? Am I so wrong?

SOLNESS. No—it's not that—But, do you know something, Hilde?

HILDE. What?

SOLNESS. I myself am obsessed by that very thought. I sit here alone, in silence, brooding over it incessantly.

HILDE. That's quite natural, it seems to me.

SOLNESS (*gives her a somewhat searching look*). You'd probably already noticed it—

HILDE. No—I can't say I had.

SOLNESS. But, a few minutes ago—when you admitted to thinking me a little—queer—in just one thing, you said—

HILDE. Oh! I was thinking of something quite different.

SOLNESS. What was it?

HILDE. I won't tell you.

SOLNESS (*crossing the room*). Just as you like. (*He stops at the bay window.*) Come here, Hilde. I want to show you something.

HILDE (*goes toward him*). What?

SOLNESS. Do you see—over there in the garden—?

HILDE. Yes?

SOLNESS. Just beyond the stone quarry—

HILDE. Oh—the new house, you mean?

SOLNESS. Yes—the one they're working on; it's nearly finished.

HILDE. It seems to have a very high tower—

SOLNESS. The scaffolding is still up.

HILDE. Is that your new house?

SOLNESS. Yes.

HILDE. The one you'll soon be moving into?

SOLNESS. Yes.

HILDE (*looks at him*). Are there nurseries in that house too?

SOLNESS. Three—just as there are here.

HILDE. And no children.

SOLNESS. No—and there never will be.

HILDE (*with a half-smile*). Well? Wasn't I right?

SOLNESS. How?

HILDE. Aren't you a little—mad, after all?

SOLNESS. So that's what you were thinking of.

HILDE. Yes—all those empty nurseries I slept in.

SOLNESS (*lowers his voice*). We *have* had children—Aline and I—

HILDE (*breathlessly*). Have you?

SOLNESS. Two little boys. They were the same age—

HILDE. Twins, then.

SOLNESS. Yes, twins. It's eleven or twelve years ago—

HILDE (*cautiously*). And are they both—? Did you lose them? Both of them?

SOLNESS (*with quiet emotion*). They only lived two weeks—not even that. Oh, Hilde—it's so good that you've come to me; now at last I have someone I can talk to!

HILDE. Can't you talk to—*her*, too?

SOLNESS. Not about this. Not as I want to—as I need to. *(Gloomily.)* And there are so many *other* things I can never talk to her about!

HILDE *(in a subdued voice)*. So *that* was all you meant, when you said you needed me!

SOLNESS. Chiefly, yes. Yesterday at least—today, I'm no longer sure—*(Breaking off.)* Sit down, Hilde—sit there, so you can look out into the garden. (HILDE *seats herself in the corner of the sofa.* SOLNESS *draws up a chair.)* Would you like to hear about it?

HILDE. Very much.

SOLNESS *(sits down)*. Good—then I'll tell you the whole story.

HILDE. I can see the garden from here—and I can see you, Master Builder—so tell me all about it—Begin!

SOLNESS *(points through the window)*. There used to be an old house where the new house stands—Aline and I spent the first years of our marriage there; it had belonged to her mother —and we inherited it, and the huge garden as well.

HILDE. Was there a tower on the old house, too?

SOLNESS. No—nothing like that! It looked like a large, ugly, gloomy wooden box from the outside; but inside it was comfortable enough.

HILDE. What happened? Did you tear it down?

SOLNESS. No. It burnt down.

HILDE. All of it?

SOLNESS. Yes.

HILDE. Was it a great loss to you?

SOLNESS. That depends on how you look at it. As a builder— that fire was the making of me—

HILDE. Was it? Then—

SOLNESS. It was just after the birth of the two little boys—

HILDE. The poor little twins, yes.

SOLNESS. They were so sturdy and healthy—and they were growing so fast—you could see a difference from day to day—

HILDE. Yes. Babies do grow quickly at first.

SOLNESS. It was such a pretty sight to see Aline lying there with the two of them in her arms. But then came the night of the fire—

HILDE *(with excitement)*. What happened? Tell me! Was anyone burnt?

SOLNESS. No, not that. Everyone got out of the house safely—

HILDE. Well—what then?

SOLNESS. Well, you see—it was a terrible shock to Aline; all

the shouts—the confusion—the flames—the sudden fear—
She and the little boys were sound asleep; they got them out
just in time; they had to drag them out of bed, and carry them
just as they were, out into that bitter night—

HILDE. Was that why they—?

SOLNESS. No, they recovered from that. But later, Aline developed a fever, and it affected her milk, she would insist on
nursing them herself—it was her duty, she said. And our two
little boys, they—they—oh!

HILDE. They didn't get over that?

SOLNESS. No, they didn't get over that. That is how we lost
them.

HILDE. How terrible for you.

SOLNESS. Hard enough for me; but ten times harder for Aline.
(Clenching his hands in suppressed fury.) Why are such things
allowed to happen in this world! *(Shortly and firmly.)* From the
day I lost them, I had no joy in building churches.

HILDE. Didn't you even like building the church tower in our
town?

SOLNESS. No, I didn't like it. I remember how glad I was when
that tower was finished.

HILDE. I remember that too.

SOLNESS. I shall never build anything of that sort again.
Neither churches nor church towers.

HILDE *(nods slowly)*. Only houses for people to live in.

SOLNESS. Homes for human beings, Hilde.

HILDE. But homes with high towers—and spires soaring above
them!

SOLNESS. If possible. *(In a lighter tone.)* Well—as I told you
—that fire was the making of me—as a builder, that is.

HILDE. Why don't you call yourself architect, like the others?

SOLNESS. My education wasn't thorough enough for that.
What I know, I've mostly found out for myself.

HILDE. But you climbed to the top just the same!

SOLNESS. Thanks to the fire, yes. Most of the old garden I cut
up into small building lots; I was free to try out my ideas—to
build exactly as I chose. Then—nothing could stop me; success
came with a rush.

HILDE *(looks at him keenly)*. What a happy man you must
be, Master Builder.

SOLNESS *(gloomily)*. Happy! You sound like all the others!

HILDE. I should think you *must* be happy. If you could only
stop thinking about the two little boys.

SOLNESS *(slowly)*. They're not so easy to forget, Hilde.

HILDE (*somewhat uncertainly*). Not even after all these years?

SOLNESS (*stares at her without answering*). So you think me a happy man—

HILDE. Well, *aren't* you? I mean—apart from that?

SOLNESS (*still looking at her*). When I told you all that about the fire—

HILDE. Yes?

SOLNESS. Weren't you struck by one particular thing?

HILDE (*after thinking in vain for a moment*). No. What do you mean?

SOLNESS. Weren't you struck by the fact that it was solely because of that fire that I had the chance to build these homes for human beings? These comfortable, warm, cheerful homes where a mother and a father and a whole troop of children could enjoy life in peace and happiness—sharing the big things and the little things—and, best of all, *belonging* to each other, Hilde?

HILDE (*ardently*). Well—isn't that a great happiness for you, to be able to build these beautiful homes?

SOLNESS. What about the price, Hilde? The terrible price I had to pay for that opportunity?

HILDE. But can't you *ever* get over that?

SOLNESS. No. In order to build these homes for others, I had to give up—give up forever—a real home of my own.

HILDE (*cautiously*). But was that *really* necessary? "Forever," you say.

SOLNESS. Yes. That was the price of this happiness. This so-called "happiness" was not to be bought any cheaper.

HILDE (*as before*). But, couldn't you still—?

SOLNESS. No. Never. That's another consequence of the fire—and of Aline's illness afterwards.

HILDE (*looks at him with an indefinable expression*). And yet you build all these nurseries!

SOLNESS (*seriously*). Haven't you ever been attracted by the impossible, Hilde? Hasn't it ever called out to you—cast its spell over you?

HILDE (*thinking*). The impossible! (*With sudden animation.*) Of course! Do you feel that too?

SOLNESS. Yes.

HILDE. Then there must be a bit of a troll in you too.

SOLNESS. Why troll?

HILDE. What would *you* call that sort of thing?

SOLNESS (*rises*). It may be so—(*Vehemently.*) But how can I help becoming a troll—when things always work out as they do for me!

HILDE. How do you mean?

SOLNESS (*in a low voice, with inward emotion*). Listen to this carefully, Hilde: All that I have been able to achieve—everything I've built and created—all the beauty, security, comfort—magnificence too, if you like—(*Clenches his hands.*) Oh, it's too terrible to think of—!

HILDE. What *is* it that's so terrible?

SOLNESS. All of this had to be paid for—not in money—but in human happiness. And I don't mean just *my* happiness either—but that of other people. Think of that, Hilde! That is the price my position as an artist has cost me—and others. And I have to look on, and watch the others paying that price for me day after day; over and over again forever!

HILDE (*rises and looks at him steadily*). I suppose now you're thinking of —her?

SOLNESS. Mostly of Aline, yes. She, too, had a vocation in life, just as I had. (*His voice quivers.*) But Aline's vocation had to be sacrificed, so that mine could force its way up to a sort of great victory. Her vocation had to be stunted, crushed—smashed to pieces! You see—Aline, too, had a talent for building.

HILDE. She? For building?

SOLNESS (*shakes his head*). Oh, I don't mean houses and towers and spires—not *my* kind of building—

HILDE. What then?

SOLNESS. Aline had a gift for building up the souls of little children, Hilde. She could teach them to become beautiful and strong in mind and body; she could help them to grow up into fine, honorable human beings. That was her talent. But it's all been wasted—it's of no use to anyone now. It's like a smoldering heap of ruins.

HILDE. Well—even if this were true—

SOLNESS. It is! It is true—I know it!

HILDE. But it's surely not your fault!

SOLNESS (*fixes his eyes on her*). I wonder. That is the great, the terrible question. It torments me day and night!

HILDE. But why?

SOLNESS. Well, you see—perhaps it *was* my fault in a way.

HILDE. You mean—the fire?

SOLNESS. Everything! The whole business! On the other hand —I may have had nothing to do with it.

HILDE (*looks at him with a troubled expression*). If you talk like that, Master Builder, I'll begin to think you are—ill, after all.

SOLNESS. I dare say I'll never be quite sane on that subject.

(RAGNAR BROVIK *cautiously opens the little door in the left-hand corner.* HILDE *steps forward.*)

RAGNAR (*as he sees* HILDE). Oh, excuse me, Mr. Solness—

SOLNESS. No, no! Don't go! Let's get it over with.

RAGNAR. I wish we could.

SOLNESS. Your father is no better, I hear.

RAGNAR. He's failing very rapidly now. That's why I must beg you to write a few encouraging words on one of my drawings; just something for Father to see before he—

SOLNESS (*vehemently*). I don't want to hear any more about those drawings of yours!

RAGNAR. Have you looked at them?

SOLNESS. Yes, I have.

RAGNAR. And they're no good? and I suppose *I'm* no good either.

SOLNESS (*evasively*). You stay on here with me, Ragnar. You can have everything your own way. You can marry Kaja—you'll have no worries—you may even be happy, too. But don't think of building on your account.

RAGNAR. I'd better go home and tell Father what you say—I promised him I would. Is this what you want me to tell him, before he dies?

SOLNESS (*with a groan*). As far as I'm concerned—tell him what you like! Why tell him anything? (*With a sudden outburst.*) There's nothing I can do about it, Ragnar.

RAGNAR. May I have the drawings to take with me?

SOLNESS. Yes, take them—take them by all means! They're there on the table.

RAGNAR (*goes to the table*). Thanks.

HILDE (*puts her hand on the portfolio*). No—leave them here!

SOLNESS. What for?

HILDE. Because I want to look at them, too.

SOLNESS. But, I thought you had—! (*To* RAGNAR.) Well—just leave them, then.

RAGNAR. Very well.

SOLNESS. And now—hurry back to your father.

RAGNAR. Yes, I suppose I must.

SOLNESS (*as if in desperation*). And, Ragnar—don't ask me to do things that are beyond my power! Do you hear, Ragnar, you mustn't!

RAGNAR. No, no. I beg your pardon. (*He bows and goes out by the corner door.* HILDE *goes over and sits down on a chair near the mirror.*)

HILDE (*looking at* SOLNESS *angrily*). That was a very ugly thing to do.

SOLNESS. You think so, too?

HILDE. Yes, it was disgusting! It was hard, and cruel, and wicked!

SOLNESS. You don't understand the facts.

HILDE. I don't care! You oughtn't to be like that!

SOLNESS. You said yourself, just now, that I alone should be allowed to build.

HILDE. I may say such things—it's not for you to say them.

SOLNESS. Who has a better right? I've paid a high enough price for my position.

HILDE. That precious domestic comfort of yours—I suppose you mean!

SOLNESS. And what about my peace of mind, Hilde?

HILDE (*rising*). Peace of mind! Yes, I see! I understand—Poor Master Builder! You think that you—

SOLNESS (*with a quiet laugh*). Sit down again, Hilde. I want to tell you something funny.

HILDE (*sits down; with intent interest*). Well?

SOLNESS. I know it sounds ludicrous! But the whole question revolves round a little crack in the chimney.

HILDE. A crack in the chimney?

SOLNESS. Yes—that's how it started. (*He moves a chair nearer* HILDE *and sits.*)

HILDE (*impatiently, taps her knee*). Well—now for the crack in the chimney, Master Builder!

SOLNESS. A long time before the fire, I'd noticed that little crack in the flue. Whenever I went up to the attic, I looked to see if it was still there.

HILDE. And it *was*?

SOLNESS. Yes, for no one else knew about it.

HILDE. And you said nothing?

SOLNESS. No. Not a word.

HILDE. And you didn't think of repairing it?

SOLNESS. I thought of it—but never got down to it. Each time I decided to get to work, it was exactly as if a hand held me back. Not today, I thought—tomorrow; and I did nothing about it.

HILDE. What made you put it off like that?

SOLNESS. I became obsessed with an idea. (*Slowly, and in a low voice.*) Through that little black crack in the chimney, I might perhaps force my way upward as a builder.

HILDE (*looking straight in front of her*). That must have been thrilling!

SOLNESS. It was almost irresistible—quite irresistible. It all seemed so simple at the time. I wanted it to happen on a winter morning, just before noon. Aline and I were to be out driving in the sleigh. At home, the servants were to have built great fires in all the stoves—

HILDE. Of course, it was to have been very cold that day—

SOLNESS. Bitterly cold, yes. And they would naturally want Aline to be nice and warm when she came in—

HILDE. I suppose she's very chilly by nature—

SOLNESS. Yes, she is. And on the way home we were to have seen the smoke—

HILDE. Only the smoke?

SOLNESS. At first, yes. But by the time we got to the garden gate, the old wooden box was to be a roaring mass of flames. That's the way I wanted it to be.

HILDE. Oh, why—*why* couldn't it have happened so!

SOLNESS. You may well say that, Hilde.

HILDE. But, Master Builder—are you quite sure the fire *was* caused by that crack in the chimney?

SOLNESS. On the contrary—I'm quite sure the crack in the chimney had nothing to do with it.

HILDE. What!

SOLNESS. It was proved quite definitely that the fire broke out in a clothes closet, in an entirely different part of the house.

HILDE. Then what's all this nonsense about a crack in the chimney!

SOLNESS. May I go on talking to you a little longer, Hilde?

HILDE. Yes—if you'll try and talk sense!

SOLNESS. I'll try. (*He moves his chair nearer. In a confidential tone.*) Don't you believe, Hilde, that there exist certain special, chosen people, who have been endowed with the power and faculty of *wishing* a thing, *desiring* a thing, *willing* a thing, so persistently, so—inexorably—that they make it happen? Don't you believe that?

HILDE (*with an indefinable expression in her eyes*). If that is true, we'll find out some day whether *I* am one of the chosen.

SOLNESS. It's not by our own power alone that we can accomplish such things; we must have the Helpers and Servers with us in order to succeed; and they never come of their own accord —we have to summon them; to call on them; inwardly—persistently.

HILDE. What *are* these Helpers and Servers?

SOLNESS. We'll discuss that some other time; let's go on talking about the fire now.

HILDE. Don't you think that fire would have happened—even if you hadn't wished for it?

SOLNESS. If old Knut Brovik had owned that house, it would never have burnt down so conveniently for him—I'm convinced of that. He doesn't know *how* to call for the Helpers—nor for the Servers either. *(Rises in unrest.)* So you see, Hilde, perhaps I *am* to blame for the death of the two little boys; and perhaps it's my fault, too, that Aline never became what she could and should have been; what she most longed to be.

HILDE. No! It's the fault of the Helpers and Servers!

SOLNESS. But who *called* for the Helpers and Servers? I did! And they came, and obeyed my will. *(In increasing excitement.)* And these good people call that "having luck on your side"! Do you know what that kind of luck feels like? It's as though I had an open wound here on my breast; and the Helpers and Servers flay pieces of skin off other people in order to heal my wound. But it goes on burning and throbbing—it never heals—never!

HILDE *(looks at him attentively)*. You *are* ill, Master Builder. I'm inclined to think you're *very* ill.

SOLNESS. Why not say mad? That's what you mean.

HILDE. No, I don't mean mentally.

SOLNESS. What *do* you mean then? Tell me!

HILDE. I wonder if you weren't born with a sickly conscience.

SOLNESS. A sickly conscience? What in the world is that!

HILDE. I mean that your conscience is too delicate and feeble; it won't face the hard things; it refuses to carry any burden that seems heavy!

SOLNESS *(growls)*. And what sort of a conscience *should* one have?

HILDE. I would prefer your conscience to be—thoroughly robust.

SOLNESS. Robust? I see. Is *your* conscience robust, may I ask?

HILDE. Yes, I think so. I've never noticed that it wasn't.

SOLNESS. I dare say it's never been put to the test.

HILDE *(with a quivering of the lips)*. I don't know about that. It wasn't any too easy for me to leave Father—I'm so awfully fond of him—

SOLNESS. Oh, well! For a month or two—!

HILDE. I feel I shall never go home again.

SOLNESS. Never? Then why did you leave him?

HILDE *(half seriously, half banteringly)*. Have you forgotten again that the ten years are up?

SOLNESS. Nonsense! Was anything wrong at home?

HILDE *(seriously)*. No. But something within me urged and

goaded me to come here—it was as though something beckoned to me and lured me on.

SOLNESS (*eagerly*). That's it. That's *it*, Hilde! There's a troll in you, just as there is in me; and it's the troll in us that summons the powers outside us; and then, whether we like it or not, we're forced to give in.

HILDE. You know—I believe you're right, Master Builder.

SOLNESS (*walks about the room*). Oh, what a lot of invisible devils there are in this world, Hilde!

HILDE. Devils, too?

SOLNESS (*stops*). Good devils and bad devils. Blond devils and dark devils! If only we could be sure which kind had hold of us— then things would be simple enough! (*He paces about.*)

HILDE (*follows him with her eyes*). Yes! Or if we had a vigorous, radiantly healthy conscience—and had the courage to follow our own will!

SOLNESS (*stops beside the table*). I'm afraid most people are as weak as I am, in that respect.

HILDE. I shouldn't wonder.

SOLNESS (*leaning against the table*). In the Sagas—have you read any of the old Sagas?

HILDE. Yes! When I used to read books—

SOLNESS. The Sagas tell about the Vikings who sailed to foreign lands, and plundered, and burned, and killed all the men—

HILDE. And captured the women—

SOLNESS. Carried them off with them—

HILDE. Took them home in their ships—

SOLNESS. And behaved to them—like the very worst of trolls!

HILDE (*looks straight before her with a half-veiled expression*). I think that must have been thrilling!

SOLNESS (*with a short, deep laugh*). To carry off women?

HILDE. To *be* carried off.

SOLNESS (*looks at her a moment*). Indeed.

HILDE (*as if breaking the thread of the conversation*). But what made you speak of these Vikings, Master Builder?

SOLNESS. What robust consciences *they* must have had! They went home again and could eat and drink, and were as happy as children. And as for the women! They must have liked those ruffians—they quite often refused to leave them! Can you understand that, Hilde?

HILDE. Of course! I understand those women perfectly.

SOLNESS. Oho! Perhaps you'd do the same yourself?

HILDE. Why not?

SOLNESS. Live of your own free will with a ruffian?

HILDE. Yes. If I loved him.

SOLNESS. But how *could* you love a man like that?

HILDE. Good Heavens, Master Builder! You know you don't *choose* whom you're going to love!

SOLNESS *(looks meditatively at her)*. No. I suppose the troll in you takes care of that.

HILDE *(half laughing)*. Yes—and all those devils that you know so well! The blond ones, and the dark ones too!

SOLNESS *(quietly and warmly)*. I hope the devils will choose well for you, Hilde.

HILDE. They've already chosen for me—once and for all.

SOLNESS *(looks at her earnestly)*. Hilde, you're like a wild bird of the woods.

HILDE. Far from it! I don't hide away under the bushes.

SOLNESS. No. Perhaps you're more like a bird of prey.

HILDE. Perhaps. *(Very vehemently.)* And why not a bird of prey? Why shouldn't I, too, go hunting? And carry off the prey I want—if I can get my claws into it—and conquer it.

SOLNESS. Hilde—do you know what you are?

HILDE. I suppose I'm some sort of strange bird—

SOLNESS. No. You're like the dawning day. When I look at you—I feel as though I were watching the sunrise.

HILDE. Tell me, Master Builder—are you sure you've never called *me* to you? Inwardly, you know?

SOLNESS *(softly and slowly)*. I'm almost sure I must have.

HILDE. What did you want of me?

SOLNESS. You are Youth, Hilde.

HILDE. Youth? That Youth you're so afraid of?

SOLNESS *(nods slowly)*. And that in my heart, I yearn toward so deeply—

(HILDE *rises, goes to the little table, and fetches* RAGNAR'S *portfolio.)*

HILDE *(holds out the portfolio to him)*. What about these drawings, Master Builder—?

SOLNESS *(shortly; waving them away)*. Put those things away! I've seen enough of them!

HILDE. But you're going to write on them for him, you know.

SOLNESS. Write on them! Never!

HILDE. But the poor old man's dying! It would make them both so happy! And he might get the commission too.

SOLNESS. That's just exactly what he would get! He's made sure of that!

HILDE. Well—if that's true—it surely couldn't hurt you to tell a little lie for once?

SOLNESS. A lie? (*Raging.*) Hilde—take those damn drawings away!

HILDE (*draws the portfolio toward her*). All right, all right! Don't bite me! You talk of trolls—it seems to me you're behaving like a troll yourself! (*Looks round the room.*) Where's the pen and ink?

SOLNESS. There isn't any here.

HILDE (*goes toward the door*). That young lady must have some in the office—

SOLNESS. Stay where you are, Hilde! You want me to lie, you say. I suppose, for the old man's sake, I might do that; I broke him—destroyed him—

HILDE. Him, too?

SOLNESS. I needed room for myself. But this Ragnar must never be allowed to get ahead—

HILDE. Poor thing—there's not much hope of that—you say he has no talent.

SOLNESS (*comes closer to her and whispers*). If Ragnar Brovik gets his chance, he'll break me—destroy me, as I did his father.

HILDE. Destroy you! You mean—he has the power for *that*?

SOLNESS. He has indeed! *He* is the younger generation waiting to thunder at my door—to make an end of Halvard Solness!

HILDE (*looks at him with quiet reproach*). And you would bar him out! For shame, Master Builder!

SOLNESS. My struggle has cost me agony enough! And I'm afraid the Helpers and Servers won't obey me any longer.

HILDE. Then you'll just have to get on without them.

SOLNESS. It's hopeless, Hilde. Sooner or later the luck will turn. Retribution is inexorable.

HILDE (*in distress, putting her hands over her ears*). Don't talk like that! Do you want to kill me? Do you want to rob me of what means more to me than life!

SOLNESS. What is that?

HILDE. The need to see you great. To see you with a wreath in your hand—high, high up, upon a church tower! (*Calm again.*) Now—get out your pencil, Master Builder— You must have a pencil in your pocket—

SOLNESS (*takes one from his pocket*). Yes—here's one—

HILDE (*lays the portfolio on the table*). Good. We'll just sit down here, Master Builder—

(SOLNESS *seats himself at the table.* HILDE *stands behind him, leaning over the back of the chair.*)

HILDE. —and we'll write on the drawings; something very nice—very kind—for this horrid Ruar—whatever his name is!

SOLNESS (*writes a few words, turns his head and looks at her*).
Tell me one thing, Hilde.

HILDE. Yes?

SOLNESS. If you were really waiting for me all these ten
years—

HILDE. Well?

SOLNESS. Why didn't you write to me? Then I could have answered you.

HILDE (*hastily*). No, no, no! That's just what I didn't want!

SOLNESS. Why not?

HILDE. I was afraid that might ruin everything—But we were
writing on the drawings, Master Builder.

SOLNESS. So we were.

HILDE (*bends forward and looks over his shoulder as he
writes*). Kindly and generously. Oh, how I hate—how I hate this
Roald—!

SOLNESS (*writing*). Have you never really loved anyone, Hilde?

HILDE (*harshly*). What? What did you say?

SOLNESS. Have you never loved anyone, I asked.

HILDE. Anyone else, I suppose you mean.

SOLNESS (*looks up at her*). Anyone else, yes. Have you never?
In all these ten years? Never?

HILDE. Oh, yes, now and then. When I was furious with you
for not coming.

SOLNESS. Then you *have* cared for other people, too?

HILDE. Maybe a little—for a week or so— Good Heavens, Master Builder! You must know all about things like that!

SOLNESS. What have you come for, Hilde?

HILDE. Don't waste time talking! The poor old man might go
and die in the meantime!

SOLNESS. Answer me, Hilde. What do you want of me?

HILDE. I want my kingdom.

SOLNESS. Hm—

(*He gives a rapid glance toward the door on the left, and
then goes on writing on the drawings. At that moment* MRS.
SOLNESS *enters; she has some packages in her hand.*)

MRS. SOLNESS. I've brought a few of the things myself, Miss
Wangel. The large parcels will be sent later on.

HILDE. You're really much too kind to me!

MRS. SOLNESS. My simple duty—nothing else.

SOLNESS (*reads over what he has written*). Aline?

MRS. SOLNESS. Yes, Halvard?

SOLNESS. Did you happen to notice whether she—whether the
bookkeeper was out there?

MRS. SOLNESS. Of course she was there. She was at her desk—as she always is when *I* go through the room.

SOLNESS *(puts the drawings in the portfolio. Rises).* Then I'll just give her these, and tell her that—

HILDE *(takes the portfolio from him).* Oh, let me have that pleasure! *(Goes to the door, but turns.)* What's her name?

SOLNESS. Miss Fosli.

HILDE. No, no! That sounds so formal! Her first name, I mean!

SOLNESS. Kaja—I believe.

HILDE *(opens the door and calls out).* Kaja! Hurry! Come in here! The Master Builder wants to talk to you.

(KAJA appears at the door.)

KAJA *(looks at him in alarm).* You want me—?

HILDE *(handing her the portfolio).* Take these home, Kaja. The Master Builder has written on them now.

KAJA. At last!

SOLNESS. Give them to the old man as soon as possible—

KAJA. I'll go home with them at once—

SOLNESS. Yes, do. Now Ragnar will have his chance to build.

KAJA. May he come and thank you—?

SOLNESS *(harshly).* I want no thanks! Tell him that from me.

KAJA. Yes—I will.

SOLNESS. And tell him, too, that I shall no longer need his services—nor yours either.

KAJA *(softly—tremulously).* Nor mine—either?

SOLNESS. You'll have other things to think of now—a great deal to attend to—that's as it should be. Take the drawings home now, Miss Fosli. At once! Do you hear!

KAJA *(as before).* Yes, Mr. Solness. *(She goes out.)*

MRS. SOLNESS. Heavens! What deceitful eyes she has!

SOLNESS. She? That poor little creature?

MRS. SOLNESS. Oh, I can see what I can see, Halvard. So you're really dismissing them?

SOLNESS. Yes.

MRS. SOLNESS. Her, as well?

SOLNESS. Wasn't that what you wanted?

MRS. SOLNESS. But how will you get on without her?—No doubt you have someone in reserve, Halvard.

HILDE *(playfully).* As for me—I'd be no good at a desk!

SOLNESS. Never mind, never mind, Aline. Everything will be all right—You just think about getting ready to move into your new home—as quickly as possible. This evening we'll hang up the wreath—*(Turns to* HILDE.*)* at the very top of the tower. What do you say to *that*, Miss Hilde?

HILDE. It'll be wonderful to see you up there again—high up!

SOLNESS. Me!

MRS. SOLNESS. Whatever put that into your head, Miss Wangel! My husband—who always gets so dizzy!

HILDE. Dizzy! He!

MRS. SOLNESS. Oh, yes. I assure you.

HILDE. But I saw him myself at the top of a high church tower!

MRS. SOLNESS. Yes—I've heard rumors about that. But it's quite impossible.

SOLNESS (*vehemently*). Impossible! Impossible! But I stood there all the same!

MRS. SOLNESS. How can you say that, Halvard. You know you don't even dare go out on the second-story balcony here—You've always been like that!

SOLNESS. You may see something different this evening.

MRS. SOLNESS (*in alarm*). No, no! God forbid that I should ever see that! I'll send word to the doctor at once. He must prevent you.

SOLNESS. But, Aline—!

MRS. SOLNESS. For you are ill, Halvard—this proves it. Oh, God! Oh, God! (*She goes hastily out to the right.*)

HILDE (*looks at him intently*). Is it so, or is it not?

SOLNESS. That I get dizzy?

HILDE. That my Master Builder *dare* not, *cannot* climb as high as he builds?

SOLNESS. Is that how you look at it?

HILDE. Yes.

SOLNESS. Is there no part of me that's safe from you, Hilde?

HILDE (*looks toward the window*). Up there then—right up there!

SOLNESS (*comes to her*). You could live in the topmost room of the tower, Hilde—you could live there like a princess.

HILDE (*indefinably; half in jest, half in earnest*). That's what you promised—

SOLNESS. Did I really?

HILDE. You said I was to be a princess—that you'd give me a kingdom—and then you went and—

SOLNESS (*cautiously*). Are you sure it wasn't all a dream—just something you imagined?

HILDE (*sharply*). You mean that you didn't do it?

SOLNESS. I scarcely know myself. (*More softly.*) But I *do* know one thing now—and that is—

HILDE. What? Tell me at once!

SOLNESS. That I *ought* to have done it!

HILDE (*exclaims, with animation*). *You* could never be dizzy!

SOLNESS. Then, this evening we will hang up the wreath, Princess Hilde.

HILDE (*with a bitter curve of her lips*). Over your new home—yes!

SOLNESS. Over the new house—that will never be a home for me. (*He goes out through the garden door.*)

HILDE (*looks straight in front of her with a faraway expression, and whispers to herself. The only words audible are*). —frightfully thrilling!

CURTAIN

ACT THREE

SCENE: *The large broad veranda of* SOLNESS' *house. Part of the house, with outer door leading to the veranda, is seen to the left. A railing along the veranda to the right. At the back, from the end of the veranda, a flight of steps leads down to the garden below. Tall, old trees in the garden spread their branches over the veranda and toward the house. Far to the right, in among the trees, a glimpse is caught of the lower part of a new villa, with scaffolding round so much as is seen of the tower. In the background the garden is bounded by an old wooden fence. Outside the fence, a street with low tumbledown cottages.*

Evening sky with sunlit clouds.

On the veranda, a garden bench stands along the wall of the house, and in front of the bench a long table. On the other side of the table, an armchair and some stools. All the furniture is of wickerwork.

MRS. SOLNESS, *wrapped in a large white crepe shawl, sits resting in the armchair and gazes over to the right. Shortly after,* HILDE WANGEL *comes up the flight of steps from the garden. She is dressed as in the last act and wears a hat. She has in her bodice a little nosegay of small common flowers.*

MRS. SOLNESS (*turning her head a little*). So you've been round the garden, Miss Wangel?

HILDE. Yes. I've been exploring it—

MRS. SOLNESS. And found some flowers too, I see.

HILDE. There are such heaps of them—in among the bushes.

MRS. SOLNESS. Fancy! Are there really? Still? You see—I scarcely ever go there.

HILDE (*comes nearer*). Really? Don't you? I should have thought you'd take a run down there every day.

MRS. SOLNESS (*with a faint smile*). I don't "run" anywhere. Not any more, Miss Wangel.

HILDE. But you must go down there sometimes—there are such lovely things to see there.

MRS. SOLNESS. It's all become so alien to me. I'm almost afraid to see it again.

HILDE. Your own garden.

MRS. SOLNESS. I don't feel that it *is* mine any longer.

HILDE. How do you mean?

MRS. SOLNESS. No—it's no longer mine, Miss Wangel. It was different when Mother and Father were alive. But they've done such dreadful things to the garden; they've divided it up and built houses for a lot of strangers—people I don't know; and they sit at their windows and stare at me.

HILDE (*brightly*). Mrs. Solness?

MRS. SOLNESS. Yes?

HILDE. Do you mind if I stay here with you for a while?

MRS. SOLNESS. Of course not. I'd be delighted—if you'd care to.

HILDE (*moves a stool over by the armchair and sits down*). Ah! How nice it is to sit and sun oneself like a cat!

MRS. SOLNESS (*lays her hand gently on the back of Hilde's head*). It's kind of you to want to sit here with me. I thought you were on your way to join my husband.

HILDE. Why should I want to join him?

MRS. SOLNESS. I thought perhaps you were helping him with something.

HILDE. No. Anyway—he's not at home just now. He's down there with the workmen. He looked so ferocious, I didn't dare talk to him!

MRS. SOLNESS. He's so kind and gentle underneath all that—

HILDE. He! Kind and gentle!

MRS. SOLNESS. You don't really know him yet, Miss Wangel.

HILDE (*gives her an affectionate look*). Are you glad to be moving into the new house?

MRS. SOLNESS. I suppose I should be glad—for it's what Halvard wants—

HILDE. Oh, not just because of that!

MRS. SOLNESS. Oh, yes, Miss Wangel. After all, it's my duty to try and please him. Still—there are times when it's very hard to force one's mind to obedience.

HILDE. That must be very hard indeed.

MRS. SOLNESS. Yes, it is. Especially when one has as many faults as I have—

HILDE. Or when one has suffered as much as you have—

MRS. SOLNESS. What do you know about that?

HILDE. Your husband told me.

MRS. SOLNESS. He seldom talks about such things to me. Yes—I've been through a great deal in my life, Miss Wangel.

HILDE (nods sympathetically). Poor Mrs. Solness! First the old house burnt down—

MRS. SOLNESS (with a sigh). Yes. I lost everything I had.

HILDE. And what followed was even worse—

MRS. SOLNESS (with a questioning look). Worse?

HILDE. That must have been the worst of all.

MRS. SOLNESS. How do you mean?

HILDE. You lost the two little boys.

MRS. SOLNESS. Oh, the little boys—yes. Well, you see—that was a thing apart. That was the will of the Almighty. One must bow before His will—yes, and be thankful too.

HILDE. Are you able to do that?

MRS. SOLNESS. Not always, I'm afraid. Although I know that it's my duty—still, I often fail in it.

HILDE. I think that's very natural.

MRS. SOLNESS. I have to keep reminding myself that it was a just punishment for me—

HILDE. Punishment? Why?

MRS. SOLNESS. Because I hadn't the strength to bear misfortune.

HILDE. But—I don't understand—

MRS. SOLNESS. No, no, Miss Wangel. Don't talk to me any more about the two little boys. We must be glad for them; they are at peace and happy now. No—it's the small losses in life that break one's heart. It's losing all the little things—things that might seem insignificant to other people.

HILDE (lays her arms on MRS. SOLNESS' knee and looks up at her affectionately). Dear Mrs. Solness—what sort of things do you mean?

MRS. SOLNESS. As I say—just little things. The old family por-

traits were all burnt on the walls. The old silk dresses were burnt
—they had been in the family for countless generations. All
Mother's and Grandmother's lace—and all the jewels—they were
burnt too. And then—all the dolls.

HILDE. The dolls?

MRS. SOLNESS (*her voice choked with tears*). I had nine lovely
dolls.

HILDE. And they were burnt too?

MRS. SOLNESS. All of them. Oh, it was hard—so hard for me.

HILDE. Were they dolls you'd played with as a little girl? Had
you stored them away all those years?

MRS. SOLNESS. They were not stored away. The dolls and I
went on living together.

HILDE. You mean, after you were grown up?

MRS. SOLNESS. Yes, long after that.

HILDE. And even after you were married, too?

MRS. SOLNESS. Oh, yes. As long as he knew nothing about it,
it was—But they were all burnt up, poor things. No one thought
of saving them. Oh, it's so tragic to think of. You mustn't laugh
at me, Miss Wangel.

HILDE. I'm not laughing in the least.

MRS. SOLNESS. In a way, you see, there was life in them, too.
I carried them under my heart. Like little unborn children.

(DR. HERDAL *comes out of the house and sees* MRS. SOLNESS
and HILDE.)

HERDAL. Are you sitting out here catching cold, Mrs. Solness?

MRS. SOLNESS. It's so pleasant and warm here today.

HERDAL. But is anything the matter! I had a note from you.

MRS. SOLNESS (*rises*). Yes. There's something I must talk to
you about.

HERDAL. Very well. Then perhaps we had better go in. (*To*
HILDE.) I see you're still dressed for mountain climbing, Miss
Wangel.

HILDE. In full regalia! But I don't intend to go breaking my
neck today. We two will sit quietly here and look on.

HERDAL. What are we to look on at?

MRS. SOLNESS (*softly to* HILDE, *in a frightened tone*). Hush,
hush! For God's sake! He's coming. Do try to get that idea out of
his head. And let us be friends, Miss Wangel. Don't you think we
can?

HILDE (*throws her arms impetuously round* MRS. SOLNESS'
neck). Oh—if we only could!

MRS. SOLNESS (*gently disengaging herself*). There, there! He's
coming, Doctor. Let me have a word with you.

HERDAL. Is it about him?

MRS. SOLNESS. Yes—of course it's about him. Do come in.

(*She and* DR. HERDAL *enter the house. Next moment* SOL-NESS *comes up from the garden by the flight of steps. A serious look comes over* HILDE's *face.*)

SOLNESS (*glances at the house door that is closed cautiously from within*). Have you noticed, Hilde? As soon as I come, she goes.

HILDE. I've noticed that as soon as you come you make her go.

SOLNESS. Perhaps. But I can't help it. (*Looks at her observantly.*) Are you cold, Hilde? You look as if you were cold.

HILDE. It's because I've just come up out of a tomb.

SOLNESS. What does *that* mean?

HILDE. I feel as if I'd been frozen through and through, Master Builder.

SOLNESS (*slowly*). I think I understand—

HILDE. Why did you come up here?

SOLNESS. I saw you from down below.

HILDE. Then you must have seen her too.

SOLNESS. I knew she'd go away at once if I came.

HILDE. Does it make you unhappy—her avoiding you like that?

SOLNESS. In a way it's almost a relief.

HILDE. Not to have her always before your eyes?

SOLNESS. Yes.

HILDE. Not to be constantly reminded of her grief at the loss of the two little boys?

SOLNESS. Yes. Mostly that.

(HILDE *crosses the veranda with her hands behind her back, and stands by the railing gazing out across the garden.*)

SOLNESS (*after a short pause*). Did you have a long talk with her? (HILDE *doesn't answer but stands there motionless.*) Did you have a long talk, I asked. (HILDE *makes no reply.*) What did she talk about, Hilde? (HILDE *still stands silent.*) Poor Aline! I suppose it was about the little boys. (HILDE *shudders and nods rapidly several times.*) She'll never get over it. Never in this world. (*He goes toward her.*) Now you're standing there again like a statue; just as you did last night.

HILDE (*turns and looks at him with great serious eyes*). I must go away.

SOLNESS (*sharply*). Go away!

HILDE. Yes.

SOLNESS. No! I won't let you!

HILDE. What can I do here now?

SOLNESS. Just *be* here, Hilde!

HILDE *(looks him up and down)*. Yes, I dare say! You know it wouldn't stop at that.

SOLNESS *(recklessly)*. So much the better!

HILDE *(vehemently)*. I can't do any harm to one whom I *know*. I can't take anything that belongs to her.

SOLNESS. Who ever said you *would*?

HILDE. A stranger, yes! That's quite a different thing. Someone I've never laid eyes on. But someone I've come close to—! No, no! Never that! No!

SOLNESS. But I've suggested nothing of that sort.

HILDE. Oh, Master Builder—you know well enough what would happen if I stayed. So I must go away.

SOLNESS. What'll become of *me* if you go away? What shall I have to live for then?

HILDE *(with an inscrutable look in her eyes)*. There's no need to worry about *you*. You have your duties to her. Live for those duties.

SOLNESS. It's too late, Hilde. All these powers, these—these—

HILDE. Devils?

SOLNESS. Yes, devils! And the troll within me, too; they have drained the lifeblood out of her. *(Laughs bitterly.)* They did it for my happiness. And now I'm chained alive to this dead woman. I! I who cannot bear to live without joy in life!

HILDE *(goes round the table and sits down on the bench, her elbows on the table and her head in her hands. Sits and stares at him a moment)*. What will you build next, Master Builder?

SOLNESS *(shakes his head)*. I don't think I'll build much more, Hilde.

HILDE. No cheerful, happy homes—for a mother and a father and a whole troop of children?

SOLNESS. I wonder—will there be any use for such homes from now on?

HILDE. Poor Master Builder! And for ten whole years you've dedicated your life to that alone!

SOLNESS. You're right there, Hilde.

HILDE *(in a sudden outburst)*. Oh, how absurd it all is! How senseless!

SOLNESS. All—what?

HILDE. This business of not daring to grasp your own happiness—your own life! And all because someone you *know*, happens to stand in the way.

SOLNESS. Someone you've no right to cast aside.

HILDE. I wonder. I wonder if that's *really* true. Perhaps, after all, one *has* the right—? And yet—somehow—Oh! To be able to sleep it all away! *(She stretches out her arms flat across the table and rests her head on them, closing her eyes.)*

SOLNESS *(turns the armchair round and sits down at the table).* Did you have a happy home up there with your father, Hilde?

HILDE *(without moving, as though half asleep).* All I had was a cage.

SOLNESS. And you really don't want to go back there?

HILDE *(as before).* Wild birds can't live in cages.

SOLNESS. They must be free to hunt in the open air—

HILDE *(as before).* Birds of prey were meant for hunting.

SOLNESS *(lets his eyes dwell on her).* Oh! To have the Viking spirit in life, Hilde!

HILDE *(in her usual voice, opens her eyes but still doesn't move).* And the other thing? Say what that was!

SOLNESS. A robust conscience.

(HILDE sits erect on the bench, once more full of animation. Her eyes are happy and sparkling.)

HILDE *(nods to him).* I know what you're going to build next, Master Builder!

SOLNESS. Then you know more than I do, Hilde.

HILDE. Yes. Master Builders are so stupid.

SOLNESS. Well? What's it to be?

HILDE *(nods again).* The castle.

SOLNESS. What castle?

HILDE. *My* castle, of course.

SOLNESS. So you want a castle now?

HILDE. You owe me a kingdom, don't you?

SOLNESS. That's what you *say.*

HILDE. All right. So you owe me this kingdom; and you can't have a kingdom without a castle, I should hope!

SOLNESS *(more and more animated).* No. They usually go together.

HILDE. Very well. Then build it for me at once!

SOLNESS *(laughs).* Must you have it this very instant?

HILDE. Of course! For the ten years are up—and I'm not going to wait any longer. So—out with my castle, Master Builder!

SOLNESS. It's no joke to owe you anything, Hilde!

HILDE. You should have thought of that before—it's too late now. So—*(raps on the table)* my castle on the table! It's my castle, and I want it at once!

SOLNESS *(more seriously, leaning toward her with his arms on the table).* How do you see this castle of yours, Hilde?

HILDE (*her expression becomes more and more veiled. She seems to be peering into her innermost being*). My castle must stand on a high hill—high, high up. It must have a clear view on all sides—so that I can see far, far around.

SOLNESS. I suppose it's to have a high tower?

HILDE. A tremendously high tower. And at the very top of the tower there must be a balcony. And I shall stand out on it—

SOLNESS (*involuntarily clutches at his forehead*). How can you bear to stand at such a dizzy height—!

HILDE. Ah, but I shall! I shall stand up there and look down at all the others—at those who are building churches. And homes for a mother and a father and a whole troop of children. And you shall come and look down at them too.

SOLNESS (*softly*). Will the Master Builder be allowed to come up to the princess?

HILDE. If the Master Builder will.

SOLNESS (*more softly still*). Then I think he will come.

HILDE (*nods*). Yes. The Master Builder will come.

SOLNESS. But he'll never build any more—poor Master Builder!

HILDE (*with animation*). Ah, but he will! We two will build together. We'll build the loveliest—the very loveliest thing in all the world.

SOLNESS (*intently*). Hilde—tell me what that is!

HILDE (*smiles at him, shakes her head a little, and talks as though to a child*). Master builders are such very—very stupid people.

SOLNESS. Yes, I know they are. But tell me what it is—this loveliest thing in all the world that we two are to build together?

HILDE (*is silent for a moment, then says with an indefinable expression in her eyes*). Castles-in-the-air.

SOLNESS. Castles-in-the-air?

HILDE (*nodding*). Castles-in-the-air, yes. Do you know what sort of a thing a castle-in-the-air is?

SOLNESS. It's the loveliest thing in the world, you say.

HILDE (*rises abruptly, and makes a gesture of repulsion with her hand*). The loveliest thing in the world! Castles-in-the-air—they're so easy to take refuge in. And they're easy to build too—especially for builders who have a—dizzy conscience.

SOLNESS (*rises*). From now on, we two will build together, Hilde.

HILDE (*with a half-doubting smile*). A real castle-in-the-air?

SOLNESS. Yes. One on a firm foundation.

(RAGNAR BROVIK *comes out of the house. He carries a large green wreath, decked with flowers and ribbons.*)

HILDE (*in a burst of happiness*). The wreath! Oh, it'll be splendid!

SOLNESS (*in surprise*). Why have *you* brought the wreath, Ragnar?

RAGNAR. I promised the foreman I would.

SOLNESS (*with relief*). Then your father must be better?

RAGNAR. No.

SOLNESS. Wasn't he pleased with what I wrote?

RAGNAR. It came too late.

SOLNESS. Too late?

RAGNAR. He was unconscious by the time she brought it. He'd had a stroke.

SOLNESS. Then you must go home to him. You must stay with him, Ragnar.

RAGNAR. He doesn't need me any more.

SOLNESS. But, surely, you ought to *be* there!

RAGNAR. She's there with him—sitting by his bed.

SOLNESS (*rather uncertainly*). Kaja?

RAGNAR (*with a dark look*). Yes, Kaja.

SOLNESS. Go home to them both, Ragnar. Give me the wreath.

RAGNAR (*suppressing a mocking smile*). You don't mean that you're going to—

SOLNESS. I'll take it down to the men. (*Takes the wreath from him.*) You go on home. We don't need you here today.

RAGNAR. No—I dare say you don't need me. But today I'm going to stay.

SOLNESS. Very well. As you like.

HILDE (*by the railing*). I'm going to stand here and watch you, Master Builder.

SOLNESS. *Watch* me?

HILDE. It'll be wonderfully thrilling!

SOLNESS (*in a low tone*). We'll discuss that later, Hilde. (*He takes the wreath and goes down the steps into the garden.*)

HILDE (*she watches him go, then turns to* RAGNAR). I should think you might at least have thanked him!

RAGNAR. Thanked him! Do you expect me to thank him?

HILDE. Yes, of course you should!

RAGNAR. It seems to me it's *you* I ought to thank.

HILDE. How can you say such a thing?

RAGNAR (*without answering her*). But I warn you, Miss Wangel. You don't really know him yet.

HILDE (*passionately*). No one knows him as *I* do—!

RAGNAR (*with a bitter laugh*). Thank him, indeed! When he's held me back year after year! When he's made my own father doubt me—made me doubt myself—and all because he wanted to—!

HILDE (*as though sensing something*). What? Tell me at once!

RAGNAR. Because he wanted to keep her with him.

HILDE (*with a start toward him*). That girl at the desk?

RAGNAR. Yes.

HILDE (*clenching her hands, threateningly*). That's not true! You're telling lies about him!

RAGNAR. I didn't believe it either until today—when she told me herself.

HILDE (*as though beside herself*). What did she say? Tell me! At once! At once!

RAGNAR. She said—that he had taken possession of her whole being—her whole being, she said. That all her thoughts were for him alone. She said she could never leave him. That she must stay here where he is—

HILDE (*with flashing eyes*). She won't be allowed to!

RAGNAR (*as if feeling his way*). Who won't allow her?

HILDE (*rapidly*). *He* won't permit it either!

RAGNAR. No—of course not. I understand everything now. From now on she'd only be in the way.

HILDE. You don't understand anything or you wouldn't talk like that. *I'll* tell you why he wanted her to stay here.

RAGNAR. Well—why?

HILDE. Because he wanted *you* to stay.

RAGNAR. Did he tell you that himself?

HILDE. No, but it's true! It *must* be true! (*Wildly.*) I will—I *will* have it so!

RAGNAR. But the moment *you* came—he let her go.

HILDE. It was *you* that he let go! Why should he care about a strange girl like her!

RAGNAR (*after a moment's thought*). Could he have been afraid of me all these years?

HILDE. *He* afraid! I wouldn't be so conceited if I were you.

RAGNAR. He must have realized long ago that I had something in me. Besides—a coward—that's just what he is, you see.

HILDE. Yes! I'm likely to believe that!

RAGNAR. Well—in some ways he is a coward—the great Master Builder! Oh, he's not afraid of destroying other people's happiness—Father's and mine, for instance—but just ask him to climb up a miserable bit of scaffolding, and see what he says!

HILDE. You should have seen him at the top of a high tower as I once saw him.

RAGNAR. You saw *that*?

HILDE. Yes—indeed I did! He fastened the wreath to the church vane—and he looked so proud and free!

RAGNAR. He's supposed to have done that once—just once in his life, they say. It's become a sort of legend among us younger men. But no power on earth would induce him to do it again.

HILDE. He'll do it again today!

RAGNAR *(scornfully)*. Yes—I dare say!

HILDE. We shall see it!

RAGNAR. We'll neither of us ever see that.

HILDE *(with passionate vehemence)*. I will see it! I *will* and I *must* see it!

RAGNAR. But he won't do it. He simply *dare* not do it. It's like an illness—don't you see?

(MRS. SOLNESS *comes out onto the veranda.*)

MRS. SOLNESS *(looking round)*. Isn't he here? Where did he go?

RAGNAR. Mr. Solness is down with the men.

HILDE. He took the wreath with him.

MRS. SOLNESS *(terrified)*. Took the wreath! Oh God! Brovik—go down to him. Try to get him to come up here.

RAGNAR. Shall I say you want him, Mrs. Solness?

MRS. SOLNESS. Yes, do—dear Brovik. No, no! Better not say *I* want him—tell him some people have just come and are asking to see him.

RAGNAR. Very well. I'll tell him, Mrs. Solness. *(He goes down the steps to the garden.)*

MRS. SOLNESS. Oh, I'm so anxious about him, Miss Wangel.

HILDE. What is there to be so afraid of?

MRS. SOLNESS. Surely you can understand? What if he really meant it? What if he were really to try and climb the scaffolding?

HILDE. Do you think he will?

MRS. SOLNESS. He's so unpredictable—it's impossible to tell. He might do anything!

HILDE. Then—perhaps you, too, think that he's—?

MRS. SOLNESS. I no longer know *what* to think of him, Miss Wangel. The doctor's just told me various things that—well—putting them together with several things I've heard him say—

HERDAL *(comes out of the house)*. Hasn't he come up yet?

MRS. SOLNESS. He'll be here soon, I think. They've just gone for him.

HERDAL *(comes toward her)*. You're wanted inside, Mrs. Solness—

MRS. SOLNESS. No, no. I'll stay on here and wait for Halvard.

HERDAL. But some ladies have come to call—

MRS. SOLNESS. Good Heavens—how tiresome! Just at this moment!

HERDAL. They insist on watching the ceremony.

MRS. SOLNESS. Then I suppose I'd better go in—after all, it's my duty—

HILDE. Why not ask them to go away?

MRS. SOLNESS. Oh, I can't very well do that. As long as they're here it's my duty to see them. But you stay out here, Miss Wangel, and talk to him when he comes.

HERDAL. Keep him up here as long as possible.

MRS. SOLNESS. Yes, do—dear Miss Wangel. Be firm with him. Make him give up that mad idea.

HILDE. Wouldn't it be best for you to do that?

MRS. SOLNESS. Yes—Heaven knows—that *is* my duty. But one has duties in so many directions that I—

HERDAL (*looks toward the garden*). Here he comes!

MRS. SOLNESS. Oh, dear! And I have to go in!

HERDAL (*to* HILDE). Don't say anything to him about my being here.

HILDE. I dare say I'll be able to find something else to talk to him about.

MRS. SOLNESS. And be sure and keep him here, Miss Wangel. I believe you can do it best.

(MRS. SOLNESS *and* DR. HERDAL *go into the house.* HILDE *remains standing on the veranda.*)

SOLNESS (*comes up the steps from the garden*). I hear someone wants to see me.

HILDE. It's only I, Master Builder.

SOLNESS. Oh, it's you, Hilde. I was afraid it might be Aline and the doctor.

HILDE. You're very easily frightened, I hear.

SOLNESS. Do you think so?

HILDE. Yes. I'm told you're afraid—afraid of climbing about— on scaffoldings, they say.

SOLNESS. Well—that's quite a special thing.

HILDE. Then you are afraid of it?

SOLNESS. Yes, I am.

HILDE. Afraid of falling down and killing yourself?

SOLNESS. No—not of that.

HILDE. Of what, then?

SOLNESS. I'm afraid of retribution, Hilde.

HILDE. Retribution? (*Shakes her head.*) I don't understand that.

SOLNESS. Hilde—sit down a minute. I want to tell you something.

HILDE. I'm listening, Master Builder! *(She sits on a stool by the railing and looks at him expectantly.)*

SOLNESS *(flings his hat on the table).* You know that I began by building churches—

HILDE *(nods).* Yes. I know that very well!

SOLNESS. You see—I came from a pious home in a little country village. I suppose that's why I thought the finest thing I could devote my life to, was the building of churches.

HILDE. Yes. I see.

SOLNESS. And I think I may say that I built those humble little churches with such honest fervor that—that—

HILDE. Well?

SOLNESS. Well—that I think He should have been pleased with me.

HILDE. *He?* What *He?*

SOLNESS. He for whom they were built, of course. To whose honor and glory they were dedicated.

HILDE. And do you think He *wasn't* pleased with you?

SOLNESS. *He* pleased with *me?* How can you say that, Hilde? Didn't He give the troll in me full power? Didn't He give me mastery over all these—these—

HILDE. Devils?

SOLNESS. Yes—devils! Of both kinds! No. I soon found out that He wasn't pleased with me. *(Mysteriously.)* That was really why He let the old house burn down.

HILDE. Was that the reason?

SOLNESS. Yes, don't you see? He wanted me to become a great master in my own sphere, so that I could go on building evermore glorious churches for Him. At first I didn't realize what He was up to—and then, suddenly, I saw it clearly.

HILDE. When was that?

SOLNESS. It was when I built the church tower at Lysanger.

HILDE. I thought so.

SOLNESS. I was up there alone in strange surroundings—I had plenty of time to think and meditate. And I suddenly understood why He had taken my little children from me. He didn't want me to become attached to anything; I was to be allowed no love or happiness, you understand. I was to be nothing but a Master Builder, and I was to devote my life solely to building for Him. But I soon put a stop to that!

HILDE. What did you do then?

SOLNESS. First I searched my own heart—put myself to the test—

HILDE. And then?

SOLNESS. Then I did the impossible. I no less than He.

HILDE. The impossible?

SOLNESS. I had never before been able to climb to a great height. But that day I did it.

HILDE. Yes, you did!

SOLNESS. And as I stood up there, high over everything, I said to Him: Listen to me, Almighty One! From now on I will be a free Master Builder; free in my sphere, just as You are in yours. I will never more build churches for You; only homes for human beings.

HILDE (*with great shining eyes*). That was the song that I heard in the air!

SOLNESS. Yes. But He won in the end.

HILDE. How do you mean?

SOLNESS. This building homes for human beings isn't worth a rap, Hilde!

HILDE. Is that **how** you feel now?

SOLNESS. Yes. Because now I see it. People have no use for these homes of theirs. Not to be happy in—no. And if I had such a home, I probably wouldn't have any use for it either. What does it all amount to—now that I look back on it? What have I ever built? What have I ever sacrificed for the chance of building? Nothing! Nothing! It all amounts to nothing!

HILDE. Then—will you never build anything any more, Master Builder?

SOLNESS. On the contrary—now I'm just going to begin!

HILDE. What will you build? What? Tell me at once!

SOLNESS. I believe there's just one possible dwelling place for human happiness—that's what I'm going to build now.

HILDE. Master Builder—you mean our castles-in-the-air?

SOLNESS. Castles-in-the-air, yes.

HILDE. I'm afraid you'd grow dizzy before you got halfway up.

SOLNESS. Not if I were to climb hand in hand with you, Hilde.

HILDE. With me alone? Will there be no others?

SOLNESS. What others?

HILDE (*with suppressed resentment*). That—Kaja—at the desk, for instance. Poor thing—don't you want to take her with you too?

SOLNESS. Aha! So *that* was what Aline was talking to you about.

HILDE. Is it so, or is it not?

SOLNESS. I won't answer that question! You must believe in me wholly and completely!

HILDE. For ten years I have believed in you so utterly—so utterly!

SOLNESS. You must go on believing in me!

HILDE. Then let me see you again free and high up!

SOLNESS *(sadly).* I can't be like that every day, Hilde.

HILDE. You must be! I want you to be! *(Imploringly.)* Just this once more, Master Builder! Do the impossible again!

SOLNESS *(looks deep into her eyes).* If I try it, Hilde, I shall stand up there and talk to Him as I did before.

HILDE *(with growing excitement).* What will you say to Him?

SOLNESS. I shall say to Him: Listen to me, Almighty Lord— You may judge me as You will. But from now on I shall build only the loveliest thing in all the world—

HILDE *(carried away).* Yes, yes, yes!

SOLNESS. I shall build it with a princess whom I love—

HILDE. Yes, tell Him that! Tell Him that!

SOLNESS. And then I'll say to Him: Now I shall go down and throw my arms round her and kiss her—

HILDE.—many times! Say that!

SOLNESS.—Many, many times, I'll say.

HILDE.—and then?

SOLNESS. Then I shall wave my hat—come down to earth again—and do as I told Him.

HILDE *(with outstretched arms).* Now I see you again as I did when there was a song in the air!

SOLNESS *(looks at her with bowed head).* Hilde—how have you become what you are?

HILDE. How have you made me what I am?

SOLNESS *(quickly and firmly).* The princess shall have her castle.

HILDE. *(joyfully, clapping her hands).* Master Builder! My lovely, lovely castle! *Our* castle-in-the-air!

SOLNESS. On a firm foundation.

(A crowd of people have gathered in the street, dimly seen through the trees. The sound of a brass band is heard from beyond the new house. MRS. SOLNESS, *wearing a fur piece round her neck,* DR. HERDAL, *carrying her white shawl over his arm, and several ladies come out on the veranda. At the same moment* RAGNAR *comes up from the garden.)*

MRS. SOLNESS *(to* RAGNAR). Are we to have music, too?

RAGNAR. Yes, it's the band from the builder's union. *(To*

SOLNESS.) I was to tell you—the foreman is ready to go up with the wreath.

SOLNESS. *(takes up his hat).* Very well; I'll go down to him.

MRS. SOLNESS *(anxiously).* Need you go down there, Halvard?

SOLNESS *(shortly).* I must be below with the men.

MRS. SOLNESS. But you'll stay down below—won't you, Halvard? You'll stay down with the men?

SOLNESS. Isn't that where I usually stay? On ordinary occasions? *(He goes down the steps to the garden.)*

MRS. SOLNESS *(at the parapet, calls after him).* And do tell the foreman to be careful! Promise me that, Halvard!

HERDAL *(to MRS. SOLNESS).* You see how right I was? He's forgotten all about that nonsense.

MRS. SOLNESS. Oh, what a relief! Twice workmen have fallen and been killed on the spot. *(Turns to HILDE.)* Thank you, Miss Wangel, for being so firm with him. I'm sure I could never have managed him.

HERDAL *(teasingly).* Just leave it to Miss Wangel! She can be firm with a man, when she puts her mind to it!

(MRS. SOLNESS and DR. HERDAL join the ladies who stand on the steps looking out over the garden. HILDE remains standing in the foreground by the railing. RAGNAR goes over to her.)

RAGNAR *(with suppressed laughter; in a whisper).* Miss Wangel —do you see all those young people down there in the street?

HILDE. Yes.

RAGNAR. Those are my fellow students. They're here to watch the Master!

HILDE. What do they want to watch him for?

RAGNAR. They like to see him obliged to stay below; they know he'd never dare climb, even to the top of his own house.

HILDE. So that's why they're here, is it?

RAGNAR. Yes—all these years he's kept us down. We like to see him forced to stay down below himself.

HILDE. Well—you won't see that this time.

RAGNAR. Really? Where will we see him then?

HILDE. High up! High up at the top of the tower! That's where you'll see him!

RAGNAR. Do you expect me to believe that?

HILDE. It is his will to climb to the top—so at the top you shall see him.

RAGNAR. His *will!* Yes, I dare say—but he simply can't do it. He'd get dizzy before he was halfway up. He'd have to crawl down again on his hands and knees!

HERDAL (*pointing toward the new house*). Look! There goes the foreman up the ladder!

MRS. SOLNESS. He has the wreath to carry too. Oh, I do hope he'll be careful!

RAGNAR (*with a shout of incredulity*). But—it's—

HILDE (*jubilant*). It's the Master Builder himself!

MRS. SOLNESS (*with a cry of terror*). Yes, it's Halvard! Oh, God! Halvard! Halvard!

HERDAL. Sh! Don't shout to him!

MRS. SOLNESS (*beside herself*). I must go to him—I must get him to come down!

HERDAL (*holding on to her*). Stand still—all of you! Not a sound!

HILDE (*motionless, follows* SOLNESS *with her eyes*). He climbs and he climbs. Higher and higher. Higher and higher! Look! Just look!

RAGNAR (*scarcely breathing*). He *must* turn back now. He can't do anything else.

HILDE. He climbs and he climbs. He'll soon be at the top now.

MRS. SOLNESS. I shall die of terror. I can't bear to look at him!

HERDAL. Don't watch him then.

HILDE. There he stands on the topmost planks—right at the very top!

HERDAL. No one must move—Do you hear!

HILDE (*exultant; with quiet intensity*). At last! At last! I see him great and free again!

RAGNAR (*almost speechless*). But this is—

HILDE. All these ten years I've seen him so! How proud he looks! Wonderfully thrilling all the same. Look at him! Now he's hanging the wreath on the vane!

RAGNAR. But—this is utterly impossible!

HILDE. It *is* the impossible that he's doing now. (*With that indefinable expression in her eyes.*) Do you see anyone else up there with him?

RAGNAR. There is no one else.

HILDE. Yes—there's someone he's striving with.

RAGNAR. No—you're mistaken—

HILDE. Don't you hear a song in the air either?

RAGNAR. It must be the wind in the tree tops.

HILDE. I hear a song. A mighty song! (*Shouts with wild joyful ecstasy.*) Look! Look! Now he's waving his hat! He's waving to us down here! Oh, wave—wave back to him—for now it is finished! (*Snatches the white shawl from* DR. HERDAL, *waves it and shouts up to* SOLNESS.) Hurrah for Master Builder Solness!

HERDAL. Stop it! Stop it—for God's sake!

(The ladies on the veranda wave their handkerchiefs, and shouts of "Hurrah!" come from the street below. There is a sudden silence—then the crowd bursts into a shriek of horror. A human body, with a few planks and fragments of wood, is seen dimly, crashing down behind the trees.)

MRS. SOLNESS and the LADIES *(simultaneously)*. He's falling! He's falling!

(MRS. SOLNESS sways and falls back in a faint. The ladies support her amidst cries and confusion. The crowd in the street breaks through the fence and storms into the garden. DR. HERDAL rushes down there too. A short pause.)

HILDE *(stares fixedly upward and says as though petrified)*. My Master Builder.

RAGNAR *(trembling, leans against the railing)*. He must have been killed outright—smashed to pieces.

ONE OF THE LADIES *(as MRS. SOLNESS is being helped into the house)*. Run for the doctor—

RAGNAR. I can't move—

LADY. Then call down to him!

RAGNAR *(makes an effort to call out)*. Is there any hope? Is he still alive?

A VOICE FROM BELOW. The Master Builder is dead.

ANOTHER VOICE *(nearer)*. His whole head is crushed in—he fell right into the stone quarry.

HILDE *(turns to RAGNAR and says quietly)*. I can't see him up there any more.

RAGNAR. What a ghastly thing. So—after all—he couldn't do it.

HILDE *(as though under a spell, with a quiet triumph)*. But he climbed to the very top. And I heard harps in the air. *(Waves the shawl and cries out with wild intensity.)* My—my Master Builder!

CURTAIN

Selma Lagerlöf[1] (1858–1940)

THE RAT TRAP

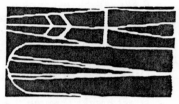

Translated from the Swedish by
Florence and Naboth Hedin

ONCE UPON A TIME there was a man who went around selling small rat traps of wire. He made them himself at odd moments, from material he got by begging in the stores or at the big farms. But even so, the business was not especially profitable, so he had to resort to both begging and petty thievery to keep body and soul together. Even so, his clothes were in rags, his cheeks were sunken, and hunger gleamed in his eyes.

No one can imagine how sad and monotonous life can appear to such a vagabond, who plods along the road, left to his own meditations. But one day this man had fallen into a line of thought which really seemed to him entertaining. He had naturally been thinking of his rat traps when suddenly he was struck by the idea that the whole world about him—the whole world with its lands and seas, its cities and villages—was nothing but a big rat trap. It had never existed for any other purpose than to set baits for people. It offered riches and joys, shelter and food, heat and clothing, exactly as the rat trap offered cheese and pork, and as soon as anyone let himself be tempted to touch the bait, it closed in on him, and then everything came to an end.

The world had, of course, never been very kind to him, so it gave him unwonted joy to think ill of it in this way. It became a cherished pastime of his, during many dreary ploddings, to

"The Rat Trap" from HARVEST by Selma Lagerlöf, translated by Florence and Naboth Hedin. Published by Doubleday & Company, Inc.
1. *Lagerlöf* (lä′gər lœf′).

think of people he knew who had let themselves be caught in the dangerous snare, and of others who were still circling around the bait.

One dark evening as he was trudging along the road he caught sight of a little gray cottage by the roadside, and he knocked on the door to ask shelter for the night. Nor was he refused. Instead of the sour faces which ordinarily met him, the owner, who was an old man without wife or child, was happy to get someone to talk to in his loneliness. Immediately he put the porridge pot on the fire and gave him supper; then he carved off such a big slice from his tobacco roll that it was enough both for the stranger's pipe and his own. Finally he got out an old pack of cards and played *mjölis* with his guest until bedtime.

The old man was just as generous with his confidences as with his porridge and tobacco. The guest was informed at once that in his days of prosperity his host had been a crofter [2] at Ramsjö Ironworks and had worked on the land. Now that he was no longer able to do day labor, it was his cow which supported him. Yes, that bossy was extraordinary. She could give milk for the creamery every day, and last month he had received all of thirty kronor [3] in payment.

The stranger must have seemed incredulous, for the old man got up and went to the window, took down a leather pouch which hung on a nail in the very window frame, and picked out three wrinkled ten-kronor bills. These he held up before the eyes of his guest, nodding knowingly, and then stuffed them back into the pouch.

The next day both men got up in good season. The crofter was in a hurry to milk his cow, and the other man probably thought he should not stay in bed when the head of the house had gotten up. They left the cottage at the same time. The crofter locked the door and put the key in his pocket. The man with the rat traps said good-bye and thank you, and thereupon each went his own way.

But half an hour later the rat-trap peddler stood again before the door. He did not try to get in, however. He only went up to the window, smashed a pane, stuck in his hand, and got hold of the pouch with thirty kronor. He took the money and thrust it into his own pocket. Then he hung the leather pouch very carefully back in its place and went away.

---

2. *crofter,* a person who cultivates a very small farm. 3. *thirty kronor,* approximately $6.00. A krona is a silver and copper coin and is the monetary unit of Sweden.

As he walked along with the money in his pocket he felt quite pleased with his smartness. He realized, of course, that at first he dared not continue on the public highway, but must turn off the road, into the woods. During the first few hours this caused him no difficulty. Later in the day it became worse, for it was a big and confusing forest which he had gotten into. He tried, to be sure, to walk in a definite direction, but the paths twisted back and forth so strangely! He walked and walked, without coming to the end of the wood, and finally he realized that he had only been walking around in the same part of the forest. All at once he recalled his thoughts about the world and the rat trap. Now his own turn had come. He had let himself be fooled by a bait and had been caught. The whole forest, with its trunks and branches, its thickets and fallen logs, closed in upon him like an impenetrable prison from which he could never escape.

It was late in December. Darkness was already descending over the forest. This increased the danger, and increased also his gloom and despair. Finally he saw no way out, and he sank down on the ground, tired to death, thinking that his last moment had come. But just as he laid his head on the ground, he heard a sound—a hard, regular thumping. There was no doubt as to what that was. He raised himself. "Those are the hammer strokes from an iron mill," he thought. "There must be people near by." He summoned all his strength, got up, and staggered in the direction of the sound.

The Ramsjö Ironworks, which are now closed down, was, not so long ago, a large plant, with smelter, rolling mill, and forge. In the summertime long lines of heavily loaded barges and scows slid down the canal which led to a large inland lake, and in the wintertime the roads near the mill were black from all the coal dust which sifted down from the big charcoal crates.

During one of the long dark evenings just before Christmas, the master smith and his helper sat in the dark forge near the furnace waiting for the pig iron, which had been put in the fire, to be ready to put on the anvil. Every now and then one of them got up to stir the glowing mass with a long iron bar, returning in a few moments, dripping with perspiration, though, as was the custom, he wore nothing but a long shirt and a pair of wooden shoes.

All the time there were many sounds to be heard in the forge. The big bellows groaned and the burning coal cracked. The fire boy shoveled charcoal into the maw of the furnace with a great deal of clatter. Outside roared the waterfall, and a sharp north wind whipped the rain against the brick-tiled roof.

It was probably on account of all this noise that the blacksmith did not notice that a man had opened the gate and entered the forge, until he stood close up to the furnace.

Surely it was nothing unusual for poor vagabonds without any better shelter for the night to be attracted to the forge by the glow of light which escaped through the sooty panes, and to come in to warm themselves in front of the fire. The blacksmiths glanced only casually and indifferently at the intruder. He looked the way people of his type usually did, with a long beard, dirty, ragged, and with a bunch of rat traps dangling on his chest.

He asked permission to stay, and the master blacksmith nodded a haughty consent without honoring him with a single word.

The tramp did not say anything, either. He had not come there to talk but only to warm himself and sleep.

In those days the Ramsjö iron mill was owned by a very prominent ironmaster whose greatest ambition was to ship out good iron to the market. He watched both night and day to see that the work was done as well as possible, and at this very moment he came into the forge on one of his nightly rounds of inspection.

Naturally the first thing he saw was the tall ragamuffin who had eased his way so close to the furnace that steam rose from his wet rags. The ironmaster did not follow the example of the blacksmiths, who had hardly deigned to look at the stranger. He walked close up to him, looked him over very carefully, then tore off his slouch hat to get a better view of his face.

"But of course it is you, Nils Olof!" he said. "How you do look!"

The man with the rat traps had never before seen the ironmaster of Ramsjö and did not even know what his name was. But it occurred to him that if the fine gentleman thought he was an old acquaintance, he might perhaps throw him a couple of kronor. Therefore he did not want to undeceive him all at once.

"Yes, God knows things have gone downhill with me," he said.

"You should not have resigned from the regiment," said the ironmaster. "That was the mistake. If only I had still been in the service at the time, it never would have happened. Well, now of course you will come home with me."

To go along up to the manor house and be received by the owner like an old regimental comrade—that, however, did not please the tramp.

"No, I couldn't think of it!" he said, looking quite alarmed.

He thought of the thirty kronor. To go up to the manor house would be like throwing himself voluntarily into the lions' den. He only wanted a chance to sleep here in the forge and then sneak away as inconspicuously as possible.

The ironmaster assumed that he felt embarrassed because of his miserable clothing.

"Please don't think that I have such a fine home that you cannot show yourself there," he said. "Elizabeth is dead, as you may already have heard. My boys are abroad, and there is no one at home except my oldest daughter and myself. We were just saying that it was too bad we didn't have any company for Christmas. Now come along with me and help us make the Christmas food disappear a little faster."

But the stranger said no, and no, and again no, and the ironmaster saw that he must give in.

"It looks as though Captain von Ståhle preferred to stay with you tonight, Stjernström," he said to the master blacksmith, and turned on his heel.

But he laughed to himself as he went away, and the blacksmith, who knew him, understood very well that he had not said his last word.

It was not more than half an hour before they heard the sound of carriage wheels outside the forge, and a new guest came in, but this time it was not the ironmaster. He had sent his daughter, apparently hoping that she would have better powers of persuasion than he himself.

She entered, followed by a valet, carrying on his arm a big fur coat. She was not at all pretty, but seemed modest and quite shy. In the forge everything was just as it had been earlier in the evening. The master blacksmith and his apprentice still sat on their bench, and iron and charcoal still glowed in the furnace. The stranger had stretched himself out on the floor and lay with a piece of pig iron under his head and his hat pulled down over his eyes. As soon as the young girl caught sight of him she went up and lifted his hat. The man was evidently used to sleeping with one eye open. He jumped up abruptly and seemed to be quite frightened.

"My name is Edla Willmansson," said the young girl. "My father came home and said that you wanted to sleep here in the forge tonight, and then I asked permission to come and bring you home to us. I am so sorry, Captain, that you are having such a hard time."

She looked at him compassionately, with her heavy eyes, and

then she noticed that the man was afraid. "Either he has stolen something or else he has escaped from jail," she thought, and added quickly, "You may be sure, Captain, that you will be allowed to leave us just as freely as you came. Only please stay with us over Christmas Eve."

She said this in such a friendly manner that the rat-trap peddler must have felt confidence in her.

"It would never have occurred to me that you would bother with me yourself, miss," he said. "I will come at once."

He accepted the fur coat, which the valet handed him with a deep bow, threw it over his rags, and followed the young lady out to the carriage, without granting the astonished blacksmiths so much as a glance.

But while he was riding up to the manor house he had evil forebodings.

"Why the devil did I take that fellow's money?" he thought. "Now I am sitting in the trap and will never get out of it."

The next day was Christmas Eve, and when the ironmaster came into the dining room for breakfast he probably thought with satisfaction of his old regimental comrade whom he had run across so unexpectedly.

"First of all we must see to it that he gets a little flesh on his bones," he said to his daughter, who was busy at the table. "And then we must see that he gets something else to do than to run around the country selling rat traps."

"It is queer that things have gone downhill with him as badly as that," said the daughter. "Last night I did not think there was anything about him to show that he had once been an educated man."

"You must have patience, my little girl," said the father. "As soon as he gets clean and dressed up, you will see something different. Last night he was naturally embarrassed. The tramp manners will fall away from him with the tramp clothes."

Just as he said this the door opened and the stranger entered. Yes, now he was truly clean and well dressed. The valet had bathed him, cut his hair, and shaved him. Moreover he was dressed in a good-looking suit of clothes which belonged to the ironmaster. He wore a white shirt and a starched collar and whole shoes.

But although his guest was now so well groomed, the iron-master did not seem pleased. He looked at him with puckered brow, and it was easy enough to understand that when he had seen the strange fellow in the uncertain reflection from the furnace he might have made a mistake, but that now, when he stood there in broad daylight, it was impossible to mistake him for an old acquaintance.

"What does this mean?" he thundered.

The stranger made no attempt to dissimulate. He saw at once that all the splendor had come to an end.

"It is not my fault, sir," he said. "I never pretended to be anything but a poor trader, and I pleaded and begged to be allowed to stay in the forge. But no harm has been done. At worst I can put on my rags again and go away."

"Well," said the ironmaster, hesitating a little, "it was not quite honest, either. You must admit that, and I should not be surprised if the sheriff would like to have something to say in the matter."

The tramp took a step forward and struck the table with his fist.

"Now I am going to tell you, Mr. Ironmaster, how things are," he said. "This whole world is nothing but a big rat trap. All the good things that are offered you are nothing but cheese rinds and bits of pork, set out to drag a poor fellow into trouble. And if the sheriff comes now and locks me up for this, then you, Mr. Ironmaster, must remember that a day may come when you yourself may want to get a big piece of pork, and then you will get caught in the trap."

The ironmaster began to laugh.

"That was not so badly said, my good fellow. Perhaps we should let the sheriff alone on Christmas Eve. But now get out of here as fast as you can."

But just as the man was opening the door, the daughter said, "I think he ought to stay with us today. I don't want him to go." And with that she went and closed the door.

"What in the world are you doing?" said the father.

The daughter stood there quite embarrassed and hardly knew what to answer. That morning she had felt so happy when she thought how homelike and Christmassy she was going to make things for the poor hungry wretch. She could not get away from the idea all at once, and that was why she had interceded for the vagabond.

"I am thinking of this stranger here," said the young girl. "He walks and walks the whole year long, and there is probably not a single place in the whole country where he is welcome and can feel at home. Wherever he turns he is chased away. Always he is afraid of being arrested and cross-examined. I should like to have him enjoy a day of peace with us here—just one in the whole year."

The ironmaster mumbled something in his beard. He could not bring himself to oppose her.

"It was all a mistake, of course," she continued. "But anyway I don't think we ought to chase away a human being whom we have asked to come here, and to whom we have promised Christmas cheer."

"You do preach worse than a parson," said the ironmaster. "I only hope you won't have to regret this."

The young girl took the stranger by the hand and led him up to the table.

"Now sit down and eat," she said, for she could see that her father had given in.

The man with the rat traps said not a word; he only sat down and helped himself to the food. Time after time he looked at the young girl who had interceded for him. Why had she done it? What could the crazy idea be?

After that, Christmas Eve at Ramsjö passed just as it always had. The stranger did not cause any trouble because he did nothing but sleep. The whole forenoon he lay on the sofa in one of the guest rooms and slept at one stretch. At noon they woke him up so that he could have his share of the good Christmas fare, but after that he slept again. It seemed as though for many years he had not been able to sleep as quietly and safely as here at Ramsjö.

In the evening, when the Christmas tree was lighted, they woke him up again, and he stood for a while in the drawing room, blinking as though the candlelight hurt him, but after that he disappeared again. Two hours later he was aroused once more. He then had to go down into the dining room and eat the Christmas fish and porridge.

As soon as they got up from the table he went around to each one present and said thank you and good-night, but when he came to the young girl she gave him to understand that it was her father's intention that the suit which he wore was to be a Christmas present—he did not have to return it; and if he wanted to spend next Christmas Eve in a place where he could rest in peace, and be sure that no evil would befall him, he would be welcomed back again.

The man with the rat traps did not answer anything to this. He only stared at the young girl in boundless amazement.

The next morning the ironmaster and his daughter got up in good season to go to the early Christmas service. Their guest was still asleep, and they did not disturb him.

When, at about ten o'clock, they drove back from church, the young girl sat and hung her head even more dejectedly than usual. At church she had learned that one of the old crofters of the ironworks had been robbed by a man who went around selling rat traps.

"Yes, that was a fine fellow you let into the house," said her father. "I only wonder how many silver spoons are left in the cupboard by this time."

The wagon had hardly stopped at the front steps when the ironmaster asked the valet whether the stranger was still there. He added that he had heard at church that the man was a thief. The valet answered that the fellow had gone and that he had not taken anything with him at all. On the contrary, he had left behind a little package which Miss Willmansson was to be kind enough to accept as a Christmas present.

The young girl opened the package, which was so badly done up that the contents came into view at once. She gave a little cry of joy. She found a small rat trap, and in it lay three wrinkled ten-kronor notes. But that was not all. In the rat trap lay also a letter written in large, jagged characters:

Honored and noble Miss:

Since you have been so nice to me all day long, as if I was a captain, I want to be nice to you, in return, as if I was a real captain: for I do not want you to be embarrassed at this Christmas season by a thief; but you can give back the money to the old man on the roadside, who has the money pouch hanging on the window frame as a bait for poor wanderers.

The rat trap is a Christmas present from a rat who would have been caught in this world's rat trap if he had not been raised to captain, because in that way he got power to clear himself.

Written with friendship and high regard,

Captain von Ståhle. ■

August Strindberg (1849–1912)

THE STRONGER

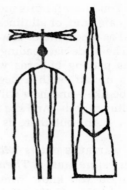

Translated from the Swedish by
Arvid Paulson

Persons in the play

MRS. X., *a married actress*
MISS Y., *an unmarried actress*
A WAITRESS

THE SETTING: *A corner of a café for ladies. Two wrought iron tables; a sofa upholstered with red shag; several chairs.* MISS Y. *is seated at one of the tables. Before her is a half-empty bottle of ale. She is reading an illustrated periodical, which she later exchanges for others on the table.* MRS. X. *enters. She is dressed in winter apparel and wears a hat and cloak. She carries a Japanese shopping bag or basket, of exquisite design, on her arm.*

MRS. X. How do you do, Amelie dear! You are sitting here all by yourself on Christmas Eve—like some poor bachelor . . .

(MISS Y. *looks up from the magazine, gives* MRS. X. *a nod, and resumes her reading.*)

MRS. X. You know it hurts me to see you sitting here—alone—alone in a café, and, of all times, on Christmas Eve. It makes me feel as bad as when I once saw a wedding party in a restaurant in Paris. The bride sat reading a comic paper, while the bridegroom was playing billiards with the wedding guests. Ugh, I thought to myself, with a beginning like that, what will the marriage be like—and how will it end? *He,* playing billiards on their wedding night!—And *she* reading a comic paper, you mean to say? . . . Ah, but there is a certain difference, don't you think?

(THE WAITRESS *enters with a cup of chocolate which she places before* MRS. X. *Then she leaves.*)

MRS. X. Do you know what, Amelie! I believe you would have been better off if you had married him. . . . You remember that I urged you from the very first to forgive him. You remember that? You could have been his wife now, and had a home of your own. . . . Do you recall how happy you were last Christmas when you spent the holidays with your fiancé's parents out in the country? How you sang the praises of domestic life and literally longed to get away from the theatre?—Yes, Amelie dear, a home is the best after all—next to the theatre. And children, you know. . . . Well, but you wouldn't understand that!

(MISS Y. *expresses disdain.*)

MRS. X. (*sips a few teaspoonfuls of her chocolate. Then she opens her shopping bag and brings out some Christmas presents*). Here—let me show you what I have bought for my little ones. (*She shows her a doll.*) Look at this one! This is for Lisa. . . . Do you see how she rolls her eyes and turns her head! Do you? Do you see?—And here is a popgun for Maja. . . . (*She loads the toy gun and pops it at* MISS Y.)

(MISS Y. *makes a gesture of fright.*)

MRS. X. Did I frighten you? You didn't think I was going to shoot you, did you? Did you?—Upon my soul, I really think you did! If *you* had wanted to shoot *me,* I wouldn't have been surprised. After all, I have stood in your way—and I realize that you can never forget that . . . even though I was entirely blameless. You still believe that I schemed to have you dismissed from the Grand Theatre—don't you? But I didn't! You may think whatever you like, but I had nothing to do with it! I realize, however, that no matter what I say, you will still believe I was responsible for it! *(She takes out a pair of embroidered bedroom slippers from the bag.)* And these are for my better half. I embroidered them myself—with tulips. You understand, I hate tulips, but my husband has to have tulips on everything. . . .

(MISS Y. *looks up from her magazine with an expression of irony mixed with curiosity.)*

MRS. X. *(places a hand inside each slipper).* See what tiny feet Bob has! See? And I wish you could see how elegantly he walks! You never saw him in slippers, did you?

(MISS Y. *laughs aloud.)*

MRS. X. Look, let me show you! *(She makes the slippers walk on the table.)*

(MISS Y. *gives another loud laugh.)*

MRS. X. And when he gets angry, he stamps his foot, like this: "Damnation! These stupid maids who never can learn to make coffee! And look at this! The idiots don't even know how to trim a lamp wick!" And when there is a draft from the floor and his feet are cold: "Heavens! It's freezing cold, and the incorrigible fools let the fire go out in the grate!" *(She rubs the sole of one slipper against the top of the other.)*

(MISS Y. *gives a shriek of laughter.)*

MRS. X. And when he comes home, he goes hunting for his slippers which Marie has put under the chiffonier. . . . Oh, but it's a shame to sit and make fun of my own husband like this. After all, he is so nice. He is a good little husband. . . . You should have had a husband like him, Amelie!—What are you laughing at, if I may ask? What is it? What's the matter?—And the best of it is that he is faithful to me—yes, that I know. He has told me so himself! . . . Why the sneering grin? He told me that Frédérique tried to seduce him while I was on a tour in Norway. . . . Can you imagine such impudence! *(There is a silence.)* I would have torn her eyes out! That's what I'd have done, if she had come near him while I was at home! *(Again there is silence.)* I was lucky enough to hear about it from Bob himself before being told by some gossip. . . . *(Silence.)* But Frédérique was not the only one, let me tell you! I can't understand it, but women seem to be absolutely crazy about my husband. They must think he has something to say about the engaging of the artists, because he is on the board of administration. . . . I would not be surprised if you, too, had used your wiles on him! I never did trust you too much. . . . But I know now that he could not be interested in you—and it seemed to me you always acted as if you bore some sort of grudge against him. . . . (*There is a silence and they regard each other with some embarrassment.* MRS. X. *continues.*) Why don't you come home to us this evening, Amelie, just to show that you have no hard feelings—at least not against *me*. . . . I can't explain just why—but I think it is so unpleasant to be bad friends— with you especially. Perhaps it is because I stood in your way that time (*In a slower tempo.*) . . . or . . . I can't imagine . . . what the reason could have been—really . . . (*There is a silence.*)

(MISS Y. *gazes fixedly and curiously at* MRS. X.)

MRS. X. (*pensively*). Our relationship was such a strange one. . . . The first time I saw you, I was frightened of you. I was so frightened that I didn't dare to let you out of my sight. No matter when or where I went—I always found myself next to you. . . . I didn't have the courage to be your enemy, and so I became your friend. But whenever you came to our home, it always led to discord. I noticed that my husband could not bear the sight of you and it made me feel ill at ease—as when a garment does not fit. I did everything I could to persuade him to show you some friendliness, but it was no use—not until you announced your engagement! Then suddenly a violent friendship blossomed between you two! At the time it appeared as if only then you dared to show your true feelings—when it was safe for you to do so! And then—what happened afterwards? . . . I didn't feel any jealousy—and that seems strange to me now! And I can remember the scene at the christening, when you were the godmother, and I had to coax him to kiss you. When he did, you were so abashed and confused—and quite frankly, I didn't notice it at the time, didn't give it a thought. I never thought of it until—until this very moment. . . . (*She rises violently, impassioned.*) Why don't you say something? You haven't uttered one single word all this time! You have let me sit here, talking on and on! You have been sitting there, drawing out of me all these thoughts that have been lying like raw silk in the cocoon —thoughts . . . yes, even suspicions. . . . Let me see! Why did you break off your engagement? Why did you never come to our home again after that? Why don't you come to our home tonight?

(MISS Y. *seems to be about to break her silence.*)

MRS. X. Don't speak! You needn't say a word! Now I understand everything! It was because of this—and that—and that! That's it exactly. Now the accounts are balanced! Now I know the answer!—For shame! I won't sit at the same table with you! (*She moves her things to the other table.*) That is why I had to

embroider tulips on his slippers—because you liked tulips. . . .
That's why we—(*She throws the slippers on the floor.*)—why we
had to spend the summers at Lake Mälar—because you didn't
like the open sea; that's why my son was named Eskil—because
that was your father's name; that's the reason I had to wear your
colors, read your authors, eat your favorite dishes, drink what
you liked—your chocolate, for instance. . . . That is why—Oh,
my God—it's frightening to think of it—horrible! Everything,
everything came to me from you, even your passions! Your soul
crept into mine, like a worm into an apple, worming its way, boring and boring, until nothing was left but the rind and a speck
of black dust inside. I tried to get away from you, but I couldn't!
You charmed me, bewitched me like a snake, with your black
eyes. . . . Every time I lifted my wings to escape, I felt myself
being dragged down again: I lay in the water with bound feet—
and the harder I fought to keep afloat, the further down I went
—down, down, until I sank to the bottom where you lay in wait
like a giant crab to seize me with your claws—and there is where
I am now.

Ugh! How I detest you, hate you, hate you! But you—all
you do is to sit there silent, cold and impassive! You don't care
whether it's new moon or full moon, Christmas or New Year—
whether people around you are happy or unhappy! You have
neither the capacity to hate nor to love; you are as cold-blooded
as a stork watching a rat-hole; you are incapable of scenting
your prey and pursuing it—but you know how to hide in holes
and corners and exhaust your prey. Here you sit—I suppose you
know people call this corner the rat trap, in your honor—scanning the newspapers in the hope that you may read about someone who has had bad luck or been struck by misfortune, or about
someone who has been dismissed from the theatre. . . . Here
you sit, lurking for victims, figuring out your chances like a pilot
in a shipwreck. Here you receive your tributes! Poor Amelie! You
know, in spite of everything, I feel sorry for you, because I am
aware that you are miserable—miserable like some wounded
beast!—and made spiteful and vicious because of having been
wounded! I find it hard to be angry with you, despite feeling
that I ought to be—but, after all, you are the weaker one. . . .
As for the episode with Bob—well, I shan't let that bother me.
. . . It hasn't really harmed me! And if *you* got me into the habit
of drinking chocolate, or if someone else did, matters little . . .
(*She takes a spoonful of chocolate; then, common-sense-like.*)
Besides, chocolate is a healthful beverage. And if you have
taught me how to dress—*tant mieux!* My husband has become

all the more fond of me as a result! That is one thing I have gained, and that you lost. As a matter of fact, judging from what I have seen, I think you have already lost him! But no doubt it was your intention that I should leave him—as you did—and which you now regret. But, you see, that's just what I don't intend to do! We must not be one-sided or selfish, you know. But why should I take only what someone else doesn't want? All said and done, perhaps I am at this moment really the stronger. . . . You never received anything from *me*—while *you gave* something to me! And now I have had the same experience as the proverbial thief had: When *you* woke up, *I* possessed what *you* had lost! And why was it that everything you touched became sterile and empty? Your tulips and your passions proved insufficient to keep a man's love—while I was able to keep it. Your authors could not teach you the art of living—as I have learned it. Nor did you bear a little Eskil—even if your father bore that name. . . . And why are you forever silent, your lips eternally sealed? I confess I used to think it a sign of strength—but perhaps it is only because you have nothing to say! Perhaps it is for lack of thoughts! *(She rises and picks up the slippers from the floor.)* Now I am going home—and I take the tulips with me. Your tulips! You found it hard to learn from others—you found it hard to bend, to humble yourself—and so you broke like a dry reed—and I survived! I thank you, Amelie, for all that you have taught me! And thank you for teaching my husband how to love! Now I am going home—to love him!

  (She leaves.)

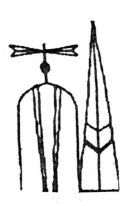

DISCUSSION QUESTIONS

Arp: BAOBAB (*page 21*)

Arp was one of the founders of *dadaism,* a movement which assumes man's helplessness to control his world. (For more on Arp and dadaism see the biographical sketch of Arp on page 402). What clue does this give you toward interpreting the poem?

1. According to many modern artists, it is possible for a work of art to appeal directly to the emotions while it defies all laws of logic. Is this true of "Baobab"? Explain. What sort of tone do the closing lines create? Does this tone accord with the view of the world assumed by dadaism? Can you make any attempt at interpreting the poem, or do you think the tone is all-important, or do you think the whole thing is nonsense?

2. Look up *baobab* in an encyclopedia to see what about this particular tree might have appealed to Arp.

Böll: ENTER AND EXIT (*page 23*)

1. The author makes two obviously intentional omissions: The narrator goes nameless and his war experiences go unmentioned. What is the probable purpose of each omission? Is there any connection between them?

2. What is the tone of the first section of the story? Give examples of episodes that help establish this tone. What would you say is the emotional high point of this part of the story? How does it prepare for the events that are to follow?

3. Has the narrator changed during the six-year interval between the two parts of the story? If so, to what extent and in what ways?

4. At one point in the second part of the story the narrator states of his fellow Germans: "What they didn't know was that I hated them, Nazis and non-Nazis . . . because they were men, men of the same species as those I had had to spend the last six years with; the words *man* and *stupid* had become almost identical for me." Do the narrator's subsequent actions show this all-inclusive hatred he here expresses? Just what does he hate? What kind of man is he?

5. Suppose the narrator, personality unchanged, had been born in the United States and was today, as he is at the beginning of the story, just under twenty. What would he probably be doing?

Brecht: GENERAL, THAT TANK (*page 53*)

1. Whom does Brecht defy in this poem, and why, perhaps, does he choose to defy him?

2. Objectivity, logic, calmness, understatement—all are present in the speaker's words and tone; what do they suggest about the speaker himself?

RETURN (*page 54*)

1. Who is the speaker? What is ironic about his homecoming?

2. Like "General, That Tank" this is an anti-war poem, but it achieves its effect by different means. Explain the difference.

IRON (*page 55*)

1. What simple yet vital concept is expressed in this poem?

CHANGING THE WHEEL (*page 55*)

1. In what ways is this poem like a Japanese haiku?

2. Brecht focuses on an inescapable attribute of human nature. How do you answer the question he poses in the last two lines?

TO POSTERITY (*page 56*)

1. For what kind of world does the speaker appeal? In what ways is he trying to help bring that world into being?

2. Discuss the meaning of the statement beginning, "Ah we/Who desired to prepare the soil . . ." in lines 69–71.

3. This poem was written in 1938, more than a generation ago. How far have we progressed toward the world Brecht foresaw for posterity?

Cohn: OF THE MAN WHO SITS IN THE CELLAR (*page 59*)

Like many other modern German poems, this is written in a deliberately cryptic style; the reader must work to find the meaning. The fact that the poet is also a psychoanalyst provides an important clue.

1. When is the man under control of the woman? When is she afraid of him?

2. If the man and the woman symbolize two opposing forces within the human personality, what do the differences in sex indicate about the nature of these forces?

3. In stanza four the speaker says, "The woman lies in bed/ but the man is awake." Does this mean the woman is necessarily asleep? Later in the same stanza the phrase "in heart beat" is used twice. What may it suggest about the symbolic meaning of the cellar door and the cellar itself? Is this symbolic meaning

supported by the final stanza? Explain. What might the "best room" symbolize?

4. What is symbolized by the woman's combing the man's hair and cleaning his ears before she displays him in front of her friends?

5. The title mentions only the man. Is there any significance in this? Discuss.

Doderer: THE MAGICIAN'S ART (*page 61*)

The magician's art succeeds when his audience is unable to distinguish illusion from reality. In this respect, much of life is like the magician's art. . . .

1. Compare the two magicians with regard to physical appearance, amount and complexity of equipment, and effectiveness of performance. What is the essential difference between the two, and how do the above factors emphasize it?

2. Explain why and how the magicians' performances cause the bee-keeper to break his engagement to the Titian-haired girl. Consider especially what may have been the content of the question he asked the second magician. Discuss the way in which both reality and illusion are involved in the broken engagement.

3. Relate the narrator's description of precious belongings, camphorized and stored away in cabinets, to his words in the final paragraph: ". . . this ten of spades was simply talked to death. This seems to be the way of all great art; it is gnawed by tiny teeth until it falls to pieces and can be argued away." What is he saying about the nature of art and of man?

4. The innkeeper, comparing the two performances, says of the second: "This one was, of course, a—a different magician's art." Why does he make the statement, and what might he mean by it?

Dürrenmatt: THE TUNNEL (*page 71*)

Since the earliest of times, travel, perhaps because of its very nature, has been used as a symbol of progress through life. Assume, for purposes of interpretation, that Dürrenmatt means his train to be representative of life, not one man's, but the world's.

1. If the train *does* symbolize life, what does the track along which it usually runs represent? What, then, does the tunnel come to mean? No one seems to know how the train got into the tunnel. What does this detail suggest?

2. By using the questions and statements in parentheses as a guide, develop your own interpretation of each of the following characters:

(a) The student. (Consider him first as a passenger: what are the responsibilities, the privileges of a passenger on a real train? What does Dürrenmatt imply by presenting the student —obese, officious, egocentric—so repugnantly? What do his occupation and his attitude toward it suggest? What one thing does he seem to have in common with the rest of the passengers in his compartment? What do you think is indicated by his growing self-awareness, by his final shedding of his defenses? Will this new-found understanding and acceptance be of any good to him now?)

(b) The Chief Conductor. (What does the railroad that employs a conductor demand of him? What do the people traveling on his train expect of him? Why might the translator accord his position a capital C? What do you think the Conductor means when he says he lives "without hope"? He knows the engineer has already left the train. Why doesn't he tell the student this instead of allowing him to find out for himself at the risk of his life?)

(c) The people in the dining car. (What seems to be their main concern, their primary interest in life? Why are they unaffected by the terrible motion of the train?)

(d) The engineer. (What is an engineer's responsibility toward the train he controls? Toward the people who ride with him? What would happen to a real train if the engineer deserted it? What does Dürrenmatt imply about his engineer by having him leave the train as soon as things seem out of control?)

(e) The freight man. (On a real train the freight, or baggage, man is put in charge of the passengers' material possessions. What might happen if such a man were to walk off his job? What is Dürrenmatt saying about the state of life by having his freight man desert?)

3. What is the significance of the ever-increasing speed of the train? Can it still be stopped? What is its destination?

4. Discuss the implications for the story and the world in the student's final words: "God let us fall. And now we'll come upon him."

5. Do you agree with the picture of life that Dürrenmatt paints in this story? Discuss.

6. The previous questions suggest variations on one basic

interpretation of the story. What other interpretations does the work support?

7. E. M. Forster's "The Celestial Omnibus" also treats of a strange journey. You might enjoy comparing these two short stories.

Eich: THE STILTS-WALKER (*page 81*)

1. Disregarding your personal opinion of stilts-walking as an art, explain whether the narrator possesses any genuine talent in this area?

2. Does the stilts-walker at any time feel any compunctions about the use to which he is putting his art? Explain.

3. What does each of the following details contribute to the story: (*a*) the piece of candy that convinces the narrator to become a stilts-walker; (*b*) the juxtaposition of "Astrol" (look up its etymology) and shoe polish; (*c*) Astrol's poison-green and purple colors; (*d*) the means by which the phonograph in the truck is activated; (*e*) the combination of clichés and poor puns, such as "Perhaps they merely lacked a trained, *rising* generation" with which the narrator tells his story.

4. Which of the following do you feel is the more correct interpretation of "The Stilts-Walker"? Why?

(*a*) The story is a bitter attack against the artist who sells out for acclaim, success. The narrator's values are those of the marketplace, not those of the art studio. Everything about him smacks of attention-getting at the expense of anything finer.

(*b*) Eich issues a warning to artists of all kinds to maintain contact with the masses, for without that contact their art is useless, "a mere hovering about in insubstantial space."

Enzensberger: FOR A SENIOR COLLEGE TEXTBOOK (*page 87*)

1. What does the speaker fear the future holds for the student (and for his fellows)? What precautionary studies does he suggest the student pursue in preparation for that future?

2. When the speaker says, "don't read odes" (line 1) and "be on your guard. don't sing" (line 3) is he really advocating that the student abandon poetry? Explain.

3. Discuss the force of the title—how effective is it in helping to establish the point of the poem?

4. In its lack of capitalization Enzensberger's poem resembles those of many modern American poets. But in Enzensberger's case the variation from the norm is even more striking because German nouns are ordinarily capitalized. What might be this poet's purpose in disregarding standard capitalization?

Goethe: THE ERL-KING (*page 88*)

1. Who are the four speakers in this ballad? How is dramatic interest sustained throughout? What does the ballad indicate about the attitude of the father (and the folk he represents) toward death?

2. Why is the ballad form especially appropriate for this particular poem?

MIGNON (*page 90*)

1. What different aspects of Italy appear in the first two stanzas?

2. How does the third stanza suggest the danger and majesty of the Alps?

3. In what way is each evocation of Wilhelm (in the last line of each stanza) appropriate to the particular aspect of Italy with which it is connected?

PROMETHEUS (*page 91*)

1. What is the tone of this poem addressed by Prometheus to Jove? Why does Prometheus refuse to honor Jove? Compare Jove's occupation as described by Prometheus (stanza 1) with Prometheus' own work (last stanza).

2. In what ways does Prometheus represent the free and unconquerable spirit of man?

3. The story of Prometheus, the immortal who stole fire from heaven and gave it to man, has been a favorite through the ages. If you are interested in further literary treatments of it, try looking into Aeschylus' tragedy *Prometheus Bound*, Shelley's verse drama *Prometheus Unbound,* or Byron's poem "Prometheus."

Grass: PLACED AMID OLD MEN (*page 93*)

1. What do the young and old struggle for in the poem?

2. How does the speaker view old age? Explain.

3. Why do the young men, placed amid old men, bite their nails? The words "we make no new growth" (line 12) can be interpreted in at least two ways. What are they?

4. Is the last stanza to be taken at face value? Explain.

POWERLESS, WITH A GUITAR (*page 94*)

1. What do lines 2–4 mean? Does the process described add to or detract from the desire of the speaker to protest?

2. Is the speaker's protest solely against napalm, or against something more? Explain.

3. In what way does the title apply to the poem, and in what way does it have a more universal application?

DO SOMETHING (*page 95*)

Like the two preceding poems, this deals with the conflict between the angry but impotent young men and the older men, the specialists in power.

1. The speaker says he is writing of the protest poem and against the protest poem. Discuss his reasons for being against it, using lines from the poem to support your answer.

2. According to the speaker, what is wrong with the therapy poems? the weapon poems?

3. The "stone" (line 55) symbolizes the specialists in power. Why does it not budge? What causes it to act as if it had been moved? How do the specialists in power react to the protest poems? What do their actions indicate about how seriously they take these protests?

4. Reread lines 102–105. Does each of the ingredients of this recipe suggest impotence? Explain.

5. What is the "something" the speaker wants us to do? Do you agree with his pessimistic view that protest is impotent, useless? If so, what remedies do you suggest?

FOLDING CHAIRS (*page 99*)

1. In the light of modern history, what might the folding chairs symbolize?

2. What do you think the speaker means by calling the chairs patented, their owners unpatented?

3. Against what is this poem a protest?

IN THE EGG (*page 100*)

1. At what point in their development are chicks normally hatched? Have the humans inside the egg reached—or passed—the hatching age? When, and if, they are finally hatched, where will they probably find themselves? What is the frying pan they fear?

2. In what ways is this poem related to "Do Something," "Placed Amid Old Men," and "Powerless, with a Guitar"?

Hauptmann: FLAGMAN THIEL (*page 102*)

1. As you read Thiel's story, did you like him or did you feel contempt for him? Why?

2. Examine Thiel's character carefully. Does he bring about his downfall through a weakness in his nature, or is he at the mercy of fate? Explain your viewpoint.

3. Why does Thiel kill Lena? Why does he kill their child? What causes him to return to the railroad tracks after the murders?

4. When, after the slayings, Thiel is found on the tracks, he is holding Toby's cap and he never lets go of it. Is Thiel deranged? Explain. What has the shaggy cap come to symbolize to him?

5. In this story built upon contrasts, one of the sharpest is between the railroad, a mechanistic, destructive force, and the pure nature of the Brandenburg forest through which it passes. Is the railroad presented as malevolent, benevolent, or neutral? How is the forest portrayed? What idea might Hauptmann have wanted to suggest by setting up the contrast between machine and nature? Where does man fit into Hauptmann's idea?

Heine: THE MESSAGE (*page 128*)

1. Like many other ballads, "The Message" focuses on a single incident but provides clues from which the entire story can be learned. Using such clues, fill in the background of this story.

THE LORELEY (*page 129*)

1. Does the melody of the translation seem to approximate the melody of an "evensong" that might be sung by the Loreley? Explain.

2. Note the recurrence of the words *gold* and *golden*. What emotional effects do they convey?

3. "The Loreley" is often regarded as one of Heine's most romantic poems. Why is it considered romantic?

4. The theme of the beautiful singer who lures boatmen to their destruction is a recurrent one in literature. What examples are you familiar with? What might be some explanations for the origin of this theme and its popularity across the centuries?

MY SONGS YOU SAY (*page 130*

1. How has the woman to whom the poem is addressed added present insult to past injury? Discuss the effectiveness of the way in which the speaker deals with her.

WHEN I AM WITH MY OWN (*page 130*

1. What truism does the speaker express here? If the poem is not a trite one, what keeps it from being so?

2. Compare the tone of this poem with the tone of "My Songs, You Say." Within the context of these two simple lyrics, how has Heine used simile and metaphor to reinforce his meaning?

ANNO 1829 (*page 131*)

1. Compare Heine's attitudes at thirty with the attitudes of much of today's youth.

2. Reread stanza 5. What does the comparison it contains add to the poem's total effect upon you?

3. In your opinion is this poem satirical or lyrical or both? Explain your answer.

4. Compare this poem with Wordsworth's sonnet, "The World Is Too Much with Us."

ANNO 1839 (*page 132*)

1. What changes appear to have taken place in the poet's life and outlook during the ten years that separate this poem from the preceding one? (Use the biography of Heine, page 405, to substantiate your findings.) What might the poet's age have to do with the changes in him?

2. Compare the tone here with that of "Anno 1829."

THE SILESIAN WEAVERS (*page 133*)

1. What phrase in the opening stanza first establishes the tone? Why is the phrase effective literally as well as figuratively?

2. According to the weavers, of what does the "threefold doom" they are weaving into Germany's shroud consist? What are their complaints against each element of the threefold doom?

3. What emotional effect is created by the refrain that ends each stanza?

4. Review the functions of the Fates of classical myth to determine whether this legend might have influenced Heine's poem in any way.

5. When this poem was written a short time after the Silesian Revolt, it was considered a topical poem. Does it have any topicality today, or do we read it for purely historical and lyrical reasons?

A WARNING (*page 134*)

1. Who is being warned? What is he being warned about?

2. Do you find any irony in the tone? Explain.

3. What does the speaker feel the poet's mission should be? Judging from what you know about Heine, are the speaker's views identical with his?

IT GOES OUT (*page 135*)

1. What is the play upon which the curtain falls? Who is the author (line 6)?

(*Heine*)

2. Analyze the imagery of "It Goes Out." Is it in keeping with the subject matter? What feelings does it convey?

3. For centuries writers have equated the world with a stage, life with a play. In a famous soliloquy Shakespeare's Macbeth exclaims, "Out, out, brief candle!/ Life's but a walking shadow, a poor player,/ That struts and frets his hour upon the stage/ And then is heard no more" (*Macbeth*, Act V, Scene 5). What similarities and differences do you find between this passage and "It Goes Out"? Try finding other quotations from literature on this subject.

DÜSSELDORF (*page 136*)

1. Who or what is the butt of this garrulous, easily-paced bit of satire?

2. What various aspects of man's nature are suggested by such grotesques as the green-veiled English ladies, the appletart vendor, crazy Aloysius, and the drunken cripple Gumpertz?

3. Discuss the boy's final statement ("They want to make us all happy! that is why there is no school today") as a summary of what Heine has been saying.

LONDON (*page 141*)

1. Why is Heine "more astonished than ever" when he has finally seen London, "the greatest wonder which the world can show to the astonished mind"?

2. What are some of the contrasts mentioned? How does Heine react to the contrasts he describes?

3. What does Heine mean when he says, "Send a philosopher to London, but, not on your life, a poet!"?

4. Relate the anger and emotion of this essay to Heine's performance in such poems as "Anno 1829," "Anno 1839," and "The Silesian Weavers."

Hesse: WITHIN AND WITHOUT (*page 145*)

The title of this story derives from Hesse's belief that an essential unity underlies the polarities of existence, such as day and night, or within and without. A major theme in Hesse's works is that the way within leads to truth, and that the individual, in overcoming polarities, realizes the essential unity of all things.

1. At the beginning of the story what is Frederick's attitude toward logic and scientific thinking? Toward religion? Toward superstition and mystical (or magical) thinking? At the end of the story what changes have taken place in his attitudes? What do you think his future course will be?

2. What is the motivating force (or symbol) in the story? How does Hesse show its increasing power over Frederick?

3. Explain in your own terms the saying on Erwin's wall: "Nothing is without, nothing is within; for what is without is within." How does the story demonstrate the truth of this paradoxical saying?

4. Hesse shows us the way to the truth that unites all through the eyes of a man who is terrified of it, so that for the reader the experience becomes filled with mystery and fear. Is this a flaw in construction, or does the writer have a purpose in presenting his thesis as he does? Discuss.

5. The little clay idol with two faces is the personification of the within and without, and, indeed, of all polarities and their underlying unities. Explain how this is so. Hesse describes the idol as Janus-like. The Roman god Janus had several manifestations: he was the god of beginnings and endings; the god of openings, entrances, and doorways; and the god for whom January was named, for as the first month of the year it looked back on the past year and ahead to the year that was to unfold itself. Explain how each of these three manifestations of Janus applies to the function of the idol in the story.

Hofmannsthal: BALLAD OF OUTER LIFE (*page 156*)

1. What impression is created by stanzas 1–4?

2. The questions about life raised in stanzas 5–6 may be equated with three of the questions with which the humanities concern themselves: Who am I? Why was I born? Where am I going? Are any answers suggested?

3. The words "And yet . . ." (line 20) signal a change in thought. Might these lines refer to man's inner life? What answer do they suggest to the three questions?

THE TWO (*page 157*)

1. In what ways does this poem epitomize the romantic concept of the power of true love? Discuss the effectiveness of the indirect method by which the poet indicates the strength of this love.

Huber: THE NEW APARTMENT (*page 158*)

1. Discuss the "circle" to which the narrator and his wife belong from three vantage points: theirs, the author's, and your own.

2. Although the Messemers describe the two old women as grotesques, they inadvertently provide details which show that these women led emotionally full though tragic lives. How does the Messemers' apartment, which symbolizes their lives, contrast with the rooms of the two old women, which symbolized their lives?

3. The Messemers' account of the former inhabitants of the apartment occupies much of the story. What light does this account shed on the Messemers? What do you learn of the narrator from his musings as the story proceeds? What do you learn of his wife from her comments? What does the account add to the total meaning of the story?

Kafka: AN OLD MANUSCRIPT (*page 167*)

1. What is the basic conflict? How did it develop? How will it probably end? In what way is the title a clue to the probable ending?

2. Kafka's stories can be interpreted in many different ways, sometimes simultaneously. Discuss the validity of each of the following attempts to explain the meaning of "An Old Manuscript":

(*a*) It is an allegory of man's inability to communicate with his fellows.

(*b*) It represents the historical cycle of the overthrow of worn-out civilizations by strong barbarian tribes.

(*c*) It is a moral allegory of the human condition in that it shows man as being overcome by worldly desires because he lacks the initiative to join with his fellows in combating them.

(*d*) It deals with alienation and shows man as the powerless victim of forces in an unremitting, ungoverned universe.

(*e*) It shows man as being threatened by an overwhelming and unsympathetic force that is all the more frightening because it is not clearly understood. As such, the story has many applications.

Kästner: LEGEND NOT QUITE HOUSEBROKEN (*page 170*)

1. Who or what is the target of satire here? Might there be more than one target?

2. What does the Christmas setting contribute to the impact of the satire?

3. Why does God say this will be his last trip to earth?

4. Discuss the title, its meaning and significance.

THE OTHER POSSIBILITY (*page 171*)

1. What is the twist that lends interest to the poem? In what ways does this unusual viewpoint seem to deal especially with Germany? Does it have universal application also? Explain.

Lichtenstein: RETURN OF THE VILLAGE LAD (*page 173*)

1. What images and pursuits of childhood does the speaker describe?

2. What is the "iron serpent" of the last line? Discuss the appropriateness of this metaphor in the context of the poem.

3. What does the title of the poem add to its content?

4. Read Dylan Thomas' "Fern Hill" and write a short paper comparing his recollections of childhood with Lichtenstein's.

Mann: TRISTAN (*page 174*)

In this novella Mann has masterfully woven together three elements or devices that have come to be identified with him. First, there is the interest in music, which Mann often makes central to his works. "Tristan" is a "parody" of Wagner's opera *Tristan und Isolde;* by *parody* Mann meant a modernized retelling of an old story. Second is the inclusion of *grotesques*—characters who are physically, mentally, or emotionally distorted in some way. Third is Mann's theory about the innate conflict between the artist and the burgher (or bourgeois).

1. Just as Wagner used a *leitmotif,* or musical phrase, to represent his characters, so Mann uses recurring descriptive phrases or details. What are the *leitmotifs* for Herr Spinell, Gabriele, and Herr Klöterjahn? How well do they serve to identify key traits in the characters described?

2. Which characters would you identify as *grotesques*? What purpose or purposes do they serve in the novella?

3. Mann's parody of *Tristan und Isolde* does not really begin until most of the patients at Einfried have left on the sleighing party. Why is Spinell so insistent that Gabriele play the piano? What does her agreement symbolize to him?

4. Just as Gabriele finishes playing the music of Act I, Frau Spatz departs hastily. What effect does her stated reason for departure have on the reader?

5. Mann describes the *Liebestod* (love-death) motif in some detail (page 196). What use does he make of this motif?

6. In his theory of the innate conflict between the artist and

the burgher, Mann sees the artist as the last flowering of a long family line that is already decaying and sapped of its strength; the burgher, not so far evolved, is ruggedly strong and healthy but lacks the ability to appreciate beauty. Relate this theory to "Tristan," tracing it through the story. Who triumphs, the artist or the burgher?

7. The artist is represented not only by Spinell, but also by Gabriele. How does her weakness differ from his?

8. Although "Tristan" contains all the ingredients of a sentimental tragedy, it is not generally so regarded. What keeps it from being tragic? How would you describe it?

9. Shortly after this novella was first published in Germany, one critic called it "a victory for vital living." Do you agree with this statement?

10. You might enjoy comparing "Tristan" with either the libretto or a prose summary of Wagner's *Tristan und Isolde*. Try your hand at a short essay in comparative literature.

Morgenstern: PALMSTRÖM (*page 209*)

1. What might Palmström find sublime about the picture of the oak and the man who holds a book?

2. Beneath the humor of the poem there is a whimsical appeal. From what does the appeal stem?

THE DAYNIGHTLAMP (*page 210*)

1. Upon what invention is Korf's daynightlamp a twist? How do the convention-goers react to it?

2. Can you think of any practical use for a lamp such as Korf's?

THE MOUSETRAP (*page 211*)

1. Palmström and Korf, pursuing their own illogical, whimsical ends, manage to install the mouse in a more proper habitat, save its life, and avoid interfering with the balance of nature. How do their actions make you feel toward them? Is the picture here consistent with those presented in the other poems? Explain.

THE GLASSES (*page 213*)

1. What remarkable property do Korf's glasses possess? If such glasses were invented, what modern enterprises might they put out of business?

2. If we are to believe the last stanza, how much value does Morgenstern place on his own poetry? Do you agree with him?

THE IMPOSSIBLE FACT (*page 214*)

1. Discuss the title: What does it mean? Is it appropriate to the content of the poem, to the logic Palmström uses?

2. Comment on the soundness of the conclusion Palmström reaches. If his brand of logic were through some cosmic event proved valid, what changes might occur in the world?

Rilke: GYM PERIOD (*page 215*)

Rilke records here, in short-story form, a painful recollection of his own childhood.

1. Describe the atmosphere of the gym class. Which factors contribute to the atmosphere? What may have caused Gruber to overcome his fears and climb to the top of the pole? What is the general reaction to his feat? How does Jerome's reaction differ from that of the other boys'?

2. How do the cadets react to Gruber's death? The officers? Jerome? Are there any indications that some of the cadets possess the callousness and brutality that characterize their officers? What is your opinion of this sort of education in molding character? What might Rilke be trying to point out through this story?

THE CADET PICTURE OF MY FATHER (*page 220*)

The situation described here is a common one: a man looks thoughtfully at a fading photograph of his father, taken while the father was still young. Reread the poem, taking note of words that indicate the father had already begun to withdraw into the distance at the time the photograph was taken . . .

1. What sort of father-son relationship would cause the son to notice such details?

2. What depth of thought and emotion do the last two lines add to what has preceded them?

JOSEPH'S SUSPICION (*page 221*)

1. What has happened to anger Joseph? How does the angel finally allay his suspicion? In the view of later events, what is ironic about the angel's reference to the tree?

2. What is the effect of retelling the biblical story as a simple narrative involving Joseph and the angel?

THE KNIGHT (*page 222*)

1. What separates the knight from the world into which he fares forth? What might his sable mail symbolize? Is Death alone in the armor, or is Death there *with* the knight?

(*Rilke*)

2. What is the significance of the sudden shift from third person to first person in line 14? Because of this shift, at what deeper level may the poem be read?

THE PANTHER (*page 223*)

1. What effect has captivity had on the panther? What is meant by "stupefied, a mighty Will may stand" (line 8)? Does the balance of the poem support your interpretation of this line? Explain.

2. Rilke is praised for writing remarkably concise yet effective poems by employing only the most essential, most distinctive details of his subject. How does this talent show itself in "The Panther"? Is there any point at which you unconsciously moved from a position outside the cage to one inside the cage, actually becoming one with the panther? Explain.

TO THE POET (*page 224*)

1. What indications are there that the speaker recognizes an evolving and rising scale of being, from animal to man to poet? How does the poet serve his fellow men? What is both unusual and appropriate in addressing the poet as "you mouth" (line 13)?

A TALE OF DEATH AND A STRANGE POSTSCRIPT THERETO (*page 225*)

Within the dialogue between the narrator and the gravedigger, three separate stories are told: that of God and His reaction to the new religion, that of the man and woman and Death, and the "strange postscript" to the second story, which is really an alternate ending.

1. Why might Rilke have used a gravedigger as the second person in the dialogue? What is meant by the gravedigger's comment that most people "bury God *up there* [in the sky] as I bury men here"?

2. In the first story God's withdrawal from His domain is similar to the belief of some Christian existentialists who claim God is too remote to intervene in man's affairs. In what way does the story's ending alter this conception?

3. In the second story, the man and woman, afraid that Death will enter their house, cut themselves off from life as well. At what point does the "strange postscript" intervene and

change this story? In the postscript, how do the man and woman cultivate death, both literally and figuratively? Which of the two endings represents allegorically the better pattern for old age? Explain.

4. The narrator makes a point of saying that the postscript was written in a woman's handwriting. Relate this fact to the door which Death first tried to enter in the original story and to the closing sentence of the postscript.

A STORY TOLD TO THE DARK (*page 231*)

1. How does the conventional view of Klara's life, as related to Georg by his brother-in-law, differ from Klara's view of it? How does Klara feel toward those who use her life as a topic for gossip? In what ways does the story seem to reverse traditional moral values? Does it really do so? Explain?

2. Through what remembered episode does Klara help Georg to rediscover his childhood? Does he discover anything else?

3. Why is it fitting that the story be told "more and more softly" to the dark? Why does the narrator say, "In this story there is nothing that children may not know. Still the children have *not* heard it" (page 239, paragraph 4)?

Schmied: ANCIENT CHINESE MAP OF THE WORLD (*page 240*)

This is a closely-knit poem in which each stanza, growing naturally out of that which preceded it, deals with a deeper level of thought.

1. Stanza 1 describes the first map of the world. Why are the speakers unable to interpret the map as they examine it?

2. Stanza 2 records the speakers' initial mental reaction to the map. What about it do they find startling?

3. Stanza 3 extends the meaning of the poem to philosophical realms. What has been the speakers' hope and how is this hope to be understood? By extension, what is signified in lines 13–14?

4. Stanza 4 brings the poem full-circle, but at a much deeper level of meaning. What startles the speakers this time? How can they call the Chinese characters, "these our own signs/on which we relied"? What is disquieting about their thoughts?

Schnitzler: THE BLIND GERONIMO AND HIS BROTHER
(*page 241*)

1. What sort of blindness, other than Geronimo's physical affliction, exists between the brothers?

2. Is Carlo really selfless, or is he a parasite dependent upon the blindness of Geronimo?

3. One reader has remarked that the most interesting character in the story is the young tourist who tells Geronimo that he gave Carlo a twenty-franc piece. Do you agree? Does the tourist also suffer from a kind of blindness?

4. Discuss the weather as (*a*) a means of setting mood and (*b*) a parallel, sometimes a symbolic one, to the action.

5. In "The Invisible Collection" (page 265), blindness becomes a blessing in disguise. How does this compare with Geronimo's blindness?

Stadler: SMALL TOWN (*page 263*)

1. What basic contrast is set up between the first two stanzas and the last stanza of the poem?

2. Explain in your own words the meaning of line 4.

3. What is it that causes the factory workers to "stop and stand," that sustains them at the end of the day?

4. Is the poem actually concerned with a small town, as the title would indicate, or with something else? Explain.

5. Stadler's style has been compared to that of the American poet Walt Whitman. Even though this poem has been translated, it retains the general appearance and rhythm of the German original. In what ways does it resemble Whitman's poetry?

Steiner: KAFKA IN ENGLAND (*page 264*)

1. Franz Kafka, who died in 1924, was a German-speaking Jew who lived in Prague. How is each of these biographical facts used in the poem?

2. What clues do the names assigned to the English people provide as to how they will react to Kafka? What is different about Geoffrey Piltzman's name and reaction? How does the speaker himself feel about Kafka?

Zweig: THE INVISIBLE COLLECTION (*page 265*)

1. Do you think that Herr Kronfeld's wife and daughter are right in keeping from him the details of the inflation and the sale of his collection? Explain.

2. Is Herr Kronfeld's blindness more of a blessing than a curse? Explain.

3. Near the end of the story, Herr Rackner says of himself, "Ashamed of lying, I was glad that I had lied" (page 275, paragraph 6). What does this mixture of emotions indicate about him as a person?

4. Is this more the story of an art collector, a humanitarian, or an era? Explain.

Couperus: ABOUT MYSELF AND OTHERS (*page 276*)

1. The tone is set in the first sentence: "There is nothing that amuses me as much as little, very little adventures." How big, really, is the adventure described in the story? What are the narrator's feelings about it? Later, the narrator says, "The case in which my friend Louis was involved is nothing else than a miniature comedy, a tiny farce" (page 277, paragraph 1). Is this an accurate description? Explain.

2. Which character has your sympathy, Louis or the narrator? Why?

3. Try retelling the same story from Louis' point of view.

Andersen-Nexø: LIFE SENTENCE (*page 286*)

1. Is this a tragic story, or an inspirational one? Explain.

2. Discuss the truth of each of the following quotations from the story, first with regard to Mattis and then with regard to life in general:

(*a*) Every child more or less carries the weight of the grown-ups' years (page 286, paragraph 1).

(*b*) Like most parents, they rated dead things above the living child (page 287, paragraph 1).

(*c*) His youth had been hard; he was passing the legacy on now (page 291, paragraph 1).

3. Read the Norwegian story, "The Father" (page 296), and compare Mattis' and Thord's attitudes toward their sons.

Bjornsen: THE FATHER (*page 296*)

1. What is Thord's sin? How is it evidenced? How does his physical appearance tend to complement it?

2. How does it happen that the greatest tragedy in Thord's life turns out to be his salvation? What change in his physical appearance accompanies the change in his personality?

3. At two key points the priest speaks directly to Thord of his son. Find these two statements. What do they reveal about the priest's insight into Thord's character?

Ibsen: THE MASTER BUILDER (*page 300*)

HERDAL. . . . that fire is what started your career; you built your success on those ruins; you were just a poor boy from a country village, and now you're at the head of your profession. You must admit, luck was on your side, Mr. Solness.

SOLNESS (*looks at him in embarrassment*). Yes—That's just why I'm so horribly afraid.

HERDAL. You afraid? Why? Because you've had the luck on your side?

SOLNESS. Yes—it fills me with terror. Some day that luck will turn, you see.

HERDAL. Nonsense! What should make the luck turn?

SOLNESS (*firmly. With assurance*). The younger generation.

The Master Builder, Act One

1. Discuss Solness' "luck." Why is he apprehensive that his luck will turn? Relate this fear to his treatment of Ragnar. What part does Kaja play in the situation?

2. In each of three acts Solness relates a story:

Act One. In his workroom he tells Doctor Herdal how Kaja came to work for him and why he keeps her.

Act Two. In the drawing room he tells Hilde about the fire and what it has done to Aline and him.

Act Three. On the veranda he tells Hilde about climbing the church tower and defying God.

Considering setting, listener, and story, explain how all three are interrelated. Can you find any connection between the subject matter of these dialogues and the idea suggested in the lines from the play quoted above?

3. Why do you think Solness remembers nothing of the incident Hilde recalls in every detail?

4. Compare Hilde in the scenes she shares with Solness and in her scenes with Kaja and Aline. What differences in her character emerge from the comparison? How do you account for them?

5. Solness talks of willing things into being (Act II, page 340). Is it possible that he willed Hilde, at least the Hilde he knows, into existence? What does he mean by saying there's a troll in her? What does he want her to do for him? What needs is she to fill?

6. Aline confesses to Hilde that she is in mourning not for her sons but for her dolls. How would you explain her attitude?

Is there any parallel between her feelings and her husband's fear of middle age? Discuss.

7. Why is Solness building a spire on his new house? For what reason—or reasons—does Solness climb the spire? In the context of the play, what does his climb symbolize? Considering the symbolism, is his fall inevitable? Why, or why not?

8. Do you consider the ending tragic or happy? Explain your answer.

9. Do you come away from the play liking Hilde? What does she represent? Is she frightening? If so, why?

Lagerlöf: THE RAT TRAP (*page 366*)

1. Was the rat-trap peddler really trapped by the thirty kronor of the old crofter, or did he merely steal the bait? Explain.

2. What is the importance of the Christmastime setting to the story?

3. State briefly the meaning of this legend.

Strindberg: THE STRONGER (*page 375*)

1. Why does Mrs. X enter the café and seat herself at the table with Miss Y?

2. Why does Mrs. X show Miss Y the embroidered slippers? Are the results what she expected?

3. Does Miss Y pose a greater threat to Mrs. X's marriage or to her career? Which do you think Mrs. X considers the greater threat? Why?

4. What does Strindberg gain by having Miss Y remain silent throughout the play? At one point she is about to speak. What might she have wanted to say? Why does she not break her silence?

5. Which of the two women is the stronger? To what extent is the weaker aware of this? Which role is more important? Which requires the better actress? Explain.

BIOGRAPHIES OF AUTHORS

Martin Andersen-Nexø (1869–1954)

Born in the slums of Copenhagen, Andersen-Nexø spent his childhood on the island of Bornholm, which he made the setting for many of his short stories and novels. Because of his family's poverty, he went to work early, first as a herdboy and later as a shoemaker's apprentice. He did not begin writing until he was almost thirty. His fiction is concerned primarily with the struggles of the working class, yet its starkness is relieved by his faith in the innate goodness of man. Among his best-known novels is *Pelle the Conqueror*.

Hans Arp (1887–1966)

Arp—German painter, sculptor, and lyric poet—was one of the founders of *dadaism*, an art movement established in 1916 by a group of pacifists, avant-garde writers, and artists. The word *dada* is supposed to have been selected in a random skimming of a French dictionary; explanations of its meaning vary from "hobby-horse" to "nothingness." The movement, which attracted both writers and painters especially in France, attempts to explore and express man's helplessness to control his world. To do this, it stresses the irrational, the destructive, and the nihilistic, yet it sometimes contains a touch of humor. Arp began publishing his poems in 1920, and they were very much in demand by avant-garde magazines. From 1926 until his death he lived in France.

Bjornstjerne Bjornsen (1832–1910)

With Ibsen, who was his friend and rival, Bjornsen is regarded as one of the fathers of modern Norwegian literature. He began his literary career as a theatrical and literary reviewer for a daily newspaper. Though Bjornsen wrote criticism, drama, poetry, novels, and short stories, his popularity and fame derive chiefly from his fictional treatments of peasant life. He sought to portray the character and the austere life of the peasant, whom he believed to be the true representative of his nation. Among the best of his peasant novels are *Arne* and *A Happy Boy*. "The Father," generally regarded as one of his greatest short stories, also deals with peasant life. Bjornsen was awarded the Nobel prize in 1903.

Heinrich Böll (1917–   )

Heinrich Böll's early manhood was interrupted by service in the infantry during World War II. He was wounded and fought on several fronts including the Russian before being captured and repatriated.

In some of his works Böll combines a compassion for the plight of the common man in postwar Germany with an indictment of the emerging materialistic society. In other works, he writes of the evils of war and of racial persecution under the Nazi regime. Among his works translated into English are *Acquainted with the Night*, published in 1954; *Billiards at Half-past Nine*, published in 1961; and *The Clown*, published in 1965.

Bertolt Brecht (1898–1956)

In 1917 Brecht began studying medicine at Munich University, but was drafted into the army. Assigned as a medical orderly, he witnessed horrors that helped to develop the humanitarian instincts visible in his plays and poems. After the war, he returned to the university and to medicine but soon established himself as a writer. Hitler's rise to power drove Brecht into exile. After living in various countries including the United States, he finally settled in East Berlin where he spent the remainder of his life. In much of his work he preaches a pro-Marxist doctrine; but his writing is also humorous, exciting, and sometimes profound. Among his plays most frequently performed in the United States are *The Three-Penny Opera, Mother Courage and Her Children,* and *The Caucasian Chalk Circle.*

Hans Werner Cohn (1916–   )

Although at first glance the admixture of poetry and psychoanalysis seems highly unlikely and doomed to failure, Cohn has been successful in combining his talents as a writer with his background in medicine and psychoanalysis. Cohn quit his medical studies to leave Germany during the Nazi persecutions in the late thirties and settled in England. He is currently a resident of London, where he serves as secretary of a psychoanalytical association.

Louis Couperus (1863–1923)

Born at The Hague, Couperus went to Java with his parents when he was ten and remained there for five years. He never forgot his experiences in that country, and he often used the Dutch East Indies as a setting for his fiction. His realistic first novel, *Elina Veere* (1889), was so successful that he gave up his position as a teacher to spend his time writing and traveling. In all, he wrote more than thirty novels, some historical, some realistic. *Old People and the Things that Pass* (1918) is generally regarded as his best work.

Heimito von Doderer (1896–1966)

A native of Vienna, von Doderer wrote principally about that city, which he knew thoroughly. Trained in psychology, he was able to give professional depth to his characterizations. His writing is sometimes termed baroque, probably because of its richness of incident and unusual use of language—he is able to mix colloquialisms with more formal means of expression, at times including archaic elements. A recurring theme in his fiction is the nature of reality and the varying ways in which people perceive—or refuse to perceive—a given reality.

Friedrich Dürrenmatt (1921–   )

Friedrich Dürrenmatt is a native-born Swiss who, like many of his countrymen, writes in German. He began his artistic career as a painter, but abandoned art for writing during his university days. Dürrenmatt's university interests (theology, philosophy, science, literature, psychology) are all more or less evident in his novels and plays. His work has been called expressionistic, fanciful, dreamlike, but—always—experimental. He has said that he writes out of a knowledge of the world's absurdity, but with an allowance for the possibility of noble and responsible choices.

Günter Eich (1917–   )

Eich has achieved recognition in two different literary fields: poetry and the radio play. Since 1932, except for the years spent in the army during World War II, he has been a full-time writer. One of the founders of Group 47, an influential coterie of writers that first met in 1947, he received their first annual award in 1950.

Hans Magnus Enzensberger (1929–   )

Enzensberger, one of Germany's postwar "angry poets," is also a leader of the New Left. Like many of his contemporaries, he was appalled at the atrocities his country committed during World War II, a war in which he took part. Perhaps because of his war experiences, he feels that poetry should be clear, politically relevant, and committed to improving man's condition in the world.

Johann Wolfgang von Goethe (1749–1832)

Goethe's is the supreme position in German letters. In literary accomplishment he ranks with Homer, Dante, Cervantes, Shakespeare, and Tolstoy. Besides artistic achievement, he won fame in science, philosophy, and politics. His belief in living intensely and fully made him a latter-day incarnation of Renaissance man. During Goethe's lifetime there occurred many events that shaped the modern world: the American Revolution, the French Revolution, the

Napoleonic Era, the beginnings of the Industrial Revolution. Cultur-
ally, he grew up in the Neoclassical Age, but he matured with the
Romantics. His work shows all these influences. Among his best
writings are two novels, *The Sorrows of Young Werther* and *Wilhelm
Meister's Apprenticeship;* the two parts of the drama, *Faust;* and his
lyric poetry, which is sensitive and personal, but, because of the
nearly perfect fusion of sound, image, and idea, virtually impossible
to translate.

Günter Grass (1927–   )

Born in Danzig of Polish-German parents, Grass, like others of his
generation, went through most of the horrors of World War II:
evacuation, wartime adolescence, military service at the age of
seventeen, wounding, and captivity. At the war's end he took up
stone-masonry and sculpture. In 1955 he won a radio poetry prize,
and after that he published regularly. His work is a relentless pursuit
and criticism of Germany's past errors, and a warning against future
mistakes through which the old could lead the young into still
another world war.

Gerhart Hauptmann (1862–1946)

Hauptmann, the son of a Silesian innkeeper, filled more than sixty
volumes with his novels, novellas, poetry, autobiography, drama, and
travel literature. His early work marked him as one of Germany's
foremost exponents of naturalistic literature, but as he grew older he
turned to romanticism, occasionally to mysticism. *The Weavers*
(1892), based on the 1844 revolt of the Silesian weavers against
their working conditions, is his best-known play. In 1912 he was
awarded the Nobel prize.

Heinrich Heine (1799–1856)

Heine spent his youth in Düsseldorf, where his father was a
tradesman. Although his first poems were published in 1821, he did
not become established as a lyric poet until the appearance of *A Trip
in the Harz Mountains* (1826), a prose work interspersed with lyrics.
Book of Songs (1827) contains most of his famous poems, many of
which were set to music by such composers as Mendelssohn, Schu-
mann, and Schubert. In 1831, finding autocratic Prussian rule unsat-
isfactory, he moved to Paris, where he remained for much of the
balance of his life. Like Lord Byron, whose works he translated, he
combined great lyric gifts with a cynical outlook.

Herman Hesse (1877–1962)

Hesse, a popular author on the modern American campus, was the
son of missionaries. His attempt to follow in his family's footsteps
failed when in 1891 he underwent a religious crisis and fled from

Maulbronn Seminary. In 1911 he made an extended trip to India, where he came into direct contact with the religion and philosophy of the East. His pacifist stance and antiwar publications during World War I turned German public opinion against him. Among his best books are *Demian*, his first and simplest, and *Magister Ludi*, generally considered his master work. He was awarded the Nobel prize for literature in 1946.

Hugo von Hofmannsthal (1874–1929)

Throughout his career the Austrian writer Hofmannsthal was concerned with the problem of communication. His early poems, to which the two included in this book belong, show the influence of expressionism in their mystic subject matter and understated method of presentation, which leaves the feeling that they mean more than they say. In 1901 Hofmannsthal went through a severe psychological crisis that changed the direction of his art. Believing that words were inadequate to express meaning because of their many connotations, he began to write drama and to combine his poetry with music in the hope of communicating more effectively. Perhaps his best play is *Jedermann*, an adaptation of the medieval *Everyman*.

Heinz Huber (1922–   )

Huber served in the German army in World War II, was taken prisoner, and after his release supported his early writing efforts by working as a window-dresser. He attained his first real success by writing radio plays. He belongs to the new school of fiction writers that developed in Germany after the "zero-point" caused by the German defeat in World War II. Concerned about the breakdown of traditional values and the increasing dehumanization brought about by a technologically oriented society, these authors examine what the "brave new world" is doing to the individual man. Their approach is often ironical or satirical, and they tend to make extensive use of symbolism, surrealism, and the theater-of-the-absurd techniques. In its tone and suggestion of surrealism, "The New Apartment" is a good example of this type of writing.

Henrik Ibsen (1828–1906)

Ibsen, whose first love was medicine, did not enter the theater until 1851, when he accepted a job as a stage manager. In 1857 he advanced to Director of the Norwegian Theater in Christiania (now Oslo); these two positions taught him the practical aspects of drama. As a playwright, Ibsen pioneered by introducing realistic themes, usually concerned with social or psychological problems, by stressing characterizations rather than plot, and by writing natural dialogue. *Peer Gynt*, one of his first successful plays, draws heavily upon Norwegian folklore for its background. *A Doll's House, Hedda Gabler*, and *The Wild Duck* are among his most widely read plays; they deal, to a large extent, with the problems of the individual in society. In later life Ibsen grew concerned with the role of the artist in the world and several of his last plays, among them *The Master Builder*, deal with this theme.

Franz Kafka (1883–1924)

Kafka studied law in his native Prague and took a job in a government insurance agency. At the prompting of his friend Max Brod, he published a few short stories but wrote nothing major before he was twenty-nine. Within the next five years, Kafka had completed the majority of his short stories, including "The Metamorphosis," and the larger part of his novel, *The Trial*. He had also contracted tuberculosis, which forced him to spend much of his remaining seven years in sanatoriums.

Little of Kafka's work was published during his lifetime, and on his deathbed, according to Max Brod, Kafka instructed him to destroy the rest, including his large though uncompleted novel, *The Castle*. Brod refused, and most of Kafka's work was published by 1931.

Erich Kästner (1899–   )

Kästner, who studied to be a teacher before serving in the German army during the last months of World War I, did not become a professional writer until 1927. Since then he has written poetry, fiction, drama, radio plays, and juveniles. His most famous juvenile is *Emil and the Detective*, a perennial favorite in German classes in American high schools. Although the Nazis banned Kästner's books in 1933, he remained, becoming what is sometimes termed "a refugee inside Germany." His literary reputation rests largely upon his satirical verse. Among his favorite targets are militarism, fascism, and middle-class morality.

Selma Lagerlöf (1858–1940)

Selma Lagerlöf, the first woman to win the Nobel prize for literature (1909), grew up in the region of Marbacka, Varmland, in Sweden. Since she was lame as a child, she studied at home, with the intention of becoming a school teacher. She pursued this career only briefly, however, for the publication of her first novel *Gosta Berling's Saga*, 1894, determined her to become a writer instead. This novel, which won her the Nobel prize, makes considerable use of legendary material as a backdrop for the adventures of its romantic hero.

Much of Selma Lagerlöf's writing has the remote and timeless quality of legend. Among her books are *Tales of a Manor*, *The Ring of the Lowenskolds*, *Memories of My Childhood*, and *Harvest*, a collection of Swedish legends from which "The Rat Trap" is taken.

Alfred Lichtenstein (1889–1914)

Born in Berlin, Lichtenstein lived and was educated there. When World War I broke out, he was sent to Belgium, where he was killed in action in 1914. Before his death he had seen a small collection of his poems, *The Twilight*, appear in print. After the end of the war, a two-volume posthumous collection of his works, *Poems and Stories* (1919), was published. His poems are often a montage of images, partially realistic, partially surrealistic, held together by the poet's controlling idea.

Thomas Mann (1875–1955)

Thomas Mann was born in Lübeck, Germany. His first novel, *Buddenbrooks*, published in 1901, demonstrated his superb talents as a storyteller. Among his principal works are *The Magic Mountain* (1924), which is considered not only a masterpiece but a major contribution to world literature; *Doctor Faustus*, a postwar novel; and *Joseph and His Brothers*, a series of four novels. In 1929 he was awarded the Nobel prize for literature.

Prior to the Nazi take-over in Germany, Mann had believed that an artist should concern himself with spiritual matters and remain aloof from politics. Once the Nazis were in power, he changed his stance and became actively involved in politics as a defender of the free, creative life. The regime burnt his books and deprived him of his German nationality.

In 1938 he moved to the United States, but settled in Switzerland after World War II; there he died with the satisfaction of knowing his works had again found favor in his native country.

Christian Morgenstern (1871–1914)

Although much of Morgenstern's writing is serious, influenced by philosophy and mysticism, he is best known for his nonsense verse. He himself insisted that the two types of writing were related, that the higher insight of the mystic displayed another aspect of itself in the higher nonsense he wrote. His whimsical verses often deal with von Korf, the talented scientist-inventor whose creations turn the expected upside-down or inside-out and sometimes give us new insights into ourselves, and with Palmström, the soft-hearted lover of beauty, who makes us smile at our own sentimental side.

Rainer Maria Rilke (1875–1926)

Rilke, who ranks with the great German poets, was born in Prague of German parents. In 1899 and again in 1900 Rilke visited Russia, where he met Tolstoy and was much impressed by the vast country and its people. Between these visits he wrote in seven successive nights *Stories of God*, from which "A Tale of Death" and "A Story Told to the Dark" are taken. In 1902 he met the sculptor Auguste Rodin, who influenced his mature style. From Rodin he learned to observe objects with meticulous accuracy and to select details that would convey the impression he wished to create. *New Poems* demonstrates this talent. Rilke's best-known collections are *Duino Elegies,* on which he labored for ten years, and *Sonnets to Orpheus,* written while he was completing the elegies.

Wieland Schmied (1929–   )

Born in Frankfurt-am-Main in the interval between two world wars, Schmied still spends part of his time there. His second residence, near Vienna, is probably better suited to his profession of art critic and essayist. "Ancient Chinese Map of the World" shows his diversity; he has used a work of art as the basis for a poem that is at least partially philosophical in outlook. The poem was included in his first collection, *Map of the Wind,* published in 1957.

Arthur Schnitzler (1862–1931)

Schnitzler, the son of a throat specialist, was born in Vienna and spent his life there. Like his father, he became a physician, and despite his success as an author never gave up his medical practice. His literary output was large: almost fifty plays, more than fifty short stories and novellas, and two novels. Schnitzler's fiction reveals his knowledge of depth psychology, his ability to convey atmosphere and mood, and his mastery of an ironically objective style. He tends to deal with extreme situations and his characters are often neurotic, even psychotic. Typically, his writing is so lucid that it does not require interpretation. "The Blind Geronimo and His Brother," one of his most famous short stories, displays many of the characteristics described above.

Ernst Stadler (1883–1914)

One of the German expressionist poets, Stadler was born in Alsace. After studying English at Strasbourg and Munich, he went to Oxford as a Rhodes scholar in 1908. He had just accepted an appointment at Toronto University when World War I broke out. He was killed in action on the Western Front in 1914. Two collections of his poems were in print before his death, but continuing interest led to the publication of a posthumous collection in 1955.

Franz Baermann Steiner (1909–1952)

Steiner's short life was troubled but busy. Born into a Jewish family in Prague, he was educated in that city, studying anthropology, sociology, and Oriental languages at the university. Later he continued his studies in many parts of the world, including Oxford, where he was when World War II broke out. Steiner remained at Oxford, but his parents were killed in a German concentration camp. Although in poor health, Steiner continued to write poetry and do research in anthropology until his death.

August Strindberg (1849–1912)

Strindberg's life is the story of a genius tortured by neurosis that at times bordered on insanity. Paradoxically, this neurosis was responsible for his great creative achievement. Through writing he found a release for the inner tensions that seemed to be tearing him apart, and his introspection led to psychologically accurate character portrayals. His literary output was prodigious; he wrote more than fifty full-length and one-act plays, prose fiction, autobiography, poetry, and nonfiction. Recognized as one of the fathers of naturalism and expressionism in modern drama, Strindberg is best known in America for two naturalistic plays, *The Father* and *Miss Julie,* and two expressionistic plays, *A Dream Play* and *To Damascus.*

Stefan Zweig (1881–1942)

Zweig, a native of Vienna, reflected that city's turn-of-the-century cosmopolitanism and background of international culture. His literary production is versatile, spanning many genres: verse, prose fiction, drama, biography, and the historical essay. Of special note is a series of *triptychs,* each dealing with three related figures; for example, *Three Masters* analyzes the French writer Balzac, the Russian Dostoevsky, and England's Dickens. "The Invisible Collection" is generally regarded as his best short tale. With the rise of Nazism, Zweig, a Jew, was exiled from Austria. In 1935 he emigrated to England where he became a naturalized citizen.

PRONUNCIATION KEY

The pronunciation of each word is shown after the word, in this way: **ab bre vi ate** (ə brē′vē āt). The letters and signs used are pronounced as in the words below. The mark ′ is placed after a syllable with primary or strong accent, as in the example above. The mark ′ after a syllable shows a secondary or lighter accent, as in **ab bre vi a tion** (ə brē′vē ā′shən).

Some words, taken from foreign languages, are spoken with sounds that otherwise do not occur in English. Symbols for these sounds are given at the end of the table as "Foreign Sounds."

a	hat, cap	o	hot, rock	ə	represents:
ā	age, face	ō	open, go		a in about
ä	father, far	ô	order, all		e in taken
		oi	oil, voice		i in April
b	bad, rob	ou	house, out		o in lemon
ch	child, much				u in circus
d	did, red				
		p	paper, cup		
e	let, best	r	run, try		
ē	equal, see	s	say, yes		**foreign sounds**
ėr	term, learn	sh	she, rush		
		t	tell, it		Y as in French *du*. Pronounce ē with the lips rounded as for English ü in **rule**.
		th	thin, both		
f	fat, if	℡H	then, smooth		
g	go, bag				
h	he, how				œ as in French *peu*. Pronounce ā with the lips rounded as for ō.
		u	cup, butter		
i	it, pin	u̇	full, put		
ī	ice, five	ü	rule, move		
					N as in French *bon*. The N is not pronounced, but shows that the vowel before it is nasal.
j	jam, enjoy				
k	kind, seek	v	very, save		
l	land, coal	w	will, woman		
m	me, am	y	young, yet		H as in German *ach*. Pronounce k without closing the breath passage.
n	no, in	z	zero, breeze		
ng	long, bring	zh	measure, seizure		

The pronunciation key is from the *Thorndike-Barnhart High School Dictionary*, copyright 1968 by Scott, Foresman and Company.

INDEX OF AUTHORS AND TITLES

413

INDEX OF TRANSLATORS